YO-ASD-760

WILD ANIMAL, WHITE MAN

WILD ANIMAL
WHITE MAN

Some Wildlife in Europe, Soviet Russia
and North America

DR BERNHARD GRZIMEK

HILL AND WANG · NEW YORK

Translated from the German by Michael Glenny

PUBLISHED IN THE UNITED STATES OF AMERICA BY HILL AND WANG, INC.
LIBRARY OF CONGRESS CATALOG CARD NUMBER: 66-12232

PRINTED IN GREAT BRITAIN

CONTENTS

PICTURE SOURCES

The following pictures were not taken by the author:

Plate 10: Detail from a painting by Professor Ungewitter, Munich
Plate 24: Photo A. Sludskij, Alma Ata (Okapia)
Plate 25: Photo A. Bannikov, Moscow
Plates 26, 52, 53, 71: Photo L. Zollinger, Zurich
Plate 36: Photo N. W. Labanoff, Askania Nova (Okapia)
Plate 39: Photo Sven Gillsäter
Plate 40: Photo H. Heimpel-Raahs
Plates 42, 56, 59: Photo H. Busse Yellowknife (Hanselmann)
Plates 46, 47: Photo Elk Research Farm, Pechora-Ilyichky, U.S.S.R.
Plate 64: Photo Jürgen Schmidt

For the past twenty years I have devoted myself to the animals of Africa. Each year I flew out to see them whenever I could, conducting my own investigations, heading research projects, and attempting to establish reserves and national parks. In order to persuade the responsible politicians of those aspiring but desperately poor countries, I collected financial aid in Europe and endeavoured to bring large numbers of tourists to see the most spectacular animal reserves of Africa.

Politicians and economists, white or black, tend to look with patronising indulgence upon our fondness for animals and unspoilt wild regions. A few well-meaning phrases about it are included in election speeches (after all, even animal lovers have a vote), but when it is a question of timber production, soil cultivation, cattle husbandry, or building of dams and new industries, wildlife has to take second place whether it concerns giraffe and rhinoceros or bears, lynx and beavers. Only a few discerning people are gradually realising that these animals are just as important for civilisation as old churches, Greek sculpture, and Egyptian temples. Realisation, however, will probably come too slowly, for orang-utans, blue whales and monkey-eating eagles are not statues, but living creatures who can die out for ever. No archaeologist will be able to resurrect them in centuries to come.

The tourists who came to see the elephants and crocodiles and brought with them hard currencies, had more and more restaurants, hotels and roads built for them; suddenly it became apparent that seemingly useless herds of antelopes were a potentially greater economic asset than bigger and better coffee plantations. This is why I advocated tourism and made enemies of many nature lovers. Anyone with a fondness for the hippopotami who inhabit the shores of central African lakes prefers to watch them in solitude and hates to see them against a background of noisy motorboats filled with camera-happy tourists. I feel the same, but luckily in every national park there are enough impenetrable regions left for the connoisseur.

Meanwhile I have been vindicated by events: today national parks are beginning to be fashionable, and not only in African countries but in other overseas countries. Foreign governments invite us to advise them on the establishment of these nature reserves.

In order to rouse compassion in the hearts of my fellow citizens in Europe and America for the plight of those last wonderful wild animals of Africa, I have produced colour films, written books and appeared on television, with the result that European nature lovers charged me with caring only for Cape buffaloes and gorillas, while ignoring the animals of my own country. They told me that charity begins at home.

Naturally there is a grain of truth in this. But there is a limit to what one person can do. If you want to achieve something you must not try to do everything at once. If one man has lost his heart to Tanganyika, there are enough others left in Germany to fight against the draining of bogs, the drying up of rivers and the destruction of natural environment. For centuries it has been the tradition to reclaim moors and to receive annual Government grants for doing so even though it has been common knowledge for some time that our natural water resources – more important even than our daily bread – are being destroyed in order to gain a few hundred acres of inferior soil which will probably not remain under cultivation for long.

At first it was only my desire to make comparisons with Africa that took me to the United States, Canada, the European countries and through the Soviet Union to the furthest corners of northern Asia. I wanted to see for myself what had become of the wild animals in the 'white' continents. Hence this book.

The result is depressing. It is true that during our short colonial rule we Europeans have senselessly and wantonly destroyed nine-tenths of Africa's wildlife; but together with the new Governments of these countries we shall be able to preserve intact for our descendants at least a few corners of the dark continent where predatory and non-predatory animals alike, plants and rivers, exist in a natural equilibrium.

In our own countries, however, we seem unable to achieve this. A hundred years hence there will still be a few wild animals left, of course, among the combine harvesters and the cancerous growth of the cities – but only stags, roedeer, hares and pheasants – free-ranging domestic animals, wild animals that have become adjusted to cultivated fields and have learnt to hop across our motorways. This I have described in my book. Europe and America must have been magnificent once, when they were still free and wild, when forests grew naturally, where red deer and elk were kept in natural balance by wolves and lynx and not by the guns of man. But this no longer exists for us to admire, not even in the remotest regions of the white man's territory.

I saw that the wolves in Canada's national parks have been largely exterminated and that in the United States' Yellowstone Park the majority of wapiti deer will have to be shot. I had hopes that in Russia, where individual species have been successfully reared again, I would find regions where nature had not been tampered with, where even wolves could proliferate unhindered. But I was disappointed.

According to Terrantianus of Mauretania – whose 'pro captu lectoris habent sua fata libelli' has been misquoted for over two thousand years now – the effect of a book depends upon the attitude of its readers. I hope, therefore, that this book will not only serve the purpose of entertaining the reader, but that it may give people enough food for thought to do something for the wildlife in our parts of this ancient planet.

BERNHARD GRZIMEK

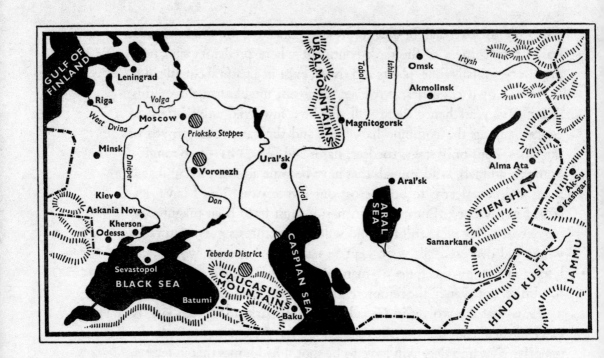

1 MOSCOW – THE CITY WITHOUT DOGS

Abruptly I walked through the great revolving door of the skyscraper Hotel Leningrad and decided to make a reconnaissance, alone and on foot, of the fourth largest city in the world, the city which houses seven million Muscovites. The gentlemen from the State Zoological Institute and the Ministry of Culture, who had fetched me from the airport and conducted me to my room, had taken their leave. It was four o'clock on a Saturday afternoon. My interpretress was not due until Monday, but I was restless and wanted to make good use of my time. I had, after all, had to wait eighteen months for permission to make this journey to the Soviet Union.

It does not normally take so long. If you travel by 'Intourist', which costs about £14 10s per day all-in, you probably get your visa in a fortnight at the most. However, I had asked to be allowed to travel around at will in any part of this, the largest country in the world, which occupies a sixth of all the dry land of the globe. Besides this I wanted to be able to take still and ciné films without restriction and bring my films undeveloped out of the Soviet Union in order to show them on television. This appeared to involve a great deal of enquiries and correspondence, but finally I received the personal assurance of Mr Smirnov, Soviet Ambassador in Bonn, that my request was granted. And so now here I was – in the USSR for the first time in my life; even during my war service I had only got as far as Poland.

The people on the street, when I asked the way to the Kremlin, understood neither German, French nor English – I unfortunately know none of the Slav languages – but they grasped the word 'Kremlin',[1] and pointed the way to me. Muscovites, it seems, only pay attention to traffic lights when there is a policeman in sight – just as in Frankfurt. It was a genuine adventure for me to be at large in a country in which I

was 'deaf and dumb'. I was able to read a little: I had made use of the
two hours in the Ilyushin jet between Copenhagen and Moscow to
memorise the Cyrillic alphabet, because I had always been annoyed by
my inability to read even the sender's name on the letters written to
me by Soviet zoologists. I had been obliged to pass them over to the
town hall in Frankfurt to have them translated and since the only
person in the whole city administration with a fluent command of
Russian was the Lord Mayor, Werner Bockelmann – he was born in
Moscow – the letters always came back translated by His Worship
himself, which I found embarrassing.

So I began spelling out the signs over the shops. In the Soviet Union
these are usually open until quite late in the evening, so that people
can shop easily after working all day. When one deciphers the illu-
minated letters over a shop such as *Parikmacher*[2] one knows at once
from this German loan-word that this is a barbershop. The chain of
food stores in Moscow is called *Gastronom*. If you ask for a sandwich
(German *Butterbrot*) in one of them, they understand you at once as
this is another German word which the Russians have borrowed. Other
German words adopted by the Russians are *Schlagbaum* (barrier), also
Kapellmeister (bandmaster), *Postamt* (post office), *Rucksack* and *Kurort*
(spa); on railway stations they announce the *Marschroute* of the trains
and *Büstenhalter* (brassières) are known only by their German name.
On my very first afternoon in Moscow, in the multi-storey department
store 'Gum' milling with thousands of people, I acquired two needles
by sign-language – not by purchase, but as a gift. As I had forgotten
my shaving gear I had to buy a razor. Ten shillings. Russian razor
blades turned out to be wafer-thin and, unexpectedly, extremely
good. The shaving brush was marked 'Made in Germany' and its
bristles were stiff. The exchange was four marks (7s) to the rouble, the
same rate as for a dollar. This official rate is high and, depending on
what you buy, things are not exactly cheap. If you come from East
Germany a rouble only costs two East German marks, so that everything is half-price. This no doubt reflects the relative warmth of
relations between the Soviets and the two parts of Germany.

The people are generally well dressed, so that no one turns to stare at a foreigner. A young Muscovite girl, who spoke fluent German (but who had never been nearer to Germany than one brief visit to Vienna) took pity on me and showed me where to find the specialist bookshops. There one can buy newspapers in every western language, but only the communist papers and only German books produced in East Germany, Czechoslovakia and Poland. Finally I found what I was looking for – an atlas of the Soviet Union containing a number of specialised maps. The girl told me how to get back to my hotel by the Metro. In the Moscow subway there is no need to buy tickets. You simply put ten kopecks into a slot near the barrier and walk through. If you are stingy enough to contrive to forget to put your money in, you only walk a few yards before a diabolical apparatus stops your passage by dropping a bar right in front of your shins. It often works a fraction of a second too late and hits your leg, which is painful and leaves bruises.

Of course I went completely wrong. When I came to the surface again it was dark. In these alien streets everyone shrugged their shoulders when I asked for the Hotel Leningrad. As I found out later, 'Hotel' in Russian is not 'Hotel', as in almost every other language, but *Gostinnitsa*. It came on to rain and just as in every other city there were suddenly no more empty taxis to be found; besides, I regarded it as a point of honour to find my way back on foot. I succeeded in this, but not until ten pm, by which time I was pretty wet. At least I had attempted to see whether a German can move about alone in Moscow. And whether one is 'tailed' everywhere.

A zoo which is a hundred years old can suffer no better fate – disregarding for a moment the lot of its poor inmates – than to be completely bombed to pieces. Even in this event the animals are no danger to the human inhabitants. In the last war there were frequent rumours of lions or elephants running amok and savaging people. After the war I sent round a questionnaire to all the European zoos: nowhere had an animal, released by an air-raid, so much as injured a human being. The reaction of even such wild beasts as tigers had always been to try and return to their damaged cage.

The Moscow Zoological Garden was founded in 1864 by a professor at the university and remained undamaged throughout all the subsequent wars and upheavals. Consequently it looks very much as the Frankfurt Zoo did in 1938: lots of bars, old fashioned, too small. But a great number of people go there, more than three million a year and there are some rare animals to be seen: Siberian wild dogs, Corsak foxes, clouded leopards, Asiatic ibex, isubras, walruses, kulan (Asiatic wild asses), alligators from China and as the *pièce de résistance* the harlequinesque black and white giant panda from Szechuan. Only four of these extraordinary beasts are in captivity, two at the Peking Zoo (to whom a cub was born in 1964, the first ever in a zoo), one in the London Zoo and this one in Moscow. The zoo runs film shows for the many school-children, there are lecture rooms, an information centre for visitors and more than a dozen resident scientists. 1965 will see the start of building a new and much bigger zoo outside Moscow's city centre. Until then the new Friedrichsfelde Zoo in East Berlin is clearly the largest and most modern zoological garden in the communist bloc. When the East and West Berliners are united again they will be able to congratulate themselves on having two generously laid-out zoos. They can do with them: London has two zoos, Paris three, New York four and Chicago two. Even Muscovites have a choice of two zoos.

I was not concerned with politics. I had no wish to film Soviet skyscrapers, lavish Metro stations or new residential suburbs: I was looking for animals. In Moscow this is by no means simple. There are plenty of pigeons, as in all big cities whose inhabitants, cut off from the world of animals, appease their hunger for contact with nature by petting them and feeding them until they multiply to the point of becoming a nuisance. As in West Germany, proposals were made to poison Moscow's surplus pigeons but the idea was vetoed by higher authority on the grounds that 'the dove is the symbol of peace'.

It was only gradually that I began to realise that Moscow is a city where there are no dogs. Among the millions of people walking through the street, among the tens of thousands in the big parks and gardens there is scarcely a quadruped to be seen. I don't know whether anyone has counted Moscow's dog population, as I was unable to obtain any statistics on it. One of my aims was to find out whether the Soviet Russians are fond of animals.

At last my interpreter appeared on Monday morning. Young as she was, she was already a high school German teacher. She had been in Dresden and Leipzig and was very fond of the German Democratic Republic, she declared, firmly stressing the GDR. Miss Zelkina was pretty, naturally a convinced Communist, and extremely anxious about my welfare. I should never eat unwashed fruit, should always wear warm clothes, never carry heavy things and *never* tip the taxi-drivers as this was an insult to a Soviet working man. In fact Moscow cab-drivers generally accept tips, having been spoilt by the numerous foreigners, but apart from them my proffered tip was otherwise refused with indignation throughout the Soviet Union.

I loaded my still and movie cameras into the taxi and we drove up to the walls of the Kremlin on Red Square. The usual long but quite fast-moving queue of thousands of people stood in front of the Lenin Mausoleum, but apart from that the square was empty, roped off for a celebration to greet the first pair of astronauts to have made a dual space flight. Seeing the yawning empty space surrounded by walls of people, Miss Zelkina wanted to turn back. I was hardly able to persuade her to ask a policeman whether we couldn't after all cross the square to take films. To her amazement he said 'Yes', so we set off across the great expanse loaded with our film equipment.

On the far side there stood among the crowd one of those special trucks used for repairing overhead trolleybus wires, with a kind of tower, surmounted by a platform for the workmen, which can be raised and lowered. At first Svetlana Zelkina again refused to ask the crew, but they allowed me to climb up on it. They even set the thing moving, drove me out into the middle of the empty Red Square and raised the tower skywards. Perched so high with my camera I felt extremely conspicuous in front of the giant red decorations, the long banners with the coats-of-arms of all the Soviet republics and the gigantic portraits of Khrushchev and Lenin.

Later I met the zoologists of Moscow University, whose buildings
dominate a hilltop on the far bank of the Moscow River with a view
over the whole city – a sea of buildings punctured by the skyscrapers
of Stalin's era, which stick up like lighthouses or great reefs. The
university itself, completed in 1953, is largely composed of skyscrapers:
thirty-seven buildings ranging in height between one and seventeen
storeys. The central building is actually seven hundred and eighty feet
high, crowned by a huge spire above the thirty-first floor which is in
turn topped by an enormous Order of Lenin carved in stone. It is
surrounded by hundreds of acres of parkland where fifty thousand
trees and a million shrubs were planted for adornment. The central
building contains twenty-two thousand rooms, the residential wings on
either side of it have five thousand seven hundred and eighty-four rooms
for students and one hundred and eighty-four teachers' rooms. In the
Soviet Union in 1963, three hundred and thirty-two thousand students
took their final exams, compared with a total of twelve thousand two
hundred in 1914, I was proudly informed. The main lecture hall seats one
thousand five hundred people; there is a library containing a million
volumes, thirty-three reading-rooms, two hundred and ten professorial
chairs, twenty thousand students, one thousand four hundred and eighty-
five post-graduate students, five hundred lecturers and two hundred
and thirty professors – including my colleagues of the Department of
Zoology: Heptner, who speaks German, the grey-bearded Bannikov
who has rowed singlehanded down most of the rivers of Siberia, and
Dementiev, the leading ornithologist of the Soviet Union, who speaks
French like a Parisian. They held a council of war to decide how I might
make the best use of my two months in their country – little enough
time to cover a land of two hundred and twenty-five million people.

My first move was to be driven next morning by professors
Bannikov and Dementiev fifty miles out of Moscow to the Prioksko
Terraces nature conservancy, the smallest in Russia proper but the home
of the finest Soviet herd of bison. We have allowed the largest European
wild animal, the aurochs, to be destroyed and the bison has only just
escaped the same fate. In the last century there remained only a single

place on earth where these huge brown beasts lived in their natural state: the virgin forest of Bialowieza, south-east of the town of Bialystok. This forest was one of the tsar's preserves and supported approximately five hundred bison, but they were decimated by the soldiery in the first World War. The last wild European bison in the world was shot there by a poacher in 1921.

This magnificent species would have been exterminated altogether had not the tsar presented a bull and three cows to the Duke of Pless in Upper Silesia in 1865. By 1918 they had increased to eighty-four head, but in the confusion that reigned in Upper Silesia until it was annexed to Poland this herd was also practically destroyed by poachers. Only two bulls and a nineteen-year-old cow remained alive, and of these poachers had already shot off the tail of the older bull. Nevertheless the bull enabled the elderly cow to produce another two bullocks and a heifer, thus ensuring the continuance of the breed. Fortunately the newly-formed state of Poland made their conservation a matter of national concern; the Polish government, with the aid of Carl Hagenbeck, the Hamburg animal dealer, was able to collect a few more bison from zoos all over the world. At the same time my predecessor as Director of the Frankfurt Zoo, Dr Kurt Priemel, founded the 'Bison Conservation Society', which made it its business to ensure that isolated cows which had survived the war in European zoos were brought together for mating purposes. Thus the bison population of the world increased to a hundred head by 1938.

Then came the second World War and again fighting raged back and forth across Poland. This time, however, the German, Russian and Polish army commanders were well aware of the irreplaceable natural treasure which was at large in the forest of Bialowieza. Care was taken to protect them and by the end of the war the world's stock of bison stood at seventy head.

The new Russo-Polish border cut right through the middle of the forest of Bialowieza and the Soviets took over the greater part of the herd. The Polish government recommenced their bison conservation scheme and their example was followed everywhere else. By the end of

B

1964 there were roughly seven hundred head of these great shaggy wild cattle throughout the world. Small breeding colonies live in zoos all over Europe, in Scandinavia, in America and even in China. With luck the species will be preserved for ever. Of these the Soviet Union houses one hundred and sixty pure-bred European bison, together with about five hundred cross-breeds which have been interbred with American bison and domestic cattle. The intention is to allow these impure strains gradually to die out.

The nature conservancy men of Prioksko treated us to a delicious country meal of hard-boiled eggs, roast meat, ham and borsch, after which we spent the night in a peasant cottage being plagued by mosquitoes – all in order to get up next morning in the pouring rain to go deep into the forest and inspect a herd of forty-three head of pure-bred European bison. What a sight! The forests of Central Europe must have looked like this when the ancient Teutonic tribes roamed Germany.

The Prioksko Nature Conservancy has its problems, as we all have. The area covers only thirty-two thousand acres and one side of it is immediately bordered by the vast factories of Serpukhov. As everywhere in the Soviet Union the herds of elk have multiplied enormously, in winter they invade the Conservancy in hundreds and damage the saplings. The Russians are loath to hunt them and the wolves which once maintained the natural balance by preying on elk have long since been exterminated.

During the following evenings in Moscow, when I got bored with being alone, I would join a table of Africans in a restaurant. They can always speak either English or French, being almost invariably students. One who came from Tanganyika almost wept when I told him that I lived much of the time in Tanganyika. As we talked, the waiter might bring a bottle of Georgian wine to our table with the compliments of some unknown Russian from another table as a gesture of friendship followed perhaps half an hour later by slices of bread and caviar or cakes. This charming Russian custom was observed nearly every evening and often Russians would join our group at which the Africans were called in to interpret between us Europeans.

The streets of Moscow are not only extremely clean, but are completely devoid of dog droppings. This is not because Russians are not fond of dogs. There are plenty of dogs in villages in the country. At the gigantic 'Exhibition of Economic Achievement' there is even a special Dogs' Pavilion with a tower containing a permanent show of all the breeds of dog in the Soviet Union. In fact it was some time before I discovered this palace of dogs. Svetlana was very proud of this great permanent exhibition with its three hundred and fifty buildings and seventy-nine pavilions, its larger-than-life statues, its fountains full of gilded figures, the marble palaces built by each Soviet republic, the bandstands, the trips by miniature railway and the crowds of happy rubber-neckers. *This* was what I should be filming.

We were sitting on a bench and eating ice-cream. (These ices, which are sold on every street corner in Moscow, are the best I have ever eaten.) 'I haven't come here,' I said, 'to take pictures of astronauts, or skyscrapers or the Five Year Plan. I want to see how you live with nature and treat your animals.' Then I discovered on the plan of the exhibition that animals were on show in halls and that there were hundreds of different breeds of sheep and an area for showing off race-horses and horses harnessed in troikas; a model fur farm; the most remarkable building ever erected to house caged rabbits – a Greek temple, whose friezes were decorated with bas-reliefs, not of gods and goddesses but of rabbits: another architectural legacy of Stalin's era. Behind the temple is an up-to-date rabbit farm. Most of the breeds were familiar to me, despite their Russian names, as the Soviet Union built up its cage rabbit population by importing over ten thousand stud animals from Germany between 1927 and 1931.

It is much quieter in this part of the exhibition, which is not devoted to tractors and space ships but to animals. There are ponds full of rare water-fowl, elk runs, pig breeding farms, halls and paddocks for cattle and quiet stretches of parkland. Here family parties sit and eat their sandwiches.

For all their lack of dogs, Muscovites must love animals, if only to judge by the ten big state-run pet shops which sell cage birds, goldfish, day-old chicks and guppys. But when the wife works as long hours as her husband and when the whole family has to live in one room, then there can be neither time nor space to keep dogs. Of course huge cranes are at work all over the city putting up giant apartment blocks out of prefabricated sections and I read that every day three hundred and fifty Muscovite families move into new quarters, but the city has grown out of all proportion and people are streaming in from all over the vast country. I think it will be some time before dogs take over the Soviet capital.

Russian love of animals has instead found another outlet, as I discovered by chance. Three big markets operate daily in Moscow selling pigeons, fish and cage birds and other small pets as a substitute for dogs. I took a taxi out to one of these markets, far away from the great boulevards of central Moscow. We carried our camera-cases through a plain gateway, which might have been a factory gate, and into the crowd of people jammed between rows of stalls. It must have numbered between seven and eight thousand. One part of the market deals entirely in pigeons and doves: carrier pigeons, scandaroons, Hungarian pigeons, barbs, fantails. Every second person was holding a pigeon or looking knowledgeably at the preening, cooing inhabitants of large wooden cages. Then came an endless row of tables carrying buckets and bowls full of brown clouds of millions of twitching water-fleas on sale by the ladleful or cupful as food for fish kept in aquaria. Other rows of tables displayed aquarium plants, birdseed and bird cages. Ten men at once were staring earnestly at a tiny multicoloured top minnow being held up in a jam jar by an eighteen-year-old boy.

I climbed laboriously between budgerigar cages on to the counter of a stall and started my movie camera buzzing. One by one I picked out faces – Muscovites, not on parades or demonstrations, but stroking cats, admiring angel-fish, whistling at birds, people just like us.

Normally nobody takes films here. A small crowd quickly gathered round me, which soon discovered that I was a German and from the

'FRG' to boot, the Russian initials which stand for the West German Federal Republic. A policeman appeared, who ordered me to pack up my gear and led us both off through the interested though not unfriendly crowds. I had indeed no pass which allowed me to take films in the Soviet Union – that was unnecessary, I had been told – but I could not help laughing. I have been arrested often enough in my time, including several occasions which took place under much more unpleasant circumstances. Svetlana, who was in any case frightened by the throng of people and animals, kept whispering to me to be 'serious', because the police could so easily become unpleasant!

When the station inspector had first dealt with the usual queue of customers he kindly let us go without more ado. But no sooner was I back again and filming a couple of canaries than we were at once arrested by another policeman. 'Haven't you done enough filming?' asked the duty sergeant back at the station. 'There are ten policemen out on the beat. If you go back there again you'll probably be arrested eight more times until they all get to know you.'

I had in any case finished and I felt sorry for the terrified Svetlana. I felt thoroughly at home here. In the Silesian town of Neisse where I grew up the weekly market had always been a great event since as a boy I had always bred chickens, pigeons, ducks and even goats. For this reason I disliked the long hours in class at High School. My means of escape was always to ask 'to be excused' ten minutes before long break and simply not to come back until the next period began. I would run down to the market stall-keepers, the cages of chickens, the horses straining at the farmers' carts, the herds of geese and baskets of pigeons. . . . I can quite understand all those Muscovites who go to the animal market.

After my return to Frankfurt several people from Moscow wrote to say that there were plenty of dogs in Moscow after all – one hundred thousand pedigree dogs alone and over a million cats. The 'Blue Cross', the first-aid service for animals, has fifty animal ambulances; the waiting rooms of veterinary hospitals are generally full and treatment is free. I don't know whether this figure for the dog population is official or whether it is a mere private estimate. As a comparison, Moscow has seven million inhabitants: Frankfurt on Main, with seven hundred thousand inhabitants has fifteen thousand seven hundred and eighty-four stray dogs. Another Muscovite wrote to me: 'The reason why you saw so few dogs in Moscow has less to do with the housing shortage (although this is undoubtedly a factor) than with the strict regulations laid down by the "Mossoviet" (city council), which has banned dogs from a great number of streets, including almost the entire city centre. In Leningrad, where housing conditions are certainly no better, but where the centre is much better off for parks, you find many more dogs, just as you do in the *dacha* suburbs round Moscow. It depends, therefore, on the Mossoviet whether the dogs will eventually take over Moscow.'

[1] The German form *Kreml* is much closer to the sound of the Russian word than is the English version.

[2] *Parikmacher* – russianised form of the German *Perückenmacher* (lit. wigmaker or *posticheur*).

My mother once had a sable coat. It was by then extremely old and somewhat shabby but whenever, in the early 'twenties, she took it to be re-styled or moth-proofed for the summer, the furrier could not keep a note of respect and admiration out of his voice. These Russian animals had then become so rare as to be regarded as almost mythical beasts. Even quite recently I read somewhere that there were only two sable coats in the world. One of them Stalin had presented to Queen Soraya on a state visit. One sable pelt was said to cost anything between £725 and £2,000.

Not unnaturally I grew up with a feeling of something like awe towards these costly, unknown Russian animals. I never imagined that I should ever see one alive, for they are a state monopoly of the Soviet Union. I believe that twenty or thirty years ago a pair of sables was sold to North America, but they had almost certainly been gelded because they never produced any progeny.

It was therefore an exciting moment when I first saw live sables, several hundred of them at once. This happened at the big state Breeding Farm for fur-bearing animals at Pushkino, about thirty kilometres outside Moscow. The stock also included twenty thousand mink and eight hundred female silver foxes. In Germany the silver fox farms, which once flourished so greatly, have all been long since given up. Around 1900, when the only silver foxes to be had were wild ones, a single good pelt fetched 1,000 gold sovereigns at the London auctions. Later silver fox farming greatly increased the numbers available and they became much cheaper. By 1940 one and a quarter million silver fox pelts were coming on the market every year and each one cost no more than £20 or £30. Also, farm-bred silver fox fur too easily acquires a slight reddish tint which furriers dislike. Long-haired pelts are in any case unfashionable nowadays, as they make women look too bulky and for this reason silver fox culture has been discontinued, even in Scandinavia and North America. Only in the Soviet Union is it kept up, no doubt waiting for D-Day when it becomes the fashion again. Meanwhile there is always a certain demand for it in Russia itself.

Much greater emphasis, however, has been placed on the blue or arctic fox. These little creatures, which even in the Arctic are extremely trusting and tame, not to say cheeky, have the great advantage that they breed like rabbits – indeed, even faster than rabbits. They produce on an average between thirteen and fifteen cubs in a litter, sometimes as many as twenty whereas silver fox vixens only have half as many.

Then there are the hundred female sables. Every April most of them drop a litter of three or four, but the number can be as many as seven. They are killed for their skins in October of the same year. The sex ratio is kept at one male for every ten female sables. There are altogether about ninety of these big fur farms in the Soviet Union.

All these animals live in cages of wire netting. They also run about on wire netting, so that the droppings fall through the mesh and can be easily collected. They sleep in little wooden boxes. These cages of foxes, mink and sables stand in long rows in clearings in the forest. Besides the sables they house eight hundred female silver foxes, seven hundred arctic foxes and two thousand mink with young. Mink fur is at the moment the most fashionable in the world. In 1964-65 the world crop is expected to amount to twenty million mink pelts. Thirty years ago it was only a million, most of them wild pelts. The total area of the Pushkino farm is sixty-six acres, roughly equivalent in size to a large zoo.

1 *The largest wild animal in Europe is the European bison. A bull bison can grow to be six feet six inches from the ground to the top of its back and to weigh seventeen hundred-weight; a human observer literally has to look up to this animal.*

2 *A view of one of Moscow's gigantic skyscraper apartment blocks, a legacy of the Stalin era, seen from the Children's Zoo of the Zoological Gardens. In the foreground, seen from inside, is the new entrance gateway to the Moscow Zoo.*

Unfortunately the long rows of covered cages between the trees, the incessant rain and the black wall of an approaching thunderstorm made lighting conditions so bad that filming a sable seemed impossible. I therefore asked a 'brigade leader' whether there wasn't a tame young sable which could be taken out and put in a clearing where there was more light. The 'brigade leader' was a girl, about twenty-five years old, dressed in trousers and with a bright kerchief round her head. Pushkino is staffed by thirteen of these 'brigades', each one eight men – or rather eight girls – strong and all of them with five years training behind them. My attractive brigadier took pity on me and picked out a young sable. He was very badly behaved and bit her ear, but the second one allowed itself to be filmed. There was just enough light, using the widest aperture, to make a film of the grey-brown beast. It had the colouring most highly sought after by furriers, known as 'water'; if there is the slightest tint of yellow in the pelt it will fetch a great deal less money.

My mother's sable coat had not originally been very costly. The pelts had formed the inner lining of my grandfather's large travelling-cloak, which she had had removed and made up into a coat. A century or more ago sables were by no means rare and were found throughout the north of Siberia and Russia all the way from Kamchatka to Scandinavia. In the year 1600 Tsar Boris Godunov despatched forty thousand three hundred and sixty pelts to Vienna in one consignment. In Kamchatka at that time sable were killed merely for their meat, the skin being looked upon as worthless, worse than dog-skin. When the Kamchatkans had to pay taxes to the tsars they were delighted to be allowed to pay them in sable pelts. It was usual in those days to

3 *This temple must be the most imposing building ever erected for cage rabbits. Instead of the usual gods and allegorical figures there are rabbits carved in relief friezes and decorating the capitals of the columns. The temple is in a remote corner of the grounds of the permanent 'Exhibition of Economic Achievements' in Moscow, which is otherwise chiefly occupied by gigantic and rather pompous exhibition pavilions devoted to the individual Soviet republics.*

barter a knife for eight sable pelts, an axe for sixteen. A trapper could easily catch seventy or eighty of these animals in one winter. In the eighteenth century several hundred thousand sable pelts changed hands every year at the great fur fair of Irbit in the Urals.

But as the price of fur rose, so the trappers' keenness to catch these martens increased with it, and the number of sables fell rapidly. Thus their pelts became ever rarer and more costly and it became still more profitable to hunt them – a vicious circle which has led to the extermination of so many animal species from the earth. Around 1900 no more than between forty-eight thousand and fifty-three thousand sable pelts were traded at Irbit, whilst in the years from 1910 to 1913 the number fell to between twenty thousand and twenty-five thousand. It grew less every year. The times were long past when a Russian official in Kamchatka could make his fortune in a few years by making fifty-fold profits in bartering food and utensils with the Kamchatkans. Even in the farthest East the natives had come to realise the value of sable pelts. These precious animals had meanwhile been virtually exterminated throughout the whole vast empire of the tsars. Only in the Altai, in the Kuznetsky Alatau and in farthest Yakutia were a few specimens still extant.

The size of a sable, making it a much easier target than many of the smaller fur-bearing animals, was undoubtedly a factor aiding its extinction. Sables are closely related to our martens, but have much longer legs, an orange fleck at the throat, a much glossier silky fur and above all larger feet. This latter characteristic is probably due to their spending much of the year in snow: their feet make marks nearly as large as those of smaller members of the bear family, compared with the delicate paw-marks made by other martens. Sables are passionate hunters of squirrels and other rodents, of birds and all kinds of fish. They even attack large geese, which have frequently been known to take off in flight with their attacker hanging on to them with its teeth, but they are gradually forced down in the sable's mortal grip. The sable is even reported to kill musk deer, creatures about half the size of roedeer. Although they are such bloodthirsty predators sables easily grow tame, as do our native martens, if they are brought up from young by humans. In the last century a tame sable is said to have lived in the palace of the Archbishop of Tobolsk and was even allowed the run of the town. After a meal it always demanded a drink and would then fall fast asleep; it was apparently almost unconscious for several hours when in this state and could be pinched and poked without giving a sign of life. It was, however, extremely hostile to cats. When it saw one it would rear up on its hind legs and had to be restrained from attacking the cat.

Originally sables were either shot or bitten to death by dogs whenever they could be flushed. As the pelts grew more valuable, hunters tried increasingly to avoid peppering the skins with gunshot. Instead they preferred to hunt them in winter with packs of dogs. They would be driven up a tree, which was then shaken or simply felled to bring down the sable. Other northern hunters would lay snares across the sables' tracks, in places where they used long branches to cross over rivers and streams. The sable when caught in one of these snares would fall into the water and drown with the long snare still round its neck. Nowadays a tree is felled at a height of about three feet from the ground, a little wooden cage is placed on the stump with the branch of a tree running up like a ramp from the ground to an opening in the cage. The cage contains a trap, baited with poultry or soured elk's liver. If the sable dies in the cage there is at the most the risk that it will be devoured by another predator before the trapper can collect the valuable pelt.

What use was it when sable pelts fetched higher and higher prices in Irbit or Leipzig, if the species itself was rapidly disappearing – indeed when the probability of complete extinction was imminent? For this reason the tsarist government decreed the establishment in 1913 of three conservancy areas in eastern Siberia in which the hunting and trapping of sable was prohibited. Unfortunately this move was completely unsuccessful, probably due in part to the outbreak shortly afterwards of the first World War. After the Russian revolution, the sables had slightly increased in numbers: now and again they were seen in regions which they had not frequented for several decades. This was clearly a result of the civil war, when there had not been many people with time to spare for hunting sable, but it was equally clear that the situation would soon deteriorate again.

Farsighted men in the new government began considering how to reintroduce the big martens with the yellowish-red throats into areas in which they had once lived unmolested for several millenia. The same problem affected other wild animals in the Soviet Union – elk, maral, beaver, saiga antelopes, European bison and ibex. To populate an area with an animal species means releasing breeding couples; but how were breeding sable to be found and caught? To catch the last few dozen alive and transport them, still alive, across thousands of miles seemed hopeless. If it were to succeed at all they would have to be held captive and bred like silver fox, mink or nutria. How could this feat be achieved?

The man who devoted himself particularly to this problem in the 'twenties was Professor B. Manteufel of the Moscow Institute of Zoology. One of the undoubted reasons for the failure of previous attempts was the completely erroneous theory concerning the gestation period of the sable. This was only disproved by the astonishing dis-covery that they had a gestation period, not of two months as had hitherto been believed, but of a full nine months, from July to April. The fertilised embryo remains dormant within the placenta for the time of hibernation and only begins to develop when this period is over. Because it had been thought that the rutting season was in early spring, the bucks had generally been put to the does too late. Professor Man-teufel now mated them considerably earlier and his caged sables in the old Moscow Zoo produced young. It was a great achievement: for the first time these regal beasts, these valuable earners of foreign currency, had bred in captivity.

But it went no further. No more broods were produced and no explanation for it could be found. In the wild the sable only eats the head, i.e. the brain, the neck and the liver of its larger prey, of grouse and of partridge. Only small animals does it eat whole. The brain is rich in lipoids. The neck and the breast cavity contain the glands of internal secretion. Manteufel therefore fed his sables on chicken heads, liver and bones. He also found that strong electric light over the cages had a good effect. They attracted insects which fell down and were greedily devoured by the sables, to which the professor added meal-worms. But the sables in the Moscow Zoo continued infertile.

At that time, in the 'twenties, the Soviets were extremely anxious to build up large-scale fur farming. They sent study groups abroad and between 1927 and 1931 they imported truckloads of silver fox, mus-quash, raccoon and mink from Canada via Hamburg. A German specialist in fur-bearing animals, Dr Paul Schöps, who is still living today in Leipzig, used to take charge of the animals in Hamburg and forward them by Russian steamer or by rail to Leningrad. In Germany a fur farm had been set up in the early 'twenties at Hirschegg-Riezlern in the Kleiner Walsertal and in 1927 its director, Dr Fritz Schmidt, went to Russia as expert adviser to the Soviet government. He built the first Russian fur farms and was also the first Scientific Director of the Central Instructional Farm at Pushkino. Schmidt stayed in Russia until 1934, by which time the first one hundred and thirty-six young sables had been bred in captivity and the further propagation of this most valuable fur-bearing animal was well under way. In Dr Schmidt's opinion his success was not due to any special knack; he simply let the animals alone, removed the night-time electric lighting, stopped the perpetual tests and experiments and – waited.

The fine young sable which grew up in wire cages were not to be simply slaughtered to gratify a few rich women. The breeders waited until they were fully grown – the body twenty inches, the tail eight inches long – and then took them in couples to all the places where sables had once flourished in old Russia. By 1957 twelve thousand five hundred had been distributed to recreate the wild sable population of the Soviet Union, a sensible policy which soon began to pay off. At the 1956 auction in Leningrad fourteen thousand one hundred and ten sable pelts were on offer and there are now more sable in Siberia than there were a century ago.

Nevertheless sable pelts are still a rarity and one can understand why a finished sable coat costs from £6,000 to £8,000 with manufacturing costs and the maker's profit. Furriers have told me that there are now probably about fifteen to twenty sable coats in the world, of which in recent years three or four have been made in West Germany alone. Dense-haired furs such as sable are in any case used more for capes, stoles and trimming on elegant dresses because as coats they are bulky and make the wearer look altogether too well covered.

These valuable animals of the marten family are a good example of how wild animals need not become extinct if the government of the country actively intervenes to preserve them.

I flew from Moscow via Kiev to Kherson on the lower reaches of the Dnieper, a rather dull provincial town which has grown from a population of ninety-seven thousand in 1939 to one hundred and seventy thousand today. There I took a taxi and drove about one hundred miles to a place which is of interest to all, at least to all German-speaking, animal-lovers in the world. In the last few decades it has become shrouded in legend and nobody has had any exact information about what has happened there. Even the Soviet Embassy at Rolands-werth near Bonn had maintained that there were no longer any wild animals there and the Ministry of Culture in Moscow said the same thing; but the Russian zoologists knew better.

The roads cross the absolutely flat land as straight as rulers. To right and left are fields of grain, an endless sequence of giant spaces. Parallel with both sides of the broad macadam road run five or six rows of young trees, which can only have been recently planted. Every ten or twelve yards stands a tall plant of some four feet high with brilliant flowers. But the most glorious show of colours grows monotonous when it is repeated again and again.

As we were driving along at forty miles an hour my thoughts wandered to Africa where not long ago during a flight stopover in Khartoum I had sailed across the Nile to the tomb of the Mahdi, the religious fanatic whose troops killed General Gordon and who was then defeated and expelled by the British. General Slatin Pasha, by birth an Austrian named Rudolph Slatin, spent twelve years, from 1883 to 1895, as a prisoner of the Mahdi and of his successor, the Khalifa. Afterwards Slatin Pasha wrote:

'It was in the month of December 1892 that I received the command to appear at once before the Khalifa. I found him surrounded by his

Kadhis, the threats and homilies which I had but recently received as a result of the slandering of Tajjib Ali were still fresh in my memory and an unpleasant feeling crept over me when the Khalifa, without offering his customary response to my greeting, ordered me to be seated within the circle of his judges. "Take this thing," he said to me, with grave expression, after a short pause, "and draw out what it contains."

'I stood up, took the proferred object and began to inspect it. I was holding in my hand a brass ring of about two inches in diameter, to which was attached a small brass capsule somewhat of the shape and size of a revolver cartridge. An attempt had already been made to open it and I could see clearly that it contained a piece of paper. It was an unpleasant moment.

'Was it a letter meant for me from my family or from the Egyptian government and had the bearer of it been discovered and seized? If it were, then the outlook was bad for me. I made an effort to remain calm. As I forced the capsule half open with a knife that had been handed to me and was attempting to withdraw the paper, I rapidly considered how I should best behave and what I had to say. Fortunately my histrionic powers were put to no great test: I had soon removed the two slips of paper from the capsule and unfolded them. In four languages, in German, English, French and Russian was written in small but legible script the following: "This crane was born and reared on my estate of Askania Nova, Tauride Province, South Russia. The finder is requested to inform me of where this bird was caught or killed. September 1892. Fr Falz-Fein."

'I raised my head feeling less constrained. "Now," demanded the Khalifa, "what news does this paper contain?" "My lord," I replied, "this ring must have hung round the neck of a bird which has been killed. Its former owner, a man living in Europe, begs to be informed of the place where the bird was caught or killed."

' "Thou hast spoken the truth," said the Khalifa in a somewhat kinder tone; "the bird was brought down by a sheikh near Dongola and this capsule found on its neck. He brought it to the Emir Yunis Noled ed Dikem whose scribe, however, was unable to decipher the

Christian script. He sent me this thing. Tell me once again, what is written on that piece of paper?" I translated the content literally and also attempted, at his request, to describe the approximate distance and position of the country from whence the bird had come.

' "This is another piece of devilry of the infidel," he finally declared, "who fritter away their lives with such useless matters. A faithful muslim would never attempt such a thing."

'I handed the capsule to the scribe who was present and withdrew, having first cast a last rapid glance at the message: "Askania Nova, Tauride, South Russia, Falz-Fein." I returned to my quarters, murmuring the words to myself in order to impress them on my memory and resolved, if God willing I should regain my freedom, to inform that man of the fate of his crane, which had caused me to pass a few extremely anxious moments.

'After some years, when I had been released and brought to Cairo, I was standing on the balcony of the consul's palace and admiring the fine park resplendent in the beauty of spring, when I saw a tame heron walking among the flower beds. The recollection which it aroused was at first unclear; then suddenly I remembered the words: "Falz-Fein, Askania Nova, Tauride Province, South Russia." I returned to my room and wrote a few lines to that address, describing how late in 1892 a female crane had been shot at Dongola. The sincere words of thanks which I soon received were proof that my interest in this little episode was warmly appreciated.'

Rudolph Slatin never reached southern Russia and even Friedrich von Falz-Fein, although one of the world's richest animal-lovers, was never able to carry out his plans for an expedition to Africa.

I now started to ask the way to Askania Nova. Not even the driver was quite sure where it was, since he hardly ever drove so far out of Kherson. We took a right-angled turn off the main road – all the roads here intersect at right angles as though laid out on a gigantic grid system. A tractor was throwing up the black earth in great clouds of dust as it pulled along an enormous box-like machine which in one operation cut and threshed the grain and compressed the straw into

c

bales. The dust cloud slowly blew away as the tractor driver halted for us. Askania Nova? The man pointed to a line of trees, a wood far away on the horizon.

These were special trees. Their story begins with sheep. After the War of the Spanish Succession, when the Spaniards finally allowed the export of their famous merino sheep, the breeding of sheep began to flourish in Germany as elsewhere. In the Duchy of Anhalt they grew so skilled at washing and sorting the wool that even England bought its wool there for preference. Over one hundred thousand merino sheep were kept on the ducal estates – the tiny duchy of Anhalt-Köthen was too small to support any more sheep. For that reason, and because he was related to the Russian imperial family, the duke had the notion of founding a kind of Anhalt-Köthen colony in the under-populated and recently conquered south of Russia. He was given a grant of land of three hundred square miles and with it a ten-year exemption from taxation. He named this huge possession 'Askania Nova' after the county of Askania at the northern end of the Harz mountains.

On August 11, 1828 began one of the most audacious overland sheep-treks in history. Two thousand eight hundred and eighty-six pedigree sheep, two bulls, eight cows, eight horses and twenty-three men and women set out on foot from Anhalt to the Black Sea. Three wagons carried supplies of clothing, tools, utensils and seed. A day's march averaged between ten and fifteen miles. About a thousand of the sheep spent the winter on an estate near Poznan and when the odyssey finally reached the south Russian steppes they had only lost thirty-five sheep. The following year five thousand three hundred sheep made the same journey with even less loss and by 1830 approximately eight thousand sheep and one hundred and thirty German settlers, including a schoolmaster, a vintner, workmen and wool-sorters, had been safely moved to Askania Nova.

But the flow of wool and money, which the Kötheners had expected, failed to materialise. Far from it proving a source of income, the treasury of the little duchy was forced to subsidise the colony. When Commissioner Aue journeyed to Russia as the duke's official inspector, he sent a damning report back to Köthen. There had been quarrels between the officials of the colony. Ten thousand vines had been planted out in the arid steppes and had withered, as had all the fruit trees; the grain had wilted for lack of water. The Chief Bailiff, who was in charge of the colony, had apparently always allowed purchasers to choose the best sheep for themselves. As a result only the poorer animals were left in the flock and their numbers had dropped to thirty-two thousand. Arrears of wages alone amounted to 40,000 roubles. 'The entire economy of Askania Nova is the object of general derision, due to inept husbandry. The people here say that the duke of Anhalt must possess immeasurable riches in order to tolerate management of such hopeless inefficiency.'

Only the magnanimity of the tsar enabled the colony to survive. Again and again he renewed its exemption from taxes and crown land dues. But when the ducal line of Anhalt-Köthen was extinguished with the death of Duke Heinrich in 1847, his heir, the duke of Anhalt-Dessau, seized the first opportunity to rid himself of the whole disastrous undertaking. He sold it in 1856 to a Russo-German landowner, Friedrich Fein, for 525,000 Prussian thalers in cash, equal to over a million and a half gold marks. Over years the duchy had lost more than a million gold marks on the colony, due to obstinate insistence on German methods of agriculture in a completely unsuitable environment.

The riches of Friedrich Fein's family all stemmed from a slap in the face. In 1760 their forefather, gigantically tall, strong and irascible, had been given a box on the ears by an officer in a Württemburg regiment. The young man seized his musket and bayonetted the officer on the spot. He managed to escape and settled, after some time, in southern Russia. His son Friedrich was his equal in brute strength and quick temper. During an argument between them the father picked up a shotgun and fired at his son, who ran away to the Caucasus. There he too made a fortune, returned home after his father's death, bred more and more sheep and bought up estate after estate including, finally, Askania Nova. He succeeded in becoming the greatest sheep-farmer in all Russia, with a herd of seven hundred and fifty thousand highly valuable sheep.

Considerable skill, of course, was required to keep these animals alive on the steppes, which do not share the mild climate of the Crimean peninsula even though they lie a mere two hundred and fifty miles to the north of the Crimea. Every winter the sheep must spend a month or two penned up and if the farmer has not made enough hay that summer the flocks starve. In the terrible snowstorms of that region it is often impossible to drive the silly animals into their pens; the only hope is to drive past them with a sleigh loaded with hay, which the half-starved sheep may follow. Above all they must never be allowed to graze in the vicinity of the pens during the summer. The grass there must be left to grow and in winter herds of horses are driven round and round the sheep-pens in order to break up the snow crust to enable the sheep to reach fresh fodder near their pens. Wool, too, did not fetch as much money in those days as it was really worth: it was too full of dust and dirt. The sparse wells, dug with much difficulty, only provided enough to water the sheep but not enough to wash them before shearing. Quantity alone earned the money.

This it did with some success. Friedrich's only daughter married an energetic partner of her father, a Saxon named Johann Gottlieb Pfalz. The tsar allowed him to assume the double name of Pfalz-Fein, which was soon modified to Falz-Fein as there is no sound for 'pf' in Russian. Once when Friedrich, who loved travelling, was sailing down the Danube in a steamer from Budapest to the Black Sea coast, he found himself in company with some Hungarian sheep-farmers. Friedrich joined in with them, talking shop about wool, shepherds, herds and grassland. The Hungarians stared haughtily at the modestly dressed foreigner, making it plain that an ignoramus had no business to join in their professional talk – until Friedrich remarked, quite by the way, that he happened to own more sheepdogs than the entire stock of sheep of all of them put together.

This was no exaggeration: the family grew more and more prosperous. They had estates in Mecklenburg, a villa near Nice, and a fairytale white castle built in the gothic style with sixty sumptuously furnished rooms on the shore of the Black Sea, where week-long birthday parties were held, attended by the entire local population.

But it would never have occurred to me to travel to that remote corner of the Ukraine if the last of the line, Friedrich Falz-Fein, had not also been a passionate amateur zoologist. While still at school he had been allowed to build an aviary. When out hunting he was delighted if he only slightly wounded a bird, as he could then take it to his aviary and nurse it back to health. Once, towards the end of a day's hunting, his shotgun went off as a result of a careless movement and the entire charge entered the upper part of his right arm. In order not to upset his parents he hastily bandaged himself, put on another jacket and joined the Christmas festivities. When one of the guests, a schoolteacher, shook him by the hand with particular warmth he was overcome and fainted with pain.

Worse befell him when in 1890 he assumed the management of the estates on the death of his father. Having been obliged to dismiss a surly and obstinate bailiff, there was an explosion in the wing of the house which contained Friedrich's bedroom. Not until the following morning were his rescuers able to drag him from the ruins unconscious, badly wounded and with several broken ribs. Luckily a beam from the ceiling had fallen across the head and foot of his iron bedstead in such a way as to form a 'roof' which had protected Friedrich from the worst of the falling rubble. An unknown culprit had filled the stove with gunpowder and exploded it with a slow-burning fuse.

Friedrich Falz-Fein, who neither smoked nor drank, turned his astounding energy to building more and bigger aviaries and bird-cages. The real beginning of the animal sanctuary of Askania Nova dates from 1887. In that year he engaged an expert English hydrologist who succeeded in sinking the first artesian well in southern Russia. Good, clear water was found at a depth of two hundred and thirty feet and a mechanical pump was installed which raised three hundred thousand gallons of water per day. Later all Falz-Fein's neighbours followed his example and sank artesian wells. By this means and with the aid of dams to control the rivers, the steppes, once uninhabited except by nomads, have come to be one of the granaries of the Soviet Union.

The water tower, built in the style of a ruin, stands to this day although it is completely overgrown with ivy. It is the source of the water which flows in canals through the 'zoological park' where ducks and geese from every land under the sun can be found swimming, until it reaches the great pond, home of flamingoes and pelicans. Friedrich Falz-Fein imported six hundred different species of trees and attempted to create a great botanical park in the middle of the steppes; of these, two hundred species became acclimatised and flourished. I spent an evening walking to the sound of nightingales along well-kept paths through this man-made paradise.

Friedrich did not have to keep his birds caged for long: they gladly stayed in this unique island of trees in the midst of the great treeless steppes. The first canaries had had their wings clipped, but after their first moult and with the next generation it was no longer necessary. More and more birds of passage came to know this oasis of greenery where there was always food. Soon orioles, nightingales, whitethroats, great tits and other small songbirds joined the canaries. Some migratory birds even spent the whole summer there and after several decades in addition to indigenous birds about forty foreign species had settled there permanently, including little owls, hoopoes, storks, crested larks, swallows, doves, sparrows, starlings, jackdaws, white-wagtails, sparrow hawks, lapwing, finches, cuckoos, laughing-doves, nightingales, magpies, marsh harriers and black-headed gulls.

Year by year the sheep magnate derived increasing pleasure from his animal reserve. He corresponded with famous German animal dealers such as Hagenbeck and Ruhe. The South American nandu ostrich found his estate particularly congenial and bred in large numbers, followed by Australian emus and African ostriches (although the latter apparently found the steppes too cold and did not breed), whilst four species of kangaroos, camels, dromedaries and llamas settled down there, as did thirteen species of deer, twenty species of antelope, ibex, aruis sheep, yaks, zebras, marmots and water buffalo. In 1889 Friedrich visited the Paris World's Fair and made the acquaintance of the famous zoologist Geoffroy St Hilaire, who aroused him to even greater enthusiasm for his private zoo: 'You are a lover of nature; you have knowledge; you have energy and you are rich,' said the Frenchman.

Unfortunately Friedrich Falz-Fein never succeeded in keeping a couple of the vanishing breed of wild horses of the Russian steppe. His attention was drawn to them too late. As early as the 1870s his father, returning home from his travels, had often described how he had seen a herd of wild horses on the steppes. Finally there were only eight of them, then five, then only two horses and always in the same area. These wild horses, which are smaller and more delicately built than Przewalski's wild horse of east Asia, were at one time common in the south Russian steppes together with imperial eagles, vultures, bustards, pelicans, jumping hares, saiga antelope and wolves. As the human population of the steppes increased, more and more wild horses were shot – generally for the sheer fun of the chase. The aggressive wild stallions had often been known to cover a grazing mare of a domestic breed, but in Falz-Fein's opinion no domestic stallion had ever managed to cover a wild mare – the wild stallions were much too jealous and fierce to allow it. Thus the last wild horses were pure-blooded and uncrossed with domestic breeds.

One day Falz-Fein senior announced that there was now only one single wild mare at large on the Rachmanov steppe and the lonely animal was slowly drawing nearer to a herd of domestic horses. When the herdsmen were absent, she would join them, but as soon as a herdsman appeared the mare would canter off and keep her distance. She was never seen to lie down, although the domestic horses always spent some of the day resting. After three years the mare grew gradually tamer and she then bore two foals by a tame stallion. Finally one winter the mare followed the herd into the pen and even into the stable. They seized this opportunity, let the tame horses out and caught the wild mare by chasing her into a loose-box. She behaved with great ferocity, leaped at the walls and refused fodder for several days. She also lost an eye while being rounded up.

In time this mare, the last specimen of the south Russian wild horse, grew tamer and bore her third foal in the stable, although she still refused to be touched or groomed. As she would even allow herself to be let out on the halter to water, Durilin the landowner who had caught her and cared for her, believed that she would now stay with the herd when they were put out to graze in the spring. But when the animals were let out she gave a loud whinny and galloped off into the steppe. She did come back to look for her foal, but then vanished again never to return. Caught and stabled, fed and cared for, she had never lost her urge for freedom.

Next autumn the peasants in the big village of Agaimany, twenty-four miles away from Askania Nova, found the lone mare in the neighbourhood. They decided to organise a hunt to catch her during the Christmas holiday, probably as a trial of speed for their own horses. They posted a widely-spaced line of mounted men and drove her from one to the other. In spite of the succession of fresh horses she managed to show them all a clean pair of heels. She jumped effortlessly over the high snowdrifts. She would never have been caught if she had not stumbled in a crack in the ground and broken her leg. The peasants

4   *Every day at various locations in the suburbs of Moscow there are three large permanent markets dealing exclusively in pet animals; budgerigars, cage-birds, pedigree pigeons, chickens, rabbits, aquarium fish, water-fleas and water-weed for the fish, food for the most varied sorts of animals, fancy poultry. Often as many as four to five thousand people at a time are to be found at these markets.*

5   *The first sable that I ever saw in my life. The Soviet Union has a monopoly of sable-breeding. There are only about a round dozen sable coats in the world and each one probably costs about £8,000–£9,000. Years of experiment were needed before sable were successfully bred in captivity.*

6   *East African gnus, which have been living in semi-captivity in Russia for generations, stand beside prehistoric Scythian stone images found in the Tauride Steppe.*

carried her by sleigh to the village where the whole population stared at her. Unfortunately she died a few days later in spite of the villagers' efforts to make her an artificial leg.

Thus perished the last of a proud race, defending her freedom to the end. Since then there will never again be a wild horse of the southern steppes on this earth. The creatures that are exhibited in many zoos under the name of 'tarpan' as having been 'bred back' to the steppe horse are nothing but domestic horses of grey colouring.

Friedrich Falz-Fein feared that the same fate might overcome Przewalski's wild horse. He therefore sent gifts to Mongolian princes and notables of all kinds and finally made the acquaintance of a merchant in the Siberian province of Tomsk, a man by the name of Asanov, engaged in the China trade. With his help the first expeditions were equipped to explore the animals' habitat and in 1897 a number of young Przewalski's horse were caught. But they all died from clumsy handling, so Falz-Fein ordered that they were not to be caught by chasing them, but by shooting the brood mares. As no tame mares were to be had from the Mongols, some had to be bought in Biisk and covered at the right time to ensure that they foaled simultaneously with the wild horses. The tame foals were killed and the wild foals draped in their skins so that the tame mares would accept them as their own.

7 *Eland have been kept at Askania Nova since the 'eighties of the last century. Many of them are as tame as domestic cattle and can be milked.*

8 *The great landowner Friedrich von Falz-Fein spent a fortune in capturing a few of the last of Przewalski's wild horse in far Mongolia and bringing them to Askania Nova. Hagenbeck of Hamburg beat him to the second consignment. Today once more a small herd of Przewalski's wild horse live at Askania Nova.*

9 *In 1892 the Khalifa (Sayyid Abdullah ibn Sayyid Mohammed, successor to the Mahdi as a leader of the rebels in the Egyptian Sudan, 1846-1899) took counsel with his khalifs over a remarkable document found attached to the neck of a crane.*

These instructions were not followed with enough care and as a result the captive wild horses again died. At the next attempt, however, the method succeeded. The first foals to survive in captivity were caught in 1899, six mares and a stallion. Five of them survived the three hundred-mile journey to the railway at Biisk and were taken by train to within forty-five miles of Askania Nova.

'In the spring of 1901 I was in Antwerp, where I met Hagenbeck,' wrote Friedrich Falz-Fein. 'He would have liked to have known how I had managed to keep my wild horses, but as he himself was never informative on such matters I likewise told him nothing. I had just bought a number of animals from the zoo and accepted Hagenbeck's offer to have them taken to Askania Nova by one of his employees who was just due to leave for southern Russia. This man questioned my people about the methods of procuring the wild horses, set off in the autumn of 1901 straight for Biisk and bought from Asanov the twenty-eight horses that had been intended for me. The horses reached Hamburg and in 1902 Hagenbeck bought another batch. In 1903 and 1904 I was able to buy a few from Asanov.'

During the 'nineties some of the exotic animals to reach this remote corner of Russia were accompanied by a Negro named Thomas, a circus hand, about whom Friedrich Falz-Fein continued: 'He had extraordinary success with the women of Askania Nova. The interest shown by the Ukrainian girls might have had undesirable consequences had not Falz-Fein taken one of the girls in hand and shown her the striped zebras as an example of what sort of children might result from a liaison between black and white. From that moment Thomas' attraction for the local girls dwindled.' Nevertheless he became engaged and would have married had not galloping consumption and violent stomach pains brought him to his grave. Although he was a heathen he was buried in the village cemetery and all Askania Nova mourned their good and faithful black brother.

In 1897 Friedrich's six brothers and sisters gave him a present of a number of American bison out of gratitude for the fair way in which he had divided up their joint inheritance from their father and for his good husbandry of the estates. Without much trouble Friedrich succeeded in producing a crossbreed of these huge buffaloes and domestic cattle. The resulting bastards were much stronger and bigger than their mothers, the ordinary cows. On hot summer days, for instance, the tough Podolian cattle had to be changed in shifts to draw the reaping machines, but the bison-domestic cattle crossbreeds worked from morning till night without respite.

This herd of bison still flourishes at Askania Nova. I drove out to see them in the steppes with N. B. Labanov in a one-horse cart pulled by a grey. It was straight out of the past – a flat cart consisting of no more than four wheels with a platform between them and a seat. It was ideal for mounting all our film equipment and nothing was easier than to stop if a herd of deer surrounded us, if the camels wanted to inspect us or a group of East African gnu flashed past and around us, cavorting and swinging their tails. Decades of life at Askania Nova have not made these frisky great black antelopes any tamer, although they have to be rounded up every winter.

The bison, on the other hand, seemed to me to behave very much like cattle. A mounted herdsman keeps watch over them on the steppes in order that they may be rounded up every evening into one of the enormous corrals. It is exactly the kind of scene that one might have seen a hundred years ago on the American prairie. We could go as near to the bisons as one can to cows, even though they were suckling new-born calves. A few crossbred animals were among the herd; the herdsman separated them so that I could film the true bisons alone. I found these mongrel beasts most unattractive.

In a book about his brother Friedrich, which was translated into German and published in Berlin in 1930, Woldemar von Falz-Fein complained that Askania Nova had been renamed 'Chapli'. That may have been true during the first few years after the revolution, but nowadays the name Askania Nova, naturally transliterated in Cyrillic letters – 'АСКАНИЯ НОВА', figures in all Russian atlases and reference books. Since 1956 the estate has been transferred to the Ukrainian Academy of Agricultural Science. It still amounts to two hundred square miles in extent, of which eighty-one square miles are virgin steppe and of these ten square miles have been maintained in their natural state without any form of human interference. The scientific side has been considerably strengthened: eighty scientists now work here, plus two hundred and twenty laboratory technicians, the total amounting to two thousand employees. Askania Nova has become almost a small town with broad, tree-lined streets and about six thousand inhabitants. The botanical park and zoological gardens are well kept. Both the houses of the Falz-Feins are today offices and institutes. Even though Askania Nova no longer belongs to his family, Friedrich von Falz-Fein would undoubtedly be pleased at the way in which his ideas and plans have been carried on.

The number of sheep on the estate has admittedly dropped from four hundred thousand to seven thousand; but whilst the Falz-Feins kept at first a mere two per cent of the land under plough, which eventually rose to seventeen per cent, today more than two-thirds of it is ploughed. The remaining sheep are experimental animals, from which good wool-bearing and resistant strains are bred. (Today in the USSR there are one hundred and thirty-five million sheep, of which in the Tashkent area alone some ten million were lost in recent years through drought. This loss has in the meantime been made good.)

Shortly before I arrived there, Askania Nova had been visited by a New Zealander, Mr Bowen. He holds the world record for sheep-shearing: five hundred and eighty-one sheep in eight hours. He has a special knack of quieting the animals which enables him to shear the thick fleece in one minute. We in Germany take five minutes to do it. Before the electric shearing machine was invented, one man would take thirty-five to fifty minutes to shear one sheep and frequently nicked the skin in the process. A man could manage up to forty sheep in a day, a woman perhaps thirty. If a sheep was badly cut the shearer got no pay for that animal and if he accidentally smothered or strangled one he was docked four roubles. At the beginning of the century these shearers were paid two and a half kopecks per sheep, later five kopecks with free board and lodging, but he had to supply his own shears. At best a man could make about ten or eleven shillings a day. Each sheep rendered about nine pounds of wool in a year, which would make two good men's suits.

Friedrich Falz-Fein introduced steam-driven shearing machines as early as the 'nineties, although no one could operate them properly. He had a passion for innovation: M. F. Ivanov, the professor of animal genetics, offered him the opportunity of trying out artificial insemination of horses on his estate. It was a great success. By this means one stallion could fertilise not twenty but a hundred mares and the mares had only to be served once instead of four or five times.

At first everyone was extremely dubious about the method. The foals born by A.I. were regarded as somehow sub-standard. But one of the grand dukes arranged for half-bred remounts, which had been produced at Askania Nova by artificial insemination, to be sent to the cavalry officers' school at Petersburg for trials. From that moment all objections to them ceased. Artificial insemination, as introduced by Professor Ivanov, came into general use throughout the Soviet Union and its use, as we know, became accepted in all other European countries during the inter-war years.

Year by year the great sheep herds of Russia used to be decimated by anthrax, which also wrought havoc among cattle and horses. Soon after Pasteur had developed his anti-anthrax serum, Falz-Fein had it made for him by the Kharkov Veterinary Institute. When trials showed it to be successful, practically all the sheep at Askania Nova were inoculated in 1887. The result was catastrophic. News came practically hourly from the steppes that the inoculated sheep were dying, not by dozens but by hundreds. Sheep corpses lay everywhere. In spite of this Friedrich insisted that the experiment be renewed and by the 'nineties it was a complete success. Later compulsory inoculation was introduced in large areas of Russia, resulting in a steady fall in losses from anthrax – another innovation which, like the artesian wells, originated at Askania Nova.

All kinds of strange people, besides the strange animals, found their way to this idyllic estate in the steppes. A certain Wilhelm Konraetz, who loved nightingales but loved alcohol almost as much, lost his post at the Paris Opera and went to southern Russia as a music teacher. He taught the Falz-Fein children not only music but also German and English; not content with listening to the song of the nightingales at Askania Nova, he caught and caged a large number of these birds and was not happy until he had taught them to sing in his room as well as they sang out of doors. If they stopped, he had a way of making them sing again – he rubbed a brush over a sheet of paper. He left Askania Nova with a whole collection of trained nightingales. One day one of the Falz-Feins saw a seedy, sleeping figure on a bench in Paris and recognised him as Konraetz. He returned in contrition to Askania Nova.

A captain of dragoons, one Leo Kovyanko, who was frequently among the many visitors to the guest wing of the 'old house', was equally addicted to alcohol. As the governor-general had forbidden him to indulge in his amusement of driving a trained pig in his carriage through the streets of Odessa, he bought a trained cockerel, dressed it in general's uniform and made it march up and down crowing in front of the sentries outside the governor's palace. But he was nevertheless a hard-working deputy to the provincial parliament and always spoke up for the peasants, so that no one took his jokes amiss.

In the years before World War I Friedrich Falz-Fein employed nearly a hundred workmen in his zoological park and paid out wages amounting to 42,000 roubles a year. Askania Nova became increasingly famous and although it was so far from the railway, four thousand six hundred visitors a year came there to gaze at the exotic fauna. At that time it contained four hundred and two different species, including three hundred and forty-four species of birds, fifty species of hoofed animals plus kangaroos, Caucasian deer and marmots. Falz-Fein never kept any beasts of prey and this is still the rule today at Askania Nova.

One day the tsar himself announced that he would visit Askania Nova. The whole village was decorated, triumphal arches were built, the old house vanished beneath its adornments of flowers, flags and greenery. A company of Don cossacks was enlisted to keep order, as peasants and others poured in from all directions to see the autocrat of all the Russias. April 23, 1914, as the tsar and his suite drove into Askania Nova from the Crimea, was undoubtedly the climax of Falz-Fein's life. It was the first occasion on which the tsar had ever visited a private person within his own four walls and then spent several days as his guest. The tours and receptions were recorded on the newly-invented motion picture film by a representative from the Paris firm of Pathé. Ten days later Friedrich was summoned by a telegram from the tsar to the imperial palace at Livadia and on taking his leave Falz-Fein and his family were elevated to the hereditary nobility.

As far as I know this is the first and only example of someone being ennobled for keeping a zoo.

Then came the revolution, the occupation of Askania Nova by the Red Army, its seizure by the Germans and re-occupation by the Red Army. Friedrich fled the country by way of Constantinople; some of his family froze to death attempting to escape over the Black Sea; his mother was shot; the coffins of his ancestors were wrenched from their vault.

While Friedrich Falz-Fein was living as a refugee in the Hotel Continental in Berlin, he wrote to the son of Hermann Ruhe, the famous animal dealer, at Alfeld near Hanover, asking him to call on him. The old gentleman than handed a thick envelope to the son of his old friend. It came from a Jewish circus owner called Lorbeerbaum and contained a wad of thousand-rouble notes, the balance of payment due for animals that Ruhe had delivered before the war. He need never have paid the money, since German property had been sequestrated and confiscated by the tsarist government – even including the property of landowners of German descent who had been naturalised Russians for generations and had been decorated for bravery. Lorbeerbaum had lost his circus, but he had nevertheless found ways and means to make a voluntary discharge of his debt. Tears came to young Ruhe's eyes as he read the accompanying letter. 'A man's word was his bond in those days,' he said as he described the occasion to me years later.

Friedrich Falz-Fein died peacefully in a sanatorium at Bad Kissingen in 1920 and lies in the Cemetery of the Twelve Apostles in Berlin under two Russian eagles carved in stone. The inscription reads: 'Here rests in peace the great creator of Askania Nova.'

If Friedrich had stood there as I did on the day of my visit to Askania Nova, he would have found much to please him. The trees which he had planted are still there, only much bigger. The house in which he was born stands unchanged and he could still walk through the old rooms, even if they do now contain office furniture and type-writers. The fat stone statues of women, dug from ancient Scythian burial mounds in the steppes, are still outside the front door where he put them.

During World War II when large areas of Russia were occupied by German troops, Askania Nova was under German administration for a considerable time. Dr Hilmar Döring, who has been living in Venezuela for some years, was then working for the German Commissioner-General for the Crimea, Frauenfeld, as an administrative official. He has written to me as follows: 'One day when it was very dry at the height of summer, Frauenfeld summoned me in desperation. He had heard news that a steam traction engine had broken down at Askania Nova and that the whole artificial "forest" was threatened with destruction by drought within a few days. Before spares could be fetched from Rovno it would clearly be doomed. I had full powers from him to make every possible exertion to prevent such a catastrophe from occurring. "Full powers" in those days meant that I could make unlimited use of sunflower-oil, butter, eggs, etc. to get various key people to co-operate.

'With forty litres of sunflower oil and other delicacies I at once set off for Askania Nova, where I sized up the situation. The whole "forest" was irrigated by an ingeniously laid out network of trenches and runnels. The water came from an artesian well and was raised by a pump driven by a traction engine. This traction engine had quietly given up the ghost from old age without there being the slightest prospect of restoring it to even temporary working order. It was possible, however, to descry from some parts of the engine that it had come from Kherson. After an adventurous night drive I reached Aleshki (Tsuriupinsk), crossed the Dnieper and was in Kherson by next morning. To keep the local people occupied an energetic Area Commissioner had collected together all available components in the engineering works and had had them assembled into three almost perfect, brand-new traction engines. One was completed and tested. Then it was towed to Askania Nova by tractor. In no more than five days Askania Nova had a new traction engine and the "forest" had water again. It was saved.

'In my travels round those parts I noticed that the wheat in the steppes had fully developed ears but grew on stalks no more than a foot high. I asked some German farmers about this and they explained that this short-stemmed wheat was a variety specially bred for the climatic conditions of the steppes. In mid-summer in this continental climate the difference in temperature between day and night is considerable. This results in a very heavy precipitation of dew in the early hours of the morning, which at that time of the year is the only irrigation that the fields receive. If one were to grow the usual long-stemmed wheat, the plant would lose so much moisture through evaporation that the dew would be insufficient to keep it alive. With short-stemmed wheat, on the other hand, the water supply is adequate. The German farmers also noted that in the Russian winter the seed was liable to be uprooted by frost almost every year. In the fields that were protected from the wind by the woods of Askania Nova, however, there was a zone about six miles in depth where the frost never attacked the winter wheat.

'In the autumn of 1943 the Red Army advanced towards Dnepropetrovsk. If they progressed fast enough there was a danger that we should be surrounded and cut off. At that moment Frauenfeld received a long telegram, which stated in brief that there were two wild horses at Askania Nova, a stallion and a mare, which were two of the last few wild horses left in Europe. These horses were to be rounded up without delay and brought to the Berlin Zoological Garden. Signed: *Reichsmarschall* Hermann Goering.

'Frauenfeld blew his top, not because he considered this a frivolous

D

order to issue in the midst of a war but because of the practical impossibility of carrying it out during a general retreat. We discussed the matter. Frauenfeld decided that if any person on his staff could do the job, it was me. I was given the order to carry out Goering's instructions.

'My first thought was: "If you pull this off you'll be out of this damned salient and in safety." My second thought was: "If you don't pull it off, Goering will have you locked up." There being no choice, I set to work. At Askania Nova there were two first-class German grooms who were privately as glad as I was to get out of the ugly situation. These two set off to round up the wild horses and brought them in a little closer every day. After a week's work they managed to get them into two wooden crates made of two-inch-thick logs.

'Meanwhile in Kherson, with the aid of some butter, sunflower-oil and radio sets, I persuaded the Reichsbahn to allocate me two large freight cars, big enough to load up the horses and bring enough steppe-grass fodder for the journey.

'Throughout the trip, without interruption, the two wild horses thundered with their hindlegs against the sides of the crate in an attempt to get out. Every two hours we had to nail up the logs again and drive in new screws. The trip was beset with difficulties. All the railway stations were jammed full. Threats (backed by Goering's telegram) or contributions of butter, oil and sausage were the only means of getting shunted out of the sidings and hitched on to the next westbound train.

'The big trouble came at Hindenburg (Zabrze) in Upper Silesia. There the whole station was jammed with rolling-stock and not a locomotive in sight. Endless calls on the railway telephone system to the Traffic Manager in Breslau produced the only concession which the Reichsbahn could grant me; if you succeed in producing, in or around Hindenburg, one single locomotive in working order, then you can use it to drive your two waggons to Breslau.

'I found a loco – hidden away in a siding. The driver and fireman, however, refused to go. They had been on shift for twenty-six hours and that on empty stomachs. They were simply physically incapable of driving, although both would have dearly liked to get to Breslau, where wives and children were anxiously awaiting them. That being the case, I made them an offer, ten loaves of bread, six pounds of butter, a gallon of sunflower oil and two pounds of sausage per man. They agreed. Both ate their fill in our waggon and were given their promised rations. Meanwhile I was getting up steam in the engine; being a mechanical engineer I had once done a stretch as a locomotive fireman. A rail telegram was sent to Breslau that the special was ready to roll and finally came the green light. We soon reached Breslau, where against all traffic operating rules we were hitched on to the back of a passenger train for Berlin and moved rapidly towards our destination. We were uncoupled at a suburban station, Oberschöneweide, where I rang up the zoo. They arranged for us to be shunted into a small depot near the Lehrter Station and no sooner were we there than a truck came from the zoo and took over our two horse-boxes. They also took my live goose which I had bought from a peasant woman en route in order to celebrate my home-coming with my mother in Königsberg. The goose was boarded at the zoo for a week, while I finished my business in Berlin. Then I fetched it, ready-plucked and trussed, and took my leave.'

Professor Mihail Fyodorovich Ivanov, who knew Friedrich von Falz-Fein well and who had made the first experiments in artificial insemination at Askania Nova, became a famous man. After the revolution he carried out the planned breeding of the 'Askania fine fleeced sheep' and the 'Ukrainian white pig', breeds which are now widespread in the Soviet Union. Ivanov died at Askania Nova in 1935, aged sixty-four, and the great institute of animal genetics is named after him. In 1957 the main building, with his statue in front of it, was built in the classical style of a French chateau of the eighteenth century. Facing the entrance in the park is a large tablet bearing the names and photographs of the workers at Askania Nova who have particularly distinguished themselves in recent years and who have been nominated as 'Heroes of Labour'.

'If you were a Soviet citizen you would be made a "Hero of Labour" too!' the director of the zoo said to me, referring to my keenness to utilise every moment of my stay there. My sleeping quarters were in the guest-house, which is always in use by visitors from all over the Soviet Union and is as comfortable as a small hotel.

Early in the morning, when the state-run restaurant opened, I would quickly spoon up my borsch, the vegetable soup made with cream and eggs. Seated between workers from the Sovkhoz I would eat my barley porridge, my ham roll and drink my tea with plenty of lemon and sugar. Then, as in Africa, I generally did not eat again until evening in order to make full use of the light. The five zoo scientists gladly did the same.

We drove out into the steppe by jeep to the grazing land of a herd of forty-five African eland. They are the offpsring of the Falz-Fein eland and have been in the Ukraine for fifteen generations, equal to sixty-five years. During lunch the mounted herdsmen drove the herd into an enclosed courtyard between some stables. We opened the gate, Labanov then laid a great balk of timber on the ground in front of it. His plan worked: every eland shied at this unknown object on the ground, then plucked up courage and leaped over it in a mighty bound several yards in length. I stood to one side and in this way was able to take some wonderful film of these largest of African antelopes in spectacular action. In a second courtyard was a herd of domestic horses that had been crossed with wild Przewalski's stallions, containing every intermediary stage of breeding from pure wild stallion to domestic horse. Like the eland, they normally grazed free on the broad steppes, guarded by mounted keepers.

For safety's sake the seven pure blooded Przewalski's wild horses are kept fenced in a corral, although it is so big that the fence is scarcely detectable anywhere and one has the impression of seeing these animals living in the wilderness. One more was caught alive in Mongolia and she has twice foaled. The stallion came from Germany.

Nearby lives a herd of Böhm's zebra, the same subspecies of zebra to be found at Serengeti in East Africa. At first they seemed very shy, but finished by crowding round us and we were able to walk right through them. Onager and kulans are bred here, Asiatic wild asses from southern and eastern Russia, Asiatic ibex, banting, Situtunga swamp antelope – five hundred head of thirty-six different ungulates and sixty-four different species of birds, making altogether two thousand creatures. Fifty men are employed to feed and care for them, and every year about fifty thousand people come to admire them. They have access to the old Falz-Fein zoological park, which is five hundred acres in extent. Besides this the zoo has a further two thousand acres of fenced land. The animals are not primarily kept to be looked at; the principal function of Askania Nova is to restock the many zoos in the Soviet Union, but above all to replace the wild animal populations of about twenty islands in the Sea of Azov and the Black Sea, nature conservancy parks in the Ukraine and the Moldavian Republic. Hence the splendid herds of East Asian spotted red deer, sika and maral which surrounded our cart.

What pictures those were! The vast sky arching with such grandeur over the limitless Eurasian plain, the brownish-green steppes, the herds upon herds of noble wild beasts. I filmed nilgai antelope, steppe eagles, wapiti, maral deer and photographed flocks of red-breasted geese and bar-headed geese. As our little horse finally turned for home at sunset and I was packing up my equipment, I discovered that I had lost a lens. It must have been lying hidden somewhere in the long grass in an area of several square miles. I jokingly mentioned it to my hosts, completely unaware of the effect this remark would produce. A rider galloped off to the village and fetched a whole cartload of schoolchildren who were put out to search in an extended line. Feeling deeply embarrassed, I explained feebly that my lens was insured and that I could manage without it.

'It would be a pity if you left here having lost something,' said Labanov. A man with a trained eye for country, he retraced our route and from tiny traces of evidence in the grass he found the spots where we had stopped to photograph and the places where the bison had galloped past. It grew darker and darker. Finally a shout of triumph –

one of the schoolboys had found the lens. I would never have believed that it was possible in that great expanse of steppe, although I dared not mention that in addition an exposure meter had slipped off the cart, otherwise no one would have had their supper that evening.

As I walked round Askania Nova I could not help seeing much of it through the eyes of the dead Friedrich von Falz-Fein, as I had only just finished reading his brother's memoirs. He would find a lot that was new, such as modern stable blocks, but his old ones dating from the turn of the century are still there, solidly built and generous in scale. What an age has passed since then: only a few weeks ago an old crossbred stallion, a cross between a zebra and a Przewalski's wild horse which was born in 1929, died aged thirty-four, a Methusaleh-like age for a horse. A few of the big African eland here are milked like cows several times a day. On an average they give about four pints of milk a day and sometimes as much as twelve pints; one even gave fourteen pints. I was given a glass of ice-cold eland milk to drink, the first antelope milk I had ever drunk in my life. It tasted pretty much like cow's milk, but it has a much higher fat content. It is given to patients in the local hospital.

In the stables next to the eland I discovered a pair of full-grown kudu. They seemed to me very familiar, especially when I noticed that they had aluminium marks in their ears. At Frankfurt we mark all new-born hoofed animals in this way so that their age and place of birth can always be traced later. And there in the courtyard were two new crates with the inscription 'Zoo Frankfurt'. We had sold the animals to a dealer in Holland and from thence they had made the same long journey by roundabout routes to the Soviet Union as I had. After that long trek I hope they become the founders of yet another Askania herd.

In March and April 1959 some dead roe-deer, which had been killed in a most unusual fashion, were found in the neighbourhood of Messkirch near Uberlingen on Lake Constance. The heads had been cut off and removed. It was thought that some kind of sadistic killer was at work, until at seven am on the morning of April 20 a game-keeper named Heigle from Illmensee found himself staring at a live lynx. The animal was only four yards away from him, enabling Heigle to identify without fail the tufts on the ears, the short tail, the side-whiskers and the dark flecks in the coat. For a moment the lynx looked at him, then vanished silently into the undergrowth.

How did the lynx come to Lake Constance? Did it escape from a zoo, from a cage in transit or from a travelling menagerie? It is not impossible. In 1936, for example, three lynxes escaped from the Munich Zoo at Hellabrunn without much fuss being made of it. It has been proved that at least one of these lived in freedom until 1950 without ever harming any domestic animals. The last native wild lynxes were killed in 1846 near Wiesensteig in Württemberg and in 1850 in Bavaria, whilst in neighbouring Switzerland the final specimen of this fierce beast of prey breathed its last in 1872 at Val Uina, Canton Grisons. Since then the lynx has only lived on in western Europe as a figure of speech. A person of unusually sharp eyesight is said to be 'lynx-eyed'. An old scholar, Dr Konrad Gessner, writing in his *Bestiary* published in Zürich in 1557, had this to say: 'There be no beast that hath such sharp sight as a lynx/ for according to the poets they are held to have the power of penetrating with their eye/ things which be otherwise impossible of seeing through/ namely walls/ wood/ stone and such like. Against such deathly eyesight nothing may resist.' Doctor Gessner tells of further wonders attributed to these beasts: 'If the lynx be sick he so burieth his piss that a precious stone, called by the Latins "lynchurium", is said to grow therefrom; some do say that this is the amber that they bring to our land from Liguria.'

Does the lynx really possess such proverbially sharp eyes? Waldemar Lindemann is a man who was fortunate enough to be able to study this question during the 'thirties in the virgin forests of Poland and the Bialowice national park. Even here, in the place which has once again become the natural habitat of the European bison, all large beasts of prey, including lynx, bear and wolf, were carefully exterminated under the tsarist régime. Consequently the roe- and red-deer increased at an incredible pace, wrought havoc among the saplings and degenerated through excess of numbers. Since the stags no longer developed fine antlers they even lost their attraction as prey for hunters, prolific though they were.

When the Poles regained their independence after World War I, they purposely allowed wolves and lynx to move into the virgin forest from the surrounding areas and even succeeded, after considerable trouble, in reintroducing zoo-born bears into the forest. The lynxes, roughly a hundred in number, which today inhabit the Bialowice forest, kill annually between November and March about two to three hundred head of sick and weak roe- and red-deer, representing ten to fifteen per cent of the stock. A lynx kills in a flash by snapping the spinal cord at one bite and then frequently removes the head altogether and hides it somewhere. Death by lynx can often be even quicker than by the hunter's bullet. In four to six hours a lynx can consume up to ten pounds of meat. Since there have been wolves, bear and lynx again at Bialowice the roe- and red-deer have not declined at an alarming rate; rather, a natural balance has been restored and the deer have grown much stronger and healthier.

10   *Friedrich von Falz-Fein riding out on a tour of inspection.*

11   *At Askania Nova various varieties and cross-breeds of deer are bred in order to re-establish the species in nature reserves and on islands of the Black Sea and the Caspian Sea where they have become extinct.*

It was in this famous Polish nature reserve that Lindemann found two lynx cubs, still blind, in May 1935 and raised them at home with a cat as foster-mother. The two were a couple, male and female, were called 'Murr' and 'Linka' and would play together like kittens as soon as their eyes opened and they could see properly. They loved to be stroked by their master and at ten weeks old each answered to its name and came at once when called. However much they might be enjoying themselves in the woods, Lindemann could always summon them with a shout or a whistle and lead them back home. Linka learned to refrain from chasing poultry, her favourite prey, although Murr, in spite of severe punishment, was a perpetual backslider. Once he was in pursuit shouting was in vain.

The lynxes paid no attention to any other humans. Linka allowed her back to be stroked, but Murr simply drew away from people. The older he grew, the rougher he became. One day he was gnawing a piece of meat by the doorway when a servant girl walked past at a distance of some ten paces. He sprang at her in fury – with the meat still in his mouth – and ripped open her thigh with his forepaw. So he was removed, still less than a year old, to Warsaw Zoo. Linka on the other hand, who lived freely with Lindemann for over a year, never became savage with humans, although both of them would immediately attack and kill dogs.

Both lynxes were violently water-shy. Even titbits would not tempt them into a stream or a pond, yet they were good swimmers as they proved during a flood. Often at night they would stare at the moon, which seemed to cast a spell on them. They would sit for hours on the window-seat looking upwards into the sky, now and again making a crooning sound 'oooh-ohh-oooh'. Neither of them were then sexually mature: a female lynx does not reach maturity until her second year, a male until his third year. When snow first fell in their lifetime they

12 *Lynx are again moving westward. In the next few years this natural progression will probably bring them to Germany. As an advance measure they have already been declared protected game.*

investigated it cautiously, then jumped in and rolled around in delight. When they were playing about out of doors or went for a walk with their master they always preferred gardens or woodland to the open fields and broken ground to flat open spaces. If it rained they would become irritable and sleepy and were frightened by storms. Thunder and lightning would send them creeping into the darkest possible corners.

When their owner let them out of their cage in the early morning they would always greet him joyfully, rubbing their heads against his hand or his body and caressing his legs with their flanks. Since they treated him in a way quite different from their behaviour towards other humans, Lindemann was able to discover by experiment the means by which they recognised him. For this purpose he changed clothes with a gamekeeper, a man of the same height and build. The lynxes refused to greet this man when he wore Lindemann's clothes. When Lindemann put a mask over his face they would only approach him with hesitation and would only show their delight when they had touched his hands and feet, but as soon as their master spoke to them under his mask they would at once jump up at him and purr. One day Lindemann even put on women's clothes. As long as he remained silent it was a long time before either, but especially Murr, recognised him. If in addition he then put on a mask they paid no attention to him at all, but if he wore a mask and spoke in his normal voice they would approach him, hesitantly at first, and then recognise him.

Linka was often allowed to join her master in bed, which she greatly enjoyed, but if a stranger were in the bed nothing would induce her to sleep with him. After Murr was sent away to Warsaw she became increasingly attached to her human companion. Everything she caught – from a mouse to a young roe-deer – she would bring to him and lay it on the ground in front of him, gazing at him and moving the prey with her paw until he picked it up. In the autumn of the following year Lindemann's contract with the Polish Forestry Commission was due to end, so he had to move and give up Linka. She was put into the Warsaw Zoo, where she was kept on a running chain.

Even a year later this lynx recognised her human friend among a crowd of hundreds of people. She stood up on her hind legs, put her forepaws on his shoulder and licked his face with her sharp tongue as she had always done.

Wild animals which have grown as tame as this are immensely valuable to the student of animal behaviour and Waldemar Lindemann made full use of his pair of lynxes for experiment. At the highest point of the dead straight highway between Bialowice and Przoany, for instance, he erected a plywood observation booth eighteen feet high. From it he ran an eight hundred-yard-long cable along the road with electric lamps connected to it at intervals of fifty yards with which to signal to his assistants. At a certain distance, to be determined by experiment, he stretched a thin wire across the road; on this wire stuffed animals were hung so that an assistant, with the aid of a fine cable, could pull them in a natural attitude along the surface of the highway. A stuffed black and white piebald rabbit, a hare, a fieldmouse, a roebuck and a mountain hare thus 'ran' as naturally as possible, although pulled somewhat jerkily, right across the field of vision of the lynx placed in the booth, whilst the plywood walls prevented it from seeing the preparations for this manœuvre. By the way the lynx pulled at its collar and leash Lindemann could easily observe whether it had noticed the supposed 'prey', and Dr Konrad Gessner's theories about the penetrating sight of the lynx were put to the test. What were the results?

When there was snow on the ground Linka did not recognise the mountain hare in its white winter coat until it was twenty-five yards away, but she spotted the grey hare at three hundred yards, the rabbit at three hundred and twenty-five yards and the roebuck at five hundred yards. Even the little fieldmouse she was able to recognise at seventy-five yards. In summer the situation was reversed: then she spied the white hare at the same distance as the roebuck, three hundred and fifty yards, proof of the value to a hunted animal of white colouring in winter. In summer the lynx did not recognise the mouse until it was fifty yards away, the hare at two hundred and twenty-five yards, the rabbit at three hundred yards. On a light summer's night the lynx spotted the alpine hare at two hundred yards, the ordinary hare at one hundred and twenty-five yards. Humans, of course, were able to see these animals equally well and even better, but one should remember that they knew in advance roughly where the animals were due to appear. It is not so very long ago that people believed in 'lynx-eyes' which could 'penetrate wood and stone'; none the less Linka one day followed a buzzard, which was circling the edge of a wood two miles distant, with very obvious movements of the eyes and head. A buzzard has a wingspan of about four feet.

A lynx in the wild state has never, incidentally, attacked a man. They are quite unafraid of dogs, even when driven into a tree by a pack of hounds. If the dogs are not protected by a breastplate or spiked collar they can be badly wounded or even killed by a lynx at bay. Nowadays the lynx has been re-established in the Allenstein district of East Prussia and is protected by the Polish Forestry Commission. During a battue in 1959 eight lynx were sighted there, of which one was shot. In central Sweden the wooded areas nowadays have far fewer human inhabitants due to the general movement of population away from the land and considerably fewer people walk the woods and forests compared with fifty years ago. This has led to an increase in the number of lynx. There are now about two hundred and fifty in Sweden, about one thousand in Roumania and not long ago Czechoslovakia reported a lynx population of four hundred head, of which three hundred and fifty inhabit the forests of Slovakia. The Finns had exterminated the lynx by 1953-54 as 'vermin'. Only occasionally does one cross the southern frontier with the Soviet Union. Other large beasts of prey such as wolves, bear and gluttons are still indigenous to Finland.

The European lynx has a 'territory', which it regards as its private preserve, often up to as much as two thousand five hundred acres in extent, but varying in size according to the amount of prey available for it to catch and eat. Between 1956 and 1961 the biologist Jack Saunders caught fifty (Canadian) lynx in Newfoundland and marked them. He caught thirty-one of them a further fifty-two times and in addition maintained a careful watch of their tracks in the snow. The marked animals had covered distances of from nought to sixty-five miles, the average being two and three-quarter miles. The territories of three lynxes, exactly mapped out from their traces in the snow, were nine and three-quarter square miles, eleven and one-third square miles and thirteen square miles in area respectively. In winter, besides sick or weakened roe-deer, the European lynx also preys on squirrels, foxes, young wild pig and is especially fond of pursuing wildcats. When there is no snow, however, it does not have much success with roe; instead, the lynx must turn its attention to water voles, fish in flooded areas, old or weak marmots and stray sheep. In years when cockchafers are prolific it will also eat huge quantities of these brown insects. In Newfoundland Saunders investigated the stomach contents of two hundred and six dead lynx and two hundred and twenty piles of droppings, which in one hundred and sixteen cases were definitely and in one hundred and four cases probably lynx-droppings. In seventy-three per cent of the cases, at all seasons over à period of five years, remains of alpine hare were found. Birds were present in twenty-one per cent, particularly in spring and summer, mice in fourteen per cent of the cases during the snow-free times of the year, remains of big-game carrion in twenty per cent during the hunting season (autumn and winter), but no remains of domestic animals.

From 1959 to 1963 in Sweden, during a planned winter-time study of lynx tracks organised by Bertil Haglund, it was found that the chief prey of the lynx consisted of reindeer, roe and mountain hare. As the tracks in the snow indicated, the attacks on roe-deer had been unsuccessful in a third of the cases, those on hares as much as two-thirds. The distance between the place where the lynx would lie up for a day and its next day's resting-place was an average of four and three-quarter miles. In one night the lynx will not usually seize game on a greater scale than any other beast of prey; it hunts by stalking its quarry and then attacks whenever possible from a distance of less than twenty yards. In Sweden the lynx seemed to have the most success with reindeer. Even a fully-grown roe, however, can scarcely shake off a lynx once it has sunk its teeth into the deer's neck: the death-struggle is generally over in less than fifty yards.

A lynx 'territory' has its fixed paths, its frequently used resting places and drinking places. Above all the older and stronger male lynxes have regular rutting-grounds. The females come from far away to mate there. Younger and weaker male lynxes never venture near such jealously guarded places and often maintain a respectful distance of up to a mile. But outside that range several younger males may be prowling; they will often pay court together to a female who has had no luck in the main rutting-ground because she has been chased off it by the reigning ladies of the harem. The result is a considerable amount of coming and going. In one winter in the eastern Carpathians, fourteen lynx were caught in gin-traps on a single rutting-ground. The mating season for lynx is not in May, but lasts from January to March.

Their young begin to be born in May and before giving birth mother lynxes move into empty badgers' earths or into natural caves. Probably in order to preserve its security, pregnant female lynxes will often hunt several miles away from their place of confinement. At any rate they carefully avoid attacking roe-deer in its immediate vicinity.

A lynx, which will grow to a length of four feet and a weight of one hundred pounds, has scarcely any enemies. Eagle owls and eagles may occasionally carry off lynx cubs, just as lynx and wolves sometimes mutually prey on each other's young. The lynx species has consequently settled in large areas of the globe, as long as its chief enemy – man – has not exterminated it in the meantime. The northern group of lynx species inhabits Europe, Asia and Canada. The Spanish lynx, smaller and marked with brighter spots, has its habitat further to the south, e.g. in Southern Spain, Central Asia and the southerly parts of North America. Further south still there are the smaller, slimmer desert lynx or karakals, which are evenly sand-coloured all over. These elegant creatures are to be found in India, in southern Central Asia, Hither Asia, Trans-Caucasia, in East Africa and in South Africa.

Knowledge of the possible age to which a lynx can live is so far confined to animals in captivity. In the Augsburg Zoo a seventeen-year-old lynx had become senile and had to be destroyed. Now and again lynxes have also bred in captivity. In the Skansen Zoo at Stockholm a pair of lynx produced two or three young for several years in succession.

There is one attribute in which the lynx is far superior to humans: it has vastly better *hearing*. Lindemann's lynxes were able to hear the sound of a police whistle at a range of two and three-quarter miles, whilst his dog, a setter, could only hear it at just over two miles, terriers and mongrels at two miles and men at no more than one and a half miles. The lynx's sense of smell, on the other hand, seems to be little better than ours.

Another of Lindemann's experiments was to construct a long zigzag run through which he made Murr and Linka run after he had blindfolded them. They bumped into the walls only half as often as domestic cats, showing that they have an unusually good sense of touch. When Lindemann put a lump of meat, while the lynx was watching, under one of a number of overturned saucers, Linka was able to remember for an hour and a half which of the saucers it lay under, whilst Murr could actually remember it for three hours: they would go straight for the correct saucer and turn it over. A wolf of mine was only able to retain this information for five minutes, my dog for sixty-three minutes. If, however, the lynxes had hidden something *themselves* they were able to remember its place of concealment for four days.

The lynx seems, in fact, to be slowly regaining its ascendancy in Central Europe. Even in Denmark, where the last lynx was destroyed on Jutland in 1689, in the winter of 1964 Mr E. Pedersen, a carpenter, shot one in the Bøtø forest on the island of South Falster. It probably came over the ice from Poland. Some lynxes that had been released on Rominten Heath in 1938 in East Prussia were apparently missing immediately after World War II, but in 1957 they were reported as settled in the area and by 1960 twelve of them had been seen. In Norway, where they were once nearly extinct, their numbers have greatly increased since 1940. In Poland in 1963 three hundred and thirty lynx were counted. At the same period there were frequent reports of lynx tracks being observed in the woods of Saxony. Polish and Soviet experts now report that there is a steady westward movement of the lynx, so before long we can expect these handsome feline beasts of prey to be found in Central Germany and then in West Germany. Since they harm neither humans nor domestic animals, they have already been declared protected game in West Germany.

I can think of worse ways of going to take a close look at beaver than getting into an express train one evening in Moscow and travelling south for ten hours alone in a sleeping compartment with a young lady. A year previously I had tried to do some work on beavers in the Canadian Rockies and had driven out of the little town of Jasper every day by car up to the Geickie River, but the beaver only let themselves be seen in the evening shortly before sunset. They would then swim across the glassily smooth little lake, which they had made themselves, dive with a plop to fetch up water-weed roots and devour them noisily, while other brown heads popped up out of the water around them and the reflections of the snow-covered mountain pinnacles shone on the water. They are at their most active again from sunset until shortly after midnight, then as morning approaches they are less and less visible. In the Soviet Union my prospects of seeing them were better; besides hundreds of wild beavers, there are a number in a colony near Voronezh which have grown accustomed to humans, some half-tame ones and beavers kept for experimental breeding purposes in enclosures.

Our train of sleeping cars rumbled through the bright evening in late June across the flat, endless countryside. I had first to get used to the Russian habit of sharing a compartment alone with anyone of either sex, in this case pretty twenty-three year old Svetlana Zelkina, whom I had asked to accompany me as interpreter. At first two others, a lady and a gentleman, had been allotted the two upper berths, but they had found an empty compartment and the friendly conductress had allowed them to move into it. Seated on snow-white bed-linen we had our lemon tea and biscuits alone, gazing out from our beds at the villages, woods, factories and interminable wheatfields as they rolled by in the

E

pale dusk. Svetlana who had been my guide and interpreter those first days in Moscow was slightly surprised at anyone travelling round the world after animals. As a big-city dweller she had only seen a beaver once in a zoo and never in freedom. But who else in the Soviet Union or in western Europe can boast of having seen wild beavers?

Once they lived in North America, Europe and Asia well into Siberia in rivers, streams and ponds, wherever ash, willow and birch grow. There were never any in Ireland, but in England, the first country in Europe where it was to happen, they had already been exterminated by the twelfth century. Three reasons lay behind their destruction, one of which was completely erroneous. The last beaver in Switzerland was killed in 1705 at Birs near Basle; in the Rhineland and Saxony they were finally exterminated in 1840, in Bavaria in 1850, in Württemberg in 1854, whilst the last beaver in Lower Saxony died in 1856 and in North Rhine-Westphalia in 1877. Only the names of a number of German villages and towns still testify to an erstwhile connection with beavers (the German word for beavers is 'Biber'): Biberach, Bevensen, Biberstein, Biebrich; in Slav regions (since 'beaver' in Russian, Polish and Czech is 'Bobr') there are towns and rivers with names such as Bober, Böbersbach, Bobich, Boberov. In Germany there are about two hundred place-names derived from the beaver, the largest rodent of the northern hemisphere. (There is only one larger rodent in the world, the South American capybara.)

The town of Biebrich near Wiesbaden illustrates to this day in its coat of arms one of the reasons why humans have so mercilessly slaughtered this little brown aquatic creature. The coat of arms includes a beaver with a fish in its mouth; for centuries it was believed that an animal which could dive and swim so well must live on fish, by analogy with the otter. Any creature which eats the same food as humans – in this case fish – was regarded for centuries with a mixture of superstition and childish ignorance (an attitude which even today persists to some extent among hunters and farmers) as a competitor for the available supply of food, as vermin. In all those centuries no one ever took the trouble to cut open the stomach of a dead beaver and find out what it had eaten. They never eat anything but vegetable matter. Worse, beaver were even counted as fish and could be eaten during Lent and on Fridays by both religious and lay people. It was held to be a fish not only because it lived in the water but because of its tail, flat and fishlike in shape and apparently covered in scales. Charlevoix, a Jesuit, wrote in 1754: 'Due to its tail it is entirely fish and has been legally certified as such by the Medical Faculty of Paris, following which declaration the Theological Faculty has decided that its flesh may be eaten on fast-days.'

The beaver's second misfortune has been two glands in the lower abdomen of both male and female. These glands secrete a substance known as castoreum or beaver-musk, which was once held to be a remedy for nearly all ills. In the seventeenth century a physician named Johannes Marinus published in Augsburg a 'Castorologia' which contained over two hundred different prescriptions; he too believed that beavers ate fish, newts and frogs. Beavers excrete this strong-smelling substance from these two glands as a method of demarcation of their 'territory'. The North American trappers quickly discovered that they needed only to bait a trap with a smear of beaver-musk and at once beavers from nearby would appear, indignant at the alien scent, to deposit their own secretion on it and in doing so they would be caught in the trap or drowned. Among many other properties attributed to it, beaver-musk was said to be effective against rheumatism and pains in the joints and to have a certain tonic and refreshing quality. After careful chemical analysis the only explanation for this was thought to be possibly due to the presence in beaver-musk of salicin, coming from the willow-bark which is frequently eaten by beavers. Nowadays the chemical industry synthesises the derivatives of salicylic acid very cheaply, e.g. to produce aspirin; this has probably saved the beaver from total extinction. In 1852 a beaver-musk gland fetched 752 marks, which by today's values represents a considerable sum. In fresh condition the gland from a male weighs about a quarter of a pound, from a female about six ounces. It came to the dealer as a brown, strong-smelling substance which could be rubbed into powder, a compound of oils, resins, fats and salicin. Today there is no more demand for it and it no longer has a market price, but the official German Pharmacopeia, where numerous outdated old remedies continue to appear for decades after they have been superseded, still contains in its edition of October 24, 1962 a price quotation for beaver-musk: one gramme = 55 pfennigs (11*d*). The book adds: 'it has a strong penetrating odour reminiscent of valerian and a taste that is powerful, bitter and aromatic'.

That beaver tails were regarded as a delicacy in the Middle Ages and could usually only be eaten by the nobility is an indication of how much our tastes have altered. I doubt whether many people would willingly eat them today. Beaver fur, on the other hand, is still greatly in demand and this is the beaver's third misfortune. A beaver has an outer coat of long, dark, glossy hairs which get wet in the water. When it comes out it looks damp and bedraggled; but under these is a waterproofed undercoat of fine, soft, brown woolly hairs which the beaver continually greases by applying oil from a gland with its hands. When it dives the outer hairs cover the woolly pelt and form a kind of sheath. Air is trapped in the woolly hairs and they and the skin itself remain dry. On reaching land the beaver does not shake itself like a dog but brushes the water out of its coat with its hands in order not to carry too much moisture into its house.

As an excuse for taking its fur and beaver-musk, it used to be said of beavers that they not only destroyed fish but flooded fields and de-forested woods. Thus Frederick the Great, for example, revoked all regulations to protect beavers in 1765, allowing 'any person to shoot and exterminate beavers'. In Prussia they were classed as 'free game' for over a century. In East Prussia, where the right to hunt beaver had long been a prerogative of the Order of Teutonic Knights, they disappeared almost at once and in Lithuania they grew so rare that as early as 1566 they were classified in the game laws as equivalent in value to a horse.

Beavers have also disappeared from France, although a few still live under careful protection in the area of the Rhone delta and its tributaries. There are even a very few beavers left in Germany, on the middle reaches of the Elbe between Torgau and Magdeburg. In 1913 there were one hundred and eighty-eight of them; during World War I, when most of the poachers were away in the army, their numbers increased, reaching two hundred and seventy-two by the year 1919, but dropped to one hundred in 1925. The beaver colony rose to two hundred and ten in 1945 and had fallen again to one hundred by 1948 – a fairly exact reflection of Germany's political fortunes. By 1964 there were once more one hundred and seventy-four head, of which sixteen were to be found in the Schorfheide, the offspring of a couple placed there before World War II. There are said to be between four and six beavers in Mecklenburg, which were set free there after having been brought from Voronezh. Only in the West German Federal Republic are there none. The German Conservation Society has plans to settle some beavers in West Germany – on the Schalsee lake in Schleswig-Holstein, on the new 'Fahle Heide' dam in the Gifhorn district of Lower Saxony or on the Tiroler Ache in Upper Bavaria.

As long as sixty-five years ago it was taken extremely amiss when a private aquarium, which at that time stood on the Unter den Linden, secretly acquired one of the beavers from the colony on the Elbe. The authorities demanded its return, but the owners of the aquarium, in an attempt to keep it at all costs, substituted a Canadian beaver. This would have meant the indigenous beavers of the Elbe being indiscriminately crossed and the strain adulterated by breeding with another sub-species, had not the half-tame Canadian beaver obliged the government commission by climbing out of the waters of the Elbe and returning voluntarily to his crate for transportation back to Berlin. Misfortune also occurred in 1713 and later in 1830 in Brandenburg, near Potsdam, where vain attempts were made to reintroduce the beaver. When they failed for the second time to produce any young and the breeding pair were examined after death it transpired that they were two males.

In Russia too, man forced the beavers into retreat. By the end of the tsarist régime beavers were only to be found at four places in the vast Russian empire: near Voronezh, in White Russia, to the north of the

Urals and in the Touvan Republic on the Yenisei river, totalling not more than nine hundred head of beaver. Even then they were very carefully protected; they are still protected to this day, even though the Soviet stock of beaver has meanwhile risen to forty thousand head. The nucleus of this planned repopulation was principally the region round Voronezh and that was now my destination.

But the beavers also suffered a tragic fate in North America. Around A D 1600 about sixty to a hundred million beavers lived there; they were hunted, but at the same time protected and revered by their friends the Indians. They believed that Manitou, the Great Spirit, first created the beaver and then man. Many Indian tribes thought that they were the descendants of the 'Great Beaver', called beavers their 'little brothers', never destroyed whole beaver families, never killed mothers with children and carefully brought the bones of beavers that they had eaten back to the water to prevent them being devoured by dogs.

The European settlers fell upon the beavers as the most desirable booty of the new continent. The Hudson's Bay Company, one of the oldest trading concerns in existence, was founded principally to trap and export beaver pelts. There were wars against the Indians, who attempted to defend their beavers from extinction and men killed and scalped each other for their sake. Before 1800 the Hudson's Bay Company exported fifty thousand beaver pelts a year and for a time they amounted in value to half the exports of North America. Even in those days a beaver pelt was worth one dollar, but the trappers of the North and West had to pay dearly in pelts for the necessities of life. At the Company's trading posts they were charged exorbitant prices for their provisions: for instance, anyone wanting to buy a rifle had to make a pile of beaver pelts reaching above the muzzle of a rifle held upright on its butt. Many of the great American fortunes were founded on beaver fur, for example that of the Astor family. The lucrative trade in beavers attracted traders, trappers and missionaries.

Those were the days when light, broad-brimmed beaver hats were in fashion. To avoid being cheated the hatters preferred to buy whole beaver pelts and would shear off the hairs themselves. One pelt gave a pound and a half of hair, enough for more than a dozen hats, for they were made as light as a feather – many weighed no more than an ounce and a half. The hatters even had a technique of sorting the hairs by means of a jet of air. Hats were graded into 'whole', 'half' and 'quarter hats' according to the amount of hare's fur which underlaid the beaver fur. In 1663 a beaver pelt in England might cost anything between £8 and £12. The climax in the export of beaver fur was reached by the Hudson's Bay Company in 1875, when they sold two hundred and seventy thousand nine hundred and three beaver pelts. Then the decline began and by 1900 beavers were almost completely extinct in the United States and had also been exterminated in large areas of Canada. . . .

Early in the morning our train came to a halt at Grafskaya, a small market town in the forest region of Voronezh. We waited on the platform while an early morning train on the adjoining platform first discharged all its passengers on their way to work and then moved on. We were met by Comrade V. Sharkov, the director of the beaver farm and of the Voronezh Nature Reserve. He lives beside an onion-domed former church and has accommodated his offices, a natural history museum and himself in the rambling buildings of what was once a convent, although they are not exactly ideal for these purposes, as unsuitable, in fact, as are the numerous secularised monastic buildings which are to be found throughout western Europe.

We were lodged in guest-rooms that fifty years ago had housed nuns. From the window one looked out on to a white statue of Lenin in what had once been the churchyard. I wonder what those girls can have thought as they gazed out? Each year brought out the lilies through the mouldering brown leaves of the year before, each year they thrust up their green stems, turned their white bells towards the church tower and then faded again, year in, year out.

The people who stare out of these windows now are thinking about beavers. Nowadays students and scientists come from all over the Soviet Union for study and experiment, for which the Voronezh

Nature Reserve is ideally suited. It is a sort of island of woodland in the midst of the steppes, seventy-seven thousand acres in area, forming part of the great Usmanska tract of wood and heathland. The local authority took the first steps to place it under protection in 1922 and by 1927 it was declared a National Nature Reserve. Here are to be found pure steppe-species such as jumping hares, birds such as the blue roller and the bee-eater alongside woodland species, the European polecat alongside the Russian polecat, mountain hares beside field hares. The elk, which has so greatly increased in numbers throughout the whole Soviet Union, moved into the region unaided after an absence of one hundred and fifty years. Besides roe- and red-deer the smaller, spotted sika deer from the Far East were introduced here many years ago as in so many other parts of the Soviet Union. Hundreds of employees work in the Nature Reserve and last year it was visited by fourteen thousand people.

But it is the beavers that have made the Voronezh Nature Reserve so famous. The Voronezh beaver (*castor fiber vistulanus*) is black or dark brown; there are two thousand of them here and they are spreading along the tributaries of the Voronezh and the Don. Every year a hundred to a hundred and fifty of them, mostly one-year-olds, are caught and shipped to other parts of the Soviet Union where they are put out to settle. Nowadays there is hardly anywhere left in the Soviet Union where Voronezh beavers have not been introduced and have

13 *Breeding pens with access to the water. The experimental beaver farm behind the former convent church at Grafskaya.*

14 *The marbled polecat* (vormela peregusna) *is such a lively creature with his brown, black, white and yellow markings that people often take it for a tropical animal. It is, however, found in southern Poland, southern Russia, Bulgaria and eastwards as far as India and China, but is nowhere prolific.*

15 *Sixty to a hundred million beavers once inhabited North America. Due to the demand for beaver-musk, beaver fur for hats and above all for beaver pelts they had been almost exterminated by the turn of the century. Now their numbers have again risen to two million.*

multiplied. Forty of them have even been sent to a farm in East Germany.

In Russia and in North America biologists have learned many of the beaver's secrets in recent years. The first is their habit of felling trees. The beaver does it with only its four orange-yellow incisors, two in the upper jaw, two in the lower. A beaver can survive without its spatulate tail and without its legs, it can even live blind: but if its incisor teeth are missing it will be dead within a week. The front of these great, long, protruding incisors is covered with dental enamel, just as the outer sides of human teeth are. On their inner sides the beaver's teeth are composed of the softer dentine. When the animal gnaws, the dentine wears down more quickly and the enamelled front edge of the tooth remains sharp. In this way the beaver's 'cutting edge' is kept permanently and automatically sharp. Besides this method it can push forward its lower jaw with the two lower incisors and sharpen the two sets of incisors by honing the lower and upper pairs against each other. The upper teeth are usually planted firmly against the wood while the lower teeth then slice to and fro. This scissors-action is carried out five to six times per second. The beaver can also close its lips behind its front teeth, enabling it to gnaw when submerged without getting water into its mouth.

Beavers have the reputation of being able to fell trees so that the tops always fall into the water; that they can calculate the fall of a tree in such a way that no beaver is ever hit by a falling trunk; and that a tree is always felled in the right direction to ensure that the tops are not caught in neighbouring trees, in which case they would be useless to the

16 Every year for the past thirty years, about two hundred beavers have been caught at the Voronezh nature reserve. They are sent all over the Soviet Union to areas where at the beginning of the century beavers had been exterminated. Where once there were millions their numbers had dropped to a total of nine hundred in the whole Russian Empire.

17 This dam which I am inspecting was built by beavers. It easily keeps a high water pressure in check. The stems and twigs of which it is made were cut down and dragged into position by beavers.

beavers. None of this is correct. Trees that are near water almost invariably do fall with their tops into the water, but that is because the
branches on the more open water side have developed more strongly
and the tree is consequently weighted more heavily on that side. Trees
which beavers cut down further from water fall in every direction.
Beavers have indeed been crushed by falling trees, but very, very
seldom. In another case a tree was once observed whose trunk had been
laboriously gnawed through by beavers, but it stood on a slope, had
been caught by nearby trees as it fell and dropped only a few yards.
The beavers sawed through the trunk again; still supported by its
neighbours the tree fell only a short distance further and the beavers
gave up.

For preference beavers cut through trunks between six and a half
and eight inches thick, especially aspen, willow, poplar; they are
slightly less interested in birch and wild cherry, whilst they avoid
conifers and hardwoods, the woods of greatest value to man, almost
entirely. The very soft woods preferred by beavers play practically no
part in the human economy. A four-inch-thick willow is gnawed
through in five minutes, whilst they may work on larger trees for
several nights in succession. Every beaver cuts down about two or
three hundred poplar stems in a year; three acres of land will feed a
beaver colony for a year to eighteen months. Often two beavers will
work together on really thick trees; when they do so, one beaver
generally does the cutting while the other keeps lookout. They will
even take on trunks as thick as a man's body. Their record is a ninety-
foot balsam poplar with a trunk five feet in diameter which they once
gnawed through in British Columbia.

Naturally the beavers prefer it when the trees stand close to the
water. They drag the trunks or the severed branches of big trees along
the shortest route to the water. Beavers hardly ever fell trees at distances of more than two hundred yards from water. When they have
cut down all suitable timber in the vicinity of their colony they prefer
to move to another place. This is then the start of a 'beaver meadow',
a treeless clearing in the forest, as the lake created by the beaver dam

gradually drains away after they have left and are no longer there to keep the dam in repair. Beavers thus produce a beneficial change in the natural landscape by creating a succession of new areas of grazing land for wild and domestic animals.

The felled tree is cut up into pieces; the thicker it is, the shorter the pieces. Even after the beavers have removed the trunk, the length of the pieces can be measured on the ground because there is always a heap of chips left at each point where a section of the trunk was cut off. Really thick tree trunks are left lying; of these the beavers simply scale off the bark and eat it.

Fresh green bark and soft wood are their principal foods. Their teeth are of a strength to cope with this tough fare. A beaver's incisors exercise a chewing strength of one hundred and seventy-five pounds compared with the eighty-eight pound strength of the human jaw; yet the average beaver only weighs between forty-two and forty-five pounds, or about sixty-five pounds at the most. In the Voronezh district each beaver family lays in a winter store under the water of an average of one hundred and eight aspen stems of from three and a half inches to fourteen inches in diameter, in addition to which they gnaw at trees which have been blown down by the wind. Captive beavers in the farm get a daily ration per head of fifteen pounds of aspen twigs with bark, five pounds of birch twigs and fifty-seven pounds of willow. Thus in a year an adult beaver consumes about four tons of wood and bark plus greenstuff, or a total of nearly eight cubic yards of wood. Of the five hundred and eighty plant species that grow in the Voronezh district, the beavers eat one hundred and forty-eight separate species.

Beavers are rather helpless on land; they cannot run as fast as a man and they tire quickly. In flat, watery countryside they will therefore often build canals which lead for considerable distances to their feeding-grounds. The canals are perhaps initially made by the beavers trampling their well-beaten paths deeper and deeper into the soft soil, but later they purposely widen and deepen them until they reach depths of up to eighteen inches and the beaver can swim along under water. These canals also enable them to move branches with greater ease and speed.

Near the 'lodges' in which they live, beavers store the harvest of branches by anchoring the severed ends deep in the muddy bottom so that they will not float to the surface. This is mainly done to create a store for the winter, since in summer they also subsist on water-weeds, berries and the roots of water-lilies. These rafts of branches often cover the entrances to their lodges.

A beaver only feels comfortable in a new location when it has built a dwelling that can only be entered from below water level. On large rivers where water is always plentiful or which are too broad for them to dam up, the beavers live in simple holes in the bank, with at least two and sometimes as many as five or six separate entrances. The German beavers on the Elbe, for instance, live almost entirely in simple holes of this kind and are known therefore as 'bank beavers'. The way in leads steeply upwards from a point below the surface of the water until somewhere below ground level. There the beaver builds a chamber, approximately two feet wide and eighteen to twenty inches high, the interior of which is carefully smoothed out. If the water level of the river rises the floor of the chamber must also be raised; to do this the beaver simply scrapes or gnaws the earth away from the ceiling and lets it drop to the floor. Generally the roof of the chamber is so strong that several men can stand on it, but if the beavers are forced to raise the level further they strengthen the roof by laying branches on the ground above until they have built a real little hill. If the water level rises still more, for instance because the beavers have dammed up the waters, the mound must be gradually raised until finally it is an island in the midst of water.

This must have been the way in which the beavers' moated lodges were originally constructed. Nowadays beavers sometimes – although not very often – also build them in the middle of their dammed-up lakes by simply heaping up water-logged branches and mud under water until an artificial island protrudes above the water, sometimes as high as from three to six feet. They are then hollowed out from inside and fitted with chambers and corridors. Especially in northerly regions the beavers cover the mound with a layer of mud and clay, often leaving a gap in the top of the roof for ventilation. Yet this random heap of sticks can bear the weight of a man and cannot easily be broken into by predators. In hard winters steam can be seen rising out of the tip of the mound like a little plume of vapour. Old mounds may have antechambers and side-rooms, but the central dwelling chamber is invariably placed at a uniform height of eight inches above the water level. They are inaccessible to most beasts of prey and even if a bear breaks its way in by force the beavers have long since escaped under water.

Beavers do not hibernate, although they become markedly less active in the winter-time and they are often not to be seen for weeks on end. Even when there are fifteen degrees of frost outside, the air temperature within the beavers' chamber is usually above zero. As soon as the rivers freeze over, the beavers swim under the ice to their supply-rafts of branches. Often they do not even need to make breathing holes in the ice, because the rivers and lakes first freeze at the sides; during the winter the water level, particularly in rivers, sinks slightly so that the ice in the middle is somewhat lower. On the banks, however, the soil and tree roots hold the ice and keep it higher, leaving a well protected air-space for the beavers' use.

They are superb divers. Old manuals of natural history record that they can stay under water for two minutes, but in February 1939 Rudolf Berendt timed a beaver with a stopwatch in the Elbe water-meadows near Steckly and recorded a dive of ten minutes, and in Grafskaya they have even measured one of fifteen minutes in an experimental tank. Beavers never leave droppings in their lodge, but only in the water. The young are bedded on heaps of soft wood-shavings.

When the water rises not much can happen to the beavers in their lodges; at the worst they may have to move into emergency quarters. On the other hand if a river or a lake dries out the entrance passages to the lodge are left high and dry and the sunken stores of branches wither. The beavers therefore build dams to keep the water at a constant level and thus create artificial lakes in which they and their food supplies are secure. To make a dam they thrust severed trunks and branches vertically into the bed of the stream, then weight it down and secure it with stones, mud, reeds and anything else they can find. As the starting-point of a dam they also often use a tree that has fallen across the river or been washed down by the current and then gradually build up on it. The more the dammed water rises and the bed of the river or stream fills up, the more they must raise the height of the dam and lengthen it at the sides as the flood rises over the banks. The longest dam in the Voronezh Reserve is at Marinika; it is a hundred and twenty yards long, three feet high and between two and three and a half feet wide. In the mountain streams of the Rockies, however, the dams can be up to ten feet high. What is probably the biggest beaver dam in the world is one on the Jefferson River at Three Forks, Montana, USA. One can walk along it for seven hundred and fifty yards. These dams may be maintained by several generations of a beaver tribe for decades, provided enough food remains available in the vicinity. There is one in Colorado which has been in place for seventy years. In time trees and bushes take root and grow in the dam and it grows constantly wider and stronger. A man has no difficulty in riding across it on horse-back. To build a dam ten yards in length a beaver family takes about a week. If the current is strong they will often construct a number of weirs upstream to relieve the main dam of some of the pressure. The dams vary in type according to the species of beaver and to the nature of the terrain. If the water breaks through at any point the beavers feverishly repair the breach during the following night – hence the expression to 'work like beavers'. A Mr J. Hall of Denver was unable to get his artificially built dam to stay watertight, although he re-peatedly enlisted the help of engineers. Then when a pair of beavers settled there they completely sealed up the dam within a few days.

They have what seems like a passion for hydraulic engineering. The overflow of a beaver pond in a zoo, for instance, disturbs them un-endingly: they spend their time trying to block it up. With man-made dams in open country where beavers are present often the only way to keep the overflow pipe functioning is by extending it for a long way under water and piercing it with holes on all sides. When trappers want to catch beavers they have only to make a hole in a beaver dam and set an underwater trap beneath it. On the other hand when there is a flood beavers have been known to make artificial breaches to allow the excess water to flow away.

On a creek running into Lake Michigan some beavers once made use of a small disused railway bridge for a dam by filling it in, above and below, to a height of six feet and blocking the flow of water. In Canada beaver dams are often twelve to eighteen feet wide at the riverbed and between three and six feet wide across the top. It can often happen that beavers will swamp a road or a railway branch line overnight with a minor flood caused by one of their dams. Even if the dam can be rapidly breached, this is only the start of a fierce race between man and beaver which lasts until the animals can be caught and removed.

Beavers, especially in mountainous country, are magnificent 'landscape architects'. Wild torrents are stemmed and the dams prevent the meadows below them from being silted over with sand and gravel by allowing only a gradual flow of water towards the lower ground. The beavers' artificial lakes are soon filled with trout and other fish and with water birds.

The sixty million beavers that once lived in the USA, with their innumerable dams and small lakes, must have greatly reduced the number of floods. Nowadays we attempt to achieve the same result with artificial dams in the mountains and highlands. Aside from the hydro-electric power which they produce (which in an age of applied atomic energy may rapidly be superseded), we spend millions upon millions on hydraulic works to recreate artificially the conditions destroyed by the removal from the natural balance of a small but essential creature. Were all those beaver hats really worth it?

If you want to see beavers in a zoo you will seldom find them. They rarely breed in captivity, which in view of their complex and specialised life and feeding habits is hardly surprising. Furthermore, they do the greater part of their work at night and bring up their young in such seclusion in the lodge that it is scarcely possible to observe them even in freedom. As a result the strangest stories have been written about them and not only in the Middle Ages: it was said, for instance, that when pursued by hunters the beaver would bite out its beaver-musk gland and leave it behind as a kind of ransom to save its own life. Even in the last multi-volume edition of 'Brehm's Animal Life' (*Brehms Tierleben*), which has incidentally not been revised since 1914, it states that young beavers are born blind and naked.

That this is false can be easily ascertained every spring here in Grafskaya. Since 1933 there has been a beaver farm established here, a series of enclosures along a dead arm of the river immediately behind the convent. They have concreted slipways which run out a few yards into the water, each with a beaver-lodge built of oak at its landward end. Inside it is lined with sheet-metal and covered with a double, steeply-pitched roof, so that the space in between can be well stuffed with straw. These artificial lodges can be opened to watch the beavers inside them, from which one could observe that they prefer to sleep on their backs, feet in the air; they often snore. The average stock of this farm is a hundred beavers, of which there are twelve to fifteen breeding couples. Five attendants and a lady veterinary surgeon look after them. Grafskaya houses not only the black Voronezh beaver, but also the Norwegian beaver (*castor fiber fiber*), the Mongolian beaver (*castor fiber birula*) from the Bulgan, Yenisei and Assas rivers, the Ural beaver (*castor fiber polae*) from the river Konder in the Northern Urals and the Canadian beaver (*castor fiber canadensis*) from the states of Wisconsin and Arizona. These Canadian beavers are infertile if mated with the European or Asiatic varieties, although Voronezh beavers, Ural and Norwegian beavers can be interbred. The animals which are settled in other regions of the Soviet Union are bred in this stud but are caught in the Nature Reserve itself from wild stock at about one year old and have a mark clipped into their ears.

The farm also breeds desmans (*desmana moschata*), an aquatic species related to the moles, squat, nearly cylindrical little animals with plush-like fur. These 'vykhukhol', as they are known in Russian, grow to about ten inches in length and have a scaly tail flattened at the sides which is seven inches long. They have no external ears, the eyes are very small and the long trumpet-shaped snout is highly mobile. Their closest relatives are to be found in the Pyrenees. Like beavers these creatures build their lairs on the bank with underwater entrances; their life resembles that of the beavers in some ways, but they eat water insects, fish, leeches and snails. Because their fur is so valuable, about six hundred of them have already been settled in other parts of the Soviet Union.

In these enclosures one can witness the astonishing sight of beavers coupling in the water. To do so the male swims belly upwards under the female. To all appearances beaver couples live in permanent mono-gamy. After a gestation period of one hundred and five to one hundred and seven days the young are born in the lodge; the father, together with last year's young, is then made to move out for a considerable length of time. The young beavers are born with hair and with their eyes partly open, although for the first two days the eyes remain half-closed and covered with a thick fluid. Even their incisor teeth are already visible. The mother suckles them for about two months, during which time they maintain a visible rate of growth. Up to the fifth day they increase their own weight daily by eight per cent and by the twenty-fifth to the thirty-fifth day their daily rate of growth is still four per cent; this drops to one per cent after two months. When the young feed the mother often lifts up one leg and lays her broad tail under her belly to allow the babies to sit on the warm cushion of her tail.

The young begin swimming and diving very early. Like so many little children and animals they are often extremely reckless. If an observer stands on the bank and imitates the call of a beaver they show great curiosity and rush in that direction. The mother has to push them back with her nose and swim between them and the spectator. In such cases an old beaver will strike the water's surface with its broad tail and immediately dive.

F

If the young beavers linger too long in the water or are too inquisitive, the mother frequently propels them back to the lodge by force. Herr Bolan, a one-time director of the now disbanded Hamburg Zoo, once wrote that the mother beaver will pick up one of her young in her outstretched arms and carry it over dry land, walking upright on her hind legs. People were unwilling to believe this statement, but over half a century later this extraordinary example of animal behaviour was observed and even photographed and filmed at the Zurich Zoo, where a beaver couple had bred and raised young for several years in succession. The young have even been carried sitting on their mother's tail.

Whenever beavers were dug out of their lodges on the Voronezh Nature Reserve (after always ensuring that all exits were secured with nets), three generations of beavers were usually found in residence. The young of the previous year are allowed to stay with their mother or to return to her after she has dropped a new litter. A litter can number from one to six, but is normally of two to four. The next year, as soon as the nursery is full again, they must finally leave their parents, which is frequently accomplished by the parents chasing them out by biting them. The following autumn, when they are two and a half years old, they are sexually mature and next spring they produce their own offspring. These young beavers migrate up- or down-stream, sometimes for distances of twelve to fifteen miles, where they settle down and start a new household. They may even go considerable distances overland in search of a new home. A beaver which was let out of captivity in North America was found four months later in the mountains nineteen miles away. It is thought, incidentally, that the life-span of a beaver is between ten and fifteen years, although at Voronezh one beaver reached the age of twenty-three and a beaver in a zoo is even known to have lived to be thirty.

Around the turn of the century the Americans' conscience began to be stirred, just in time before their beavers were totally exterminated. Not only were protective laws passed, but beavers were also settled in many places from which they had completely disappeared. Nine pairs of beaver, for instance, which had been settled in New York State in 1906, multiplied to such an extent that in 1924 their progeny supplied pelts to the value of a million dollars. In Norway, too, beavers were placed under protection in 1899; today Norway has twelve to fourteen thousand beavers and Norwegian beavers have been settled in Latvia, Finland and Sweden. Their ability to colonise new regions unaided has been confirmed by the Game Conservancy of the State of Maine: the beaver population of the island of Vinalhaven reached it from the mainland by swimming eleven and a half miles across the sea.

Just as the beavers in Canada had barely recovered their numbers, unrestricted hunting was allowed again during World War I. A wild slaughter began. Once more the get-rich-quick hunters moved in and improvidently destroyed whole beaver colonies. This savage and unreasonable mass-destruction was opposed with particular vigour in many articles, lectures and books by the Indian (or half-Indian) known as Grey Owl. He turned, like so many, from hunter into keeper, largely as a result of an incident when he found a mother beaver caught in a trap: 'Screaming with pain she was trying to shake off the trap, which had caught one of her forelegs. With the other paw she pressed her cub to her breast, where he sucked all unaware. As carefully as possible I freed the mother, who made no attempt to bite me. Then with a sharp blow of my axe I severed her crushed and useless foot and the wretched beast, tortured by hellish thirst, began to drink the spurting blood like water. Then she limped slowly and painfully to the lake, but turned back to fetch her cub who was playing with my shoe and could hardly be persuaded to follow its mother. My companion approved of my action, although he thereby lost a valuable pelt. His heart had softened when he saw the cub. The incident made me think and contributed largely to my subsequent decision to abandon beaver-hunting altogether. Since then I have saved the lives of several young beavers by following the tracks of the trappers who go out in spring, picking up the little orphans and keeping them for a year. I could not keep them longer, as they ravaged my camp supplies mercilessly.'

Beavers, indeed, can wreak havoc in man's houses: 'We entered the hut and the sight that met our eyes remained long in our memories. A whirlwind seemed to have been there. The table had been over-turned and everything on it removed. A long, thick wooden pole was sticking with one end through a broken window and beneath the other undamaged window stood a pile of wood. The washstand, which had been broken into its component parts, was found carefully heaped up on the bunk, from which the blankets had been removed and together with other things such as pots, dishes, mocassins, etc., had been built up into a barricade in front of the stove. With many apologies to my guest I assessed the damage, but apart from what I have described nothing more had happened, that is to say there were no further casualties. I had gone out for a little walk and tempted by the mild weather had stayed out somewhat longer. The good weather had also encouraged the beavers, so that for lack of anything better to do they had attacked my little property as if possessed. Now they had vanished, having withdrawn on the arrival of my friends. But later they appeared again, were properly introduced and hopped away again like little dwarfs, not forgetting to take with them my guests' peace-offering of a few apples and some chocolate.'

Grey Owl and other nature lovers succeeded in winning the Canadians' sympathy for the beavers. In large tracts of Canada white men were forbidden to hunt beaver and only Indians were allowed to. The trappers' trails along the St Lawrence River were registered in the names of individual Indians who wished to hunt them as a regular

II   *This young Canadian lynx will grow into a formidable beast of prey. Dogs are frequently worsted if they encounter a lynx. With a bite in the nape of the neck lynx kill sick and weak roe-deer and young stags as quickly as a hunter's bullet. Afterwards they often decapitate the animal and conceal the head, a habit which accounts for the mystery of 'headless' bodies of roe-deer or hares found in the woods.*

III   *Young hares are seldom seen with their mothers. They are suckled only two or three times in a day and if necessary they can be independent of the mother after three weeks. A little leveret found in the open without its mother is therefore far from being an orphan; no one should feel bound to take it home and feed it from a bottle.*

source of income. In 1960 thirty thousand pelts were taken in the Province of Quebec, selling at a dollar apiece. 1961 was the first year in which white trappers were allowed to hunt beaver again and the take amounted to thirty-three thousand four hundred pelts. Each trapper was allowed to catch a maximum of twenty beavers without shooting. The pelts had to be officially stamped and could only be sold to authorised fur-dealers. In the State of Idaho every trapper must hand over alive ten per cent of all the beavers he catches, which are then settled in areas where there are no beavers. They are taken by aeroplane to forest clearings and mountain districts that are difficult of access and are dropped to the ground in cages by parachute from a height of five hundred to one thousand feet. The pull of the parachute lines keeps the door of the cage shut during the fall. As soon as the cage touches ground and the parachute collapses, a coil spring automatically opens the door. Even a small airship has been hired for this operation.

When their chief enemy, man, is removed the re-establishment of beavers goes ahead quite smoothly, because most of their other natural foes, such as wolves, lynxes, wolverines, otters and bears have themselves either been exterminated or become very rare. Nowadays the beaver is said to have completely re-occupied its former area of distribution in North America, although in much smaller numbers than before. The beaver population is now calculated at two hundred and fifty thousand in the USA, and a million and a half in Canada.

Efforts are being made to re-establish the beaver in Europe too. Canadian and Norwegian beavers were settled in Finland in the

IV   A few decades ago the elk was regarded almost everywhere in Europe as a species threatened with extinction. Since then its numbers have increased markedly in Sweden and many parts of Russia. Elk are gradually penetrating westward throughout Europe. The picture shows a Canadian elk.

V   The musk-ox was almost exterminated because it was too courageous. Not only will they not run away from bears and wolves but they are not afraid of human hunters; they close up into a defensive circle, the heads facing outward. In this way they form an easy target.

'thirties and by 1958 it was possible to allow some four to five hundred to be shot, for the first time in ninety years. In Poland beavers have been living in the state forestry reserve at Oliva near Danzig since 1950, having been imported from the Soviet Union. Canadian beavers have been established in the Allenstein district of East Prussia since 1914. They have been preserved there, as they have in other parts of Poland by the stringent preservation laws, which prescribe a fine of 20,000 zlotys and several years imprisonment for killing a beaver. In Switzerland French beavers from the Rhone delta were settled at Versoix in the canton of Vaud, which produced their first young in 1959.

Never in my life have I seen, heard and read so much about beavers as I did during those days at Grafskaya. On the return journey the stationmistress recommended us to take a sleeping-car train in which 'there were always places available'. For the other train, which we were supposed to have taken, she would first have to telegraph or telephone to Voronezh and she was not sure whether she would be successful. This alone should have made us suspicious, for as soon as we had gone two stops along the line in the train she had recommended we realised that it was a sleeper that halted at every single stop – an arrangement which I had never met in any other country. Consequently it did not reach Moscow in the early morning, but six hours later shortly after noon, and furthermore at a completely different station from the one at which we had set out.

As there were only Russian newspapers to be had *en route*, for lack of any other reading matter I spent the whole journey studying all the available monographs and books on beavers that I had with me. I thus reached Moscow as something of an expert on the subject. They are so interesting, however, that I did not regret a single moment that I had devoted to these industrious little creatures who invented moated fortresses and built dams thousands of years before we humans.

In the middle of the last war, while I was on active service, a letter which had been sent all the way to my home and forwarded to my army address reached me from another field post office somewhere on the Eastern front. 'We have made a bet: four of my friends won't believe it but another friend and I maintain that there are such things as white mice. You, dear Dr Grzimek, have been chosen as umpire. Please write and tell us whether white mice really exist!'

This question, as to whether there really are any white mice, has dogged me all my life. At first I thought that the man who wrote the letter was trying to pull my leg; after all, white mice are bred in tens of thousands. All laboratories and scientific institutes have special rooms given over to nothing but white mice and rats. They are infected with painful and nauseating diseases, operated on, subjected to tests to see how long they can subsist on indigestible foods – all as a means of helping sick humans and other animals. White mice can also be bought in every pet shop; young animal lovers have a habit of horrifying their mothers by bringing them home and breeding them. In spite of this many people obviously still believe that white mice only exist as products of delirium tremens and not in reality. Only a few days ago I had another enquiry about them. I have long since ceased to be surprised at this.

I once used to think that the people who write me postcards like this perhaps only wanted to know whether there are any white mice living *in freedom*, but this too I have ceased to believe: they doubt whether such creatures exist at all. Whereas the first blue budgerigar only dates from 1882, white mice living in freedom under natural conditions have been known for far longer. Chinese priests, for instance, have used them for thousands of years as aids to prophecy and for this reason Chinese governments always enjoined their historiographers to note the capture of a white mouse as a special event. We therefore know on good authority that this has occurred thirty times in the period between AD 307 and AD 1641.

White animals or albinos in general are not particularly rare and this is especially true among domestic animals. Wherever they occur they are seldom missed, because they are so obvious. A study of natural history will show that albinos exist among such varied species as kangaroos, shrews, moles (three per cent of all moles are albino), bats, hares, wild rabbits, lemmings, marmots, leopards, tigers, pumas, jaguars, martens, otters, raccoons, seals, wild pig, Cape buffalo, camels, chamois, waterbuck, apes, cheetah, zebra, cobras, trout, and other fish. In 1938 the first white giraffe was seen and photographed in East Africa, recently one in Uganda, and one in the Garamba National Park in the Republic of the Congo; an almost entirely white male giraffe lives in Northern Tanganyika, south of the Tsavo National Park, anxiously protected from harm by the superstitious game poachers. Albino brown bears, which of course have a completely different physique from polar bears, are indeed very rare but they have been known. Most bird species produce albinos, including crows, ravens, robins, blackbirds, sparrows, and swallows. Since white colouring is generally transmitted unadulterated to the offspring, it is quite easy for a breeder to mate two albinos and create a new breed or species. White fallow deer are quite frequent. The park at Klampenborg near Copenhagen once had as many albino red-deer as brown. Anyone so inclined could in time produce a white or even a black breed of our indigenous roe-deer by a controlled policy of shooting more of the brown ones.

Many farms in the Orange Free State and Cape Province of South Africa have specimens of pure white blesbok (a normally reddish-brown species of antelope). They have less resistance to the weather; they get sunburned, particularly on their ears and with time their eye-sight grows so weak that the animals become nearly blind. This makes them the special prey of dogs, who chase them unmercifully.

Sir Edward Hallstrom of the Sydney Zoo breeds a herd of white kangaroos on his private estate and exchanges them for rare animals from other zoos. Until 1962 it was believed that in contrast to the other big cats, lions never produced albinos, but in the spring of that year visitors to the Kruger National Park were able to film a white lioness. For decades an Indian maharajah has been breeding white tigers and a few years ago he sold offspring of this breed to zoos in the United States and to Bristol in England. These animals have the usual black tiger's stripes, but on a white and not a golden yellow background.

For a zoologist, therefore, it is not a very special event when some-one reports an albino. It would be more remarkable if there were any species which did *not* produce the occasional albino. At the Darwin Museum in Moscow a special section has been set aside for an albino collection, containing stuffed white specimens of capercaillie, black-cock, golden eagle, white-tailed eagle, raven, owls, falcon, fox, wolves, lynx, leopard and tiger – in short white specimens of practically every breed of creature are to be seen there.

There are even human albinos. In every race, from pale-skinned Scandinavians to the ebony black of many Negro tribes, there occur men who lack any trace of pigment in their skin, indeed, in their whole body including, for example, the brain. The actual colour of our skin itself is a creamy white. The presence of yellow colouring particles gives it a yellowish tone. Another colouring element is black, which derives from tiny grains of a substance called melanin; they are really sepia or dark brown but in the mass they absorb so much light that they give the appearance of being black. Finally the colour of the blood circulating in the ultra-fine blood vessels of the skin adds a reddish tinge. By mixing the colours white, yellow, red and black in different proportions every possible variation of human skin colouring can be reproduced. Human albinos completely lack the black pigment and the yellow is only present in very small quantities; the colouring effect of the blood in the skin gives such people a hint of pale red in their colouring. Since the pigmentation is also completely lacking in the iris of the eye – as with white mice and white rabbits – albino humans

G

have red eyes which are highly translucent; this causes them to keep their eyelids permanently half closed. Their constant need to blink causes the wrinkles round their eyes which are a characteristic mark of an albino. Among Europeans there is approximately one albino per ten thousand people, but among the San Blas Indians of Darien in Central America albinism is seventy times more common.

For a long time the ticket collector at the entrance to Serengeti National Park was an albino Negro; there is a picture of him in my book *Rhinos Belong to Everybody*. Naturally albinos who lack hair are particularly sensitive to light and are very prone to sunburn. Albinism even occurs in all species of cultivated *plants*, although albino specimens quickly die as they lack all chlorophyll, the essential component of all vegetable metabolism.

Herr Gustav Dietrich is a keeper who was trained at the Frankfurt Zoo, but who has now been living for many years in Bangkok, the capital of Thailand – or Siam, as it used to be called. He once spent a few weeks with us on a visit and then stopped for a day on the way back in Rangoon, the capital of Burma. We at Frankfurt have for long been on friendly terms with the director of the Rangoon Zoo. Our leopardess 'Mausi', who has been breeding in our zoo for more than thirty years, came as a gift from Rangoon and in turn animals born in Frankfurt are to be found in Burmese zoos. Herr Dietrich sent me greetings from Mr Kyan Thein, the director of Rangoon Zoo, together with a few snaps of a young white elephant from this zoo. Herr Dietrich added:

'The zoo is very proud of its "white elephant" (not exactly white, but pink all over with white eyes). Compared to our animals in Thailand this animal is sensational.'

In Thailand the royal household includes experts in the characteristics of white elephants and who are always summoned whenever the capture of one of these creatures is announced. The elephant must have white toes, white eyes and other distinctive marks; altogether the Thais recognise twelve 'degrees' of white elephants. (The white elephant cult is described in detail in the periodical *Das Tier*, Vol 2,

No 11.) In Bangkok I passed round a picture of the white Burmese elephant – apparently no one in Thailand had ever seen anything like it. In view of what is known about albinism in other species, a white elephant should not be such a great rarity, but true white elephants are found very seldom. On a postcard from the zoo, which Herr Dietrich also sent me, the little elephant appears so incredibly white beside another big, grey elephant that I could hardly credit the whole thing. Even *Brehms Tierleben* reports that in Siam, where albino animals of all kinds are highly prized, where the white elephant is regarded as sacred and where the king bears the title of 'Lord of the White Elephant', despite every effort extremely few pale specimens have ever been caught and they seem never to have actually possessed a truly white elephant.

When C. Bock was in Bangkok in 1881 he was shown two of these animals that were paler in colour than usual and had a few white flecks on their ears, but the difference in colouring was scarcely detectable. Just at that time, however, an elephant was caught in the upland country which was said to be truly white and was to be presented to the king.

'On the day announced for its arrival the whole city was in festive array and an extraordinary pageant was arranged.' Bock, who witnessed the solemn disembarkation of the sacred animal, described it as follows:

'I would undoubtedly be accused of being colour-blind if I were to describe it as white, but it is a pure albino; its whole body is a pale reddish-brown; there are a few completely white hairs on its back. The iris of its eyes, which is considered a good indication of albinism, was a pale Naples yellow. The beast gazed peacefully about and was led, not ridden, by its mahout; its obvious calm, as if conscious of its own importance, was in sharp contrast to the general excitement.'

There seems, therefore, to be no doubt that albino elephants exist. But even the nineteenth century authorities on the subject report that their colouring was obviously given artificial help by washing, bleaching and white paint. I know from my own experience how easy it is to deceive even the most critical onlooker. Shortly after the war – it must have been in 1947 or 1948 – we at the Frankfurt Zoo played an April Fool's trick on the press and the public, by spraying one of our great, grey asiatic elephants with a solution of French chalk. Old Simla, as she was called, looked so pure and white that she would have passed in Thailand for an incarnation of the Buddha. A few days before April 1 we put a little notice in the press that a white elephant from Siam was on its way to the Copenhagen Zoo and would break its journey in Frankfurt for a day or two. For a joke we made a small special charge for entrance to the elephant house for the privilege of seeing this miraculous beast.

We never imagined, however, that the American pressmen would really take the thing seriously. They came early in the morning and photographed the animal from every possible angle. The radio broadcast a description of the white elephant and yet another American news agency telephoned me in the night for a story, as all the Scandinavian papers were already running big headlines about the impending arrival of this extraordinary creature from Siam. Only the director of the Copenhagen Zoo seemed unaware of his good fortune, so a Danish news agency telephoned me at midnight for news. I had great difficulty in explaining that the whole story, which had aroused such attention all over Europe, was nothing more than a mild hoax. This and similar incidents are described in my book *Twenty Animals, One Man*.[1]

That is the reason, and only that, for my slight suspicions when I saw the pictures of such a beautifully white elephant from Rangoon.

After I had published a report in *Das Tier* on albinos and on the enquiries I had received about white mice, etc., I received several letters, including the two following:

I was greatly amused to discover – as were doubtless many other ex-soldiers who had served on the Eastern front – that there were still people, including yourself, who were so ignorant as to be taken in by the old hoax about white mice which was played again and again during the war.

I must begin my reply by talking like an expert; but please read to the end or you will not understand me properly.

There really are no white mice; certainly not in freedom, nor strictly speaking are there even any in captivity. Those which are bred in laboratories are perfectly normal grey mice; but according to the law of 1924 these must be dyed white with magnesium carbonate to mark them as animals for laboratory use. The same applies to guinea pigs. These animals come into the pet shops from laboratories. I have often bought some and turned them back to grey by using strong vinegar. They have red eyes because fine particles of the white dust get into their eyes which are reddened by the resulting inflammation. The redness, however, disappears a few days after bathing them in vinegar. Which proves that there are no white mice.

But joking aside, it is a fact that during the war someone would often start this game wherever there were groups of bored men, in dug-outs, in barrack rooms or in trains. Somebody would declare that there are no white mice, that they only existed as drunkards visions or in the military police.[2] Whoever did not know the game would maintain, to the secret amusement of the others, first calmly and then with increasing heat using all the usual arguments, that there were such things. It was particularly funny when there were several who were 'pro' white mice and the sceptical ones who understood the joke were in the minority. Then things used to get really heated.

Yours, Karl Imhoff, Münchengladbach.

It is most regrettable that you should recently have stated that white mice exist.

There are always people who will declare, against all the evidence of reason, that there are white mice and that they have once owned or seen some. . . . This is a piece of nonsense on the same level as the jokers who try to convince people that a stone is small because it hasn't been in the ground for very long but it will grow if left there. . . . Really refined examples of this sort of joke need a great deal of careful thought and time to perfect them; it is therefore an ideal pastime for troops in war, much of whose time is spent in soul-destroying boredom.

I know nothing about the geographical distribution and the various rare sub-species of these non-existent animals, but I suspect that they are confined to German-speaking countries. Practically everybody who went through the last war knows how to play the game. Now and again the 'white mice' have a practical purpose – to show up a know-all.

Yrs etc., Dr Ferdinand Merz, Rimpar nr Würzburg.

So that is the secret of those enquiries about white mice. The game, incidentally, obviously goes on in peacetime too. Ten weeks ago an old lady wrote to me in desperation that she had quarrelled tearfully with her son and grandsons, so badly in fact that she had shut herself in her room for the last two days. The reason – they all wanted to convince her that there were no white mice. Would I, as an expert, please write and prove to them that this was not true. So it goes on. I have the feeling that for the rest of my days I shall continue to be regarded as the final authority on the question of whether there are white mice or not.

[1] *Twenty Animals, One Man* published by Andre Deutsch, London.
[2] German military police wore white accoutrements and were nicknamed white mice.

It was not an easy matter to go to see the saiga antelope. To do so I had to journey as far as Kazakhstan near the frontier with Communist China. This Soviet Republic does not belong to the R S F S R; if I were to travel there and needed assistance it might not be so easily arranged from Moscow, I was told. They would first have to write to the President of Kazakhstan and request permission; this they were willing to do, but it would have been better if I had notified them before leaving West Germany. I have had a lot of experience with bureaucratic obstruction and I persevered. The Soviets are said to have organised a model example of nature conservation in Kazakhstan: a dying species, of which only a few animals remained alive, has been transformed in three decades into the most prolific breed of hoofed animal in the whole Soviet Union. These animals now provide meat for hundreds of thousands of people, on land which is otherwise agriculturally worthless. We have similar plans for Africa.

I went to the Bolshoi Opera and to the zoo, I went to see the beavers and the bisons in the forests of Prioksko. When I returned there was still no reply from Kazakhstan. Very well, I said, I shall proceed without formal permission. No one objected, so on a Monday I boarded one of the gigantic modern jets and took off from one of the Moscow airports which handles Soviet domestic air traffic. Like every airliner in the Union it was fully booked; my companions were without exception Soviet citizens. Because international air traffic regulations do not apply, the baggage allowance is generous. I was lugging about a hundredweight of cameras, film and apparatus with me because I was not sure whether my gear would have reached me safely if I had had it freighted out from Germany or if I had posted my exposed film from the Soviet Union, but it was never necessary to pay for excess baggage on any of my flights. Many of the other passengers also had very heavy suitcases. Air tickets are cheap, no doubt due to the high utilisation factor of the machines.

It was a long flight. The Republic of Kazakhstan is equivalent in size to England, Sweden, Norway, France, Spain, Portugal, Italy, Holland, Denmark and West Germany put together and with a little to spare. Since we West Europeans are usually a little weak in the geography of Soviet Asia, I should just mention that Kazakhstan extends from the lower reaches of the Volga and the Caspian Sea eastward to the far Altai, the Chinese frontier and Mongolia. Fifty years ago the romantic Kazakhs still led a nomadic existence with their tents, their camels and herds of sheep. Their wanderings took them over stretches of land of which neither they nor any one else dreamed would one day be covered with golden-yellow seas of wheat. Speedy though it is, the flight by jet still takes six hours and at Alma Ata, the Kazakh capital, there is three hours difference from Moscow time. From Moscow to Alma Ata is equivalent to flying from Frankfurt to central Egypt or via Iceland to Greenland, yet it takes twice as long again to fly from

18   *It is difficult to see from a live beaver how wonderfully soft its fur is. Long dark gloss hairs cover the soft woolly coat and keep it from becoming completely saturated.*

19   *When the female beaver has a litter the father and last year's young are made to leave the 'lodge', often for several weeks. Female beavers, walking upright, carry their young on their two fore-paws and frequently give them rides on their broad tails.*

20   *The lady veterinary surgeon of the beaver farm is here administering a worm mixture directly into the stomach of an old male beaver with a rubber tube. An assistant holds the animal's teeth apart with a metal wedge to prevent it from biting through the tube.*

21   *Incredible as it may sound people still place bets on whether or not white mice really exist.*

22   *In Alma Ata, the capital of Kazakhstan, there is a beautiful zoological garden founded twenty-five years ago. Every year it has a million and a half visitors. This picture shows the entrance gate.*

Alma Ata to the most easterly extremity of the Soviet Union, Kam-chatka. The stewardesses brought us trays with fried chicken, Crimean wine and caviar sandwiches.

Professor Sludski from the university and the people from the Alma Ata Zoo were waiting for me at the airport with enormous bouquets, although my visit was in no way official. I had, however, taken the precaution of sending a telegram to Konstantinidi, the director of the zoo, as I knew that there was an extremely go-ahead zoo in this remote spot. I had received a long telegram in Russian in reply to our last Easter greeting card, which we send out every year from Frankfurt, from the 'Zoo Collective of Alma Ata'. Our Easter card showed two soldiers bayonetting each other in the stomach whilst lions, elephants, buffalo, bears and giraffe (which never kill members of their own species) stare with amazement at the lords of creation. *Punch* in London and a number of French, American and Russian newspapers asked our permission to reproduce this drawing by A. Paul Weber.

Unfortunately I was unable to sell or to barter any young African hippos from our all too-prolific stud in Frankfurt: far away in Asia though he is, he had several already. The zoo was only founded in 1937; it covers two hundred and thirty acres of beautiful parkland with one thousand eight hundred animals from two hundred different species, many of whom live in the most modern types of enclosure. Two hundred employees work here and it receives a million and a

23   *The onager, which the Soviets generally group with the kulans, are a wild species of ass which are bred in Askania Nova and in large herds on an island in the Sea of Azov.*

24   *During their first two days of life new-born saiga antelope can be practically picked up by hand. It is then that they are in particular danger from wolves, prowling dogs and human poachers. As the saigas give birth to an entire generation of young within the space of a few days on large communal 'breeding grounds', they are easily protected.*

25   *The saiga antelopes have a remarkable nose. It is enlarged like a proboscis, can be moved to and fro, and on the bucks in rut it grows to four or five times its normal size. This organ has been the chief means of their adaptation to life in the dusty desert.*

half visitors every year. Every evening we sat for hours with scientists and zoo workers; I talked about Africa and other parts of the world and they described what was happening in Siberia, Mongolia and on the shores of the Arctic Ocean – and of course in Kazakhstan. I accepted an invitation to appear on Kazakh television.

Alma Ata is one of the most beautiful cities in the world. What fifty years ago was only a Russian fort is today the home of five hundred and eighty thousand people, for each one of whom there are twenty-seven square feet of open public parks and ten trees per inhabitant along the streets. Once camel caravans with bales of cloth passed through here along the famous 'silk road' from China on the way via Frunze and Tashkent to the Near East. Today the silk road is a broad tarmac avenue carrying a stream of cars. In spring the air of Alma Ata (which means 'the father of apples' in Kazakh) is laden with the scent of apple-, cherry- and apricot-blossom. Through the parks and along the streets flashes the clear water carried down from the glaciers of Ala-Tau, the 'Many-Coloured Mountains'. One hundred and twenty-five miles away is the Chinese frontier, but in recent years few visitors have crossed that border. Fountains play in the squares, palaces house the government offices; there are parks, department stores and a childrens' playground with a half-scale railway, made in East Germany. There is a Russian and a Kazakh opera house, although only fifteen per cent of the population of the capital is Kazakh and only thirty per cent of the country as a whole.

The zoologists took me by car along forty miles of a fine new road far into the 'Mountains of Many Colours' to Lake Issyk, with its glaciers above the greenish-blue waters, its pleasure steamers and paddle-boats, restaurants, a holiday camp of four-bed chalets, childrens' homes and waterfalls. There is a Communist peace slogan engraved into a cliff in huge letters, reminiscent of the gigantic presidential effigies carved in a cliffside in the USA.

I came across a group of conductresses of the Moscow–Alma Ata railway, who had spread out mountains of cakes, fruit, sandwiches and cheese on cloths by the lakeside. I had to take photographs and be photographed, drink vodka, join in the dancing and singing. A young man spoke to me in German; he was an expatriate German born in Russia. (When I was back in Frankfurt someone sent me a postcard from Alma Ata to tell me that a glacier had broken off, crashed into Lake Issyk and caused a flood. All the carefully built houses, the road and everything else had been destroyed; I was thus one of the last to see this little bit of Switzerland in Asia. Not a word about the catastrophe appeared in the newspapers.)

Kazakhstan is not only a country of fruit-growing collective farms and wheatfields, copper ore mines in the Altai, lush meadows and hydro-electric works along the valleys of the Karatau. Half the country is desert, once the habitat of millions of a most unusual species of animal.

Nearly two thousand years ago, in the first century AD, the Greek geographer Strabo described how these remarkable 'saigas' carried their drinking water with them by storing up several days' supply in their nose. In 1660 Beaplan reported that they had no bridge to their nose and could thus only pluck grass with it by walking backwards as they grazed. They are indeed rather clumsy-looking creatures about the size of a sheep with misshapen noses and little thin legs, in no way as elegant as the African or Indian antelope. The saiga antelope is not even closely related to them, as they are a unique sub-species of ruminant.

During the Ice Age, when woolly rhinoceros and long-haired mammoths were still plentiful, herds of saiga antelopes grazed over the steppes of Europe and Asia from England, across Germany and Russia, as far as the extremity of Siberia and beyond to Kamchatka and Alaska. Their bones are still found today in Germany and Denmark, but by the sixteenth and seventeenth centuries their western limit had withdrawn to the foothills of the Carpathians and the River Bug. The explorer Pallas described the Kirghiz Steppe in 1773: the number of saiga antelopes was so vast that his cossacks could kill them in abundance. In 1850 Ewersmann saw them swimming across the lower reaches of the Ural River in 'incredible numbers'; the entire steppe between the Volga and the Urals was teeming with them.

Just as the rhinoceros of Africa and Asia is being exterminated today thanks to superstitious Chinese apothecaries who believe that powdered rhino horn is an aphrodisiac, so too was the saiga slaughtered in the nineteenth century to satisfy the Chinese. Between 1840 and 1850 the merchants of Bukhara and Chibinsk alone sold no less than three hundred and forty-four thousand seven hundred and forty-seven pairs of the semi-translucent fluted horns of the male saiga. Their flesh was simply left to rot. They were shot from ambush at their waterholes, horsemen drove whole herds of them towards lines of armed hunters. The Kirghiz hunted them with greyhounds and trained eagles. In winter they were chased into reed-beds or on to frozen lakes where they were powerless to move and then struck down with clubs.

But these methods were not drastic enough. Ingenious men built long fences, which were three miles apart at the beginning and then gradually came closer and closer together until they formed no more than a narrow defile. Herds numbering thousands and tens of thousands were driven between the lines of fencing until they reached the funnel-like defile; as they raced through it in panic haste they impaled themselves on spikes, so placed as to rip open the animals' breast or belly. Thousands were butchered in this way; even more escaped wounded, crippled or dying.

Thus the saiga antelope, which as a species had survived and flourished for hundreds of millennia, was threatened with ever more rapid destruction the closer it came into touch with man. During the severe winter of 1828-29 saiga finally died out in the area between the Volga and the Ural River. Since then the 'European' saiga west of the Volga and the asiatic herds have been out of contact for over a century and by the end of World War I the saiga antelope was one of those species apparently due for extinction in a few years – another candidate for the long list of breeds which man has eradicated from the globe in the last two hundred years. The advance of the plough and the harvesting machine from the North towards the southern steppes and the semi-desert was progressively reducing the area of their habitat. No more than a few were now to be found at the furthest limit of Europe; a few dozen in West Kazakhstan, and some at scattered points in Asia – Ust-

Urt and the Sary-Su valley – making a bare thousand in all. A lost, vanishing race.

At the last possible moment, in the year 1919, the RSFSR promulgated a total ban on hunting the saiga antelope; in 1923 the Republic of Kazakhstan followed suit. At the same time Russian zoologists began investigating the habits of this dwindling, yellowish-red breed of animal. Foremost among them were Professor A. T. Bannikov of Moscow and his numerous colleagues, together with Professor A. A. Sludski in Alma Ata. They now proceeded to give me a detailed description of this gigantic experiment, showing me how since the end of the 'twenties the saiga antelope had slowly repopulated its former area of distribution in Europe and since the 'thirties in Kazakhstan.

At first they tried to locate the animals by car, then they tried aeroplanes, sometimes using eight machines at once. But since the minimum speed of these aircraft was between seventy-five and one hundred mph – in contrast to the much slower type of machine which we used in Africa to count the herds in Serengeti – and since the colour of the saiga is identical with that of its background, it was extremely difficult to identify the animals from the air. The best time was towards evening when the animals threw long shadows on the ground. A total of twenty-five thousand miles was flown during this aerial operation, a distance equivalent to flying right round the equator.

Later Professor Bannikov's assistants were able to mark more than ten thousand new-born saiga. The scientists' chief aim was to discover where and why the saiga migrated, as we have done with the herds of gnu and zebra in Tanganyika.

Saiga antelope are constantly on the move. They are extremely sensitive to the slightest change in the weather which may presage drought or snow and move on at once. When they graze their progress is very slow – two to four mph. They only increase their speed when they have to pass human habitation, which they do at about twelve mph. In some places, especially in winter, they will venture quite near to houses; but when the situation grows serious, i.e. if a heavy snowfall begins and threatens to cut them off from their food or if there is a severe frost, they can suddenly move off and reach a point seventy-five to one hundred and twenty-five miles further south in twenty-four hours. In normal, reasonably mild winters with intermittent periods of thaw, when it freezes they will trot south to places where the snow-cover is seldom deeper than four inches or where it quickly thaws, such as on the salt-impregnated soil along the shores of the Caspian Sea. As it grows warmer they move north again where there is more to eat.

If it is very cold and the snowfall heavy they must literally run for their lives. The saiga follow precisely the direction of the wind, even if it carries them over railway tracks or through villages – they pay no heed to danger. Winter is the only time when they will cross the Volga. The last time a massed army of saiga crossed the Volga was in the winter of 1953-54 when there was a westerly wind. In the very severe winters which recur at intervals of about ten to twelve years, with heavy snow, strong winds and extreme cold, the wretched animals will even stray on to the ice of the Caspian and into the reed-beds where they devour the withered stems and die from it. A snow-cover of more than eight inches which lasts more than a fortnight means death for whole herds of saiga. Since they all start running in the same direction once snow begins to fall, the herds coalesce and grow to enormous size.

In normal times the distance between the saiga's summer and winter feeding grounds is from one hundred and fifty to two hundred and fifty miles. In lean years, such as the period from 1945 to 1951 or the very snowy winters from 1948 to 1950 and 1953-54 they are forced to migrate very far afield. Although the hard winter of 1953-54 caused the death from hunger and cold of eighty thousand of the one hundred and eighty thousand 'European' saiga which had been re-established west of the Volga, it caused the remainder to be scattered over wide areas and thereby obliged these tireless animals to re-occupy much of their original stamping grounds.

Nowadays when saiga once more migrate in herds they form an unbroken stream of up to a mile in width. Sixty to a hundred thousand beasts move forward at a speed of between six and twelve mph, often for six days without a stop, as they did in spring 1958 when the bad weather had held them up in the south and they even kept moving at night in order to regain their northern breeding grounds in good time.

Of the numerous plants on which saiga feed thirteen per cent are avoided by other animals, especially by domestic animals, due to their toxic and saline content; it is just these species, in fact, which constitute the saiga's staple items of diet. As long as they can graze on succulent vegetation they do not drink. The drier it gets the further they must move each day to find sufficient green fodder. Only when the vegetation becomes very desiccated do they drink; then they will queue up at a water-hole in single file. They stretch their trunk, move it gently from side to side, put their forefeet into the water and drink, turning their nose to one side as they do so. Each antelope spends only seven to eight minutes in the water.

Their curious noses are a sign of their age-long adaptation to fast, constant running in dusty, desert places. The frontal chamber is inflatable, the nostrils are small and turned downwards. Generally the nose contains pellets of dust stuck together with mucus. Something similar, although not so clearly marked, is found in the big African topi antelope, a few of the small duikers and in camels.

Saigas usually amble along, but without a change of gait they can raise their speed to forty-five to fifty mph. When they take flight they begin by leaping into the air in order to have a better sight of the danger, then change to a gallop. When in flight they always seek out flat features in the landscape such as dried-out lakes and they run round obstacles instead of jumping over them. Their hearing is weak and their sense of smell is insignificant as their natural habitat is characterised by strongly rising airstreams. On the other hand their sight is excellent: they can see danger at a range of over a thousand yards.

Saiga bucks prefer older mates to young ones. Mating begins in late November, when the cold winter weather is on the way. By this time the bucks are carrying a one and a half to two inch-thick layer of fat, chiefly on their hindquarters and their nose is considerably more swollen than usual. It hangs down like a trunk and swings to and fro; the effect is far from elegant. Long, thick tufts of hair have grown under the eyes and the bucks are recognisable at a great distance by the dirty brown mane which grows out of both sides of their neck. A sticky, dark brown fluid exudes from the glands in front of their eyes; this has a powerful smell and enables them to detect a rival even in the dark. A buck can have two or three, even twenty and sometimes as many as fifty mates, which he is constantly striving to keep in a tight pack. During the rutting season the bucks eat nothing but snow.

Bucks frequently poach each other's does. Fandeyev, a Russian who has made first-hand observations of saiga in rut, describes how a buck with a pack of sixteen does attacked another with a smaller herd of nine. They butted one another so hard that the buck with fewer does lost its balance and fell over. His opponent immediately robbed him of three does and chased them into his own harem. A minute later the fight was repeated. After a violent collision the weaker buck again fell to the ground, whereupon the victor drove the remainder of the smaller troop of does into his own pack. The whole battle lasted about five or six minutes. The butting had been so fierce that the vanquished buck lay on the ground for another eight minutes before it could raise itself. Then it got up, quickly ran to its rival's herd and made off in haste taking with it three does from the fringe of the pack. The rival did not give chase but collected its scattered mates into a tight group.

The main rutting season lasts for seven or eight days; but the mating herds remain in existence for a further forty-five days, during which time the buck covers the young does of that year's brood who are only seven or eight months old. Finally the mating packs join up to form one great herd. The bucks who were fighting each other with such violence two days ago now graze peacefully side by side.

They have every reason now to cease their rivalry and eat their fill, for saiga bucks suffer a fate similar to that of the male of many sorts of spider, even though they are not actually eaten by their mates as the spiders are. Unlike the bucks, the does eat heartily throughout the rutting season and put on weight. The bucks face the winter in a debilitated condition. In March they often die in masses; in hard winters nearly all the males may die. The scarce winter fodder is thereby kept for the pregnant does, who ensure the continuance of the species. Young bucks are not sexually mature by their first November, as their sisters are. By this means they survive the winter in far greater numbers than the mature males and are ready to perpetuate the breed again the following autumn; nor does the leader of a rutting pack drive away young, immature males. Ninety-six per cent of the older does and eighty-six per cent of the yearling does conceive. Three out of four give birth to twins, although they never bear triplets.

Their fertility and their skill in running away from cold and bad weather is the secret of the saiga's power not only to survive but to flourish in such inhospitable surroundings. Even without human intervention mass death from natural causes occurred in 1855, 1866, 1879, 1891, 1903, 1917, 1927, 1948, 1950 and 1953. After a disaster such as this, called a 'djut', in 1949 half the saigas were dead. 1953-54 brought a snowfall of eighteen inches to two feet and temperatures of up to minus forty degrees centigrade, which caused forty per cent of the saiga antelopes west of the Volga to perish. First the old bucks, then the young bucks died, lastly the old and the young does; but only a year after this disaster the saiga west of the Volga had regained their former numbers. Male and female young are born in an equal ratio of 1 : 1 – but the adult sex ratio is one buck to 2·6 does! Sometimes after a very hard winter as few as three to four per cent of the bucks survive.

Thanks to the saiga's aptitude for running away from bad weather, whereas they lost thirty to fifty per cent during a severe winter in Western Mongolia, the goitred-gazelle in the same area who do not have this gift, lost eighty to ninety per cent of their herds. Ten years later the goitred-gazelle had not yet regained their original numbers whereas the saiga antelope made up their losses in a year or two. In millions of years of evolution nature has bred into them an incredible capacity to reassert their species in spite of all natural disasters – yet human stupidity almost succeeded in annihilating this astonishingly hardy breed.

H

In late March or early April the saiga begin to leave the lowlands bordering the Caspian Sea and move north, sometimes travelling one hundred and eighty-five to two hundred and twenty-five miles. There they have their breeding grounds, flat or gently undulating ground with short grass. Like the zebra and gnu in Serengeti they give birth, not as one might imagine in tall grass for concealment from their enemies, but on bare, open ground. They choose the open because it offers no cover to any lurking predators who might otherwise creep up unseen. In early May the steppe is literally alive with saiga as far as the eye can see. The air resounds with the bleating of young and the answering cries of their mothers. A big herd can cover an area of one hundred and eighty square miles and may number one hundred and fifty thousand and two hundred thousand head when counted from the air. Ninety-five per cent of them are does with young.

Newborn saiga fawns wait from six to eight hours after birth before starting to suckle. During their first days of life they lie pressed close to the ground and suck only for a few minutes or seconds at a time. The milk has a butterfat content of 6·7 per cent, somewhat more than normal cow's milk, and contains 5·4 per cent albumen. From the third or fourth day the young begin to crop greenstuff in addition to taking milk and are fully weaned at the age of eight to ten weeks; after this only a few of the fawns will still occasionally suck.

A man will have considerable difficulty in catching even a day-old saiga fawn if it decides to run away; fortunately the young generally lie so still that they can easily be picked up. When this happens the mother runs five or six hundred yards off and returns later having run in a wide arc; but by the time they are five or six days old the fawns nearly always run away when approached. When they do so they have a curious trick: they fall down in full career and crouch on the ground so suddenly that a pursuer usually fails to notice where they have stopped and loses them. When the mother comes bleating back, three or four other fawns usually run towards her bleating in response. She sniffs them and passes them by; her own fawn will continue to give tongue until the mother finds it. Five- or six-day-old fawns can run for up to thirty minutes at twenty to twenty-five mph; at ten days old they have the speed and stamina of adults.

Eight to ten days after they begin to drop their litters, the does and their young start to leave the breeding grounds and set off in hordes across the steppes. In a few days they may have moved one hundred and fifty miles. The noise of these migrating herds can be heard far away and the clouds of dust which they throw up are visible from a great distance. They will flow round a stationary car, for instance, like a river.

Apart from man, the saiga antelope's chief foe is the wolf. A wolf cannot catch a healthy adult saiga alone in the open, but preys instead on males in winter weakened after the rut, pregnant does and on the new-born young. They are specially vulnerable to wolves in deep snow, as the saiga with its narrow, pointed hooves exerts a relative pressure on the snow crust four and a half times greater than that of the wolf with its broad, hairy paws. Wolves also hunt in packs. The antelopes flee, as do most wild animals, by running round in an arc and returning more or less to the point of departure. Part of the wolf-pack stays and waits for them to come back.

In Kazakhstan in the 'fifties there was one wolf to a hundred saiga and twenty to twenty-five per cent of the antelope fell victim to these beasts of prey. After that eighty thousand wolves were shot in five years; after ten years a total of two hundred and ten thousand wolves had been shot in Kazakhstan, resulting in a sharp rise in the saiga population. There were, of course, no wolves west of the Volga, so in that area they did not affect the numbers. It is to be hoped that this policy does not have the unfortunate effects that so often result from artificially exterminating the natural enemies of a particular species. These enemies have a proper function in preventing a 'population explosion' and in assisting the selection of the fit.

The adults of this boss-nosed breed of antelope no longer have any enemies, although eagles, ravens and foxes still prey on the young saiga. If a bird attacks from the air the mother jumps up and strikes at it with forelegs and head. Incidentally, they show the same reaction to an aeroplane flying low over the ground where the young are being born. About one fawn in ten dies within ten days of birth; often the proportion is much higher. In May 1947, when it was very dry, the mortality rate of the young was twenty per cent and in May 1959 it reached sixty per cent. Even in normal weather conditions only two out of five fawns survive the first year of life, but that is quite a healthy proportion when one remembers that each doe bears young at the rate of 1·6 per year.

There was a time when the saiga were plagued by warble-fly, which laid its eggs under the antelope's skin. This resulted in painful boils when the insects developed into larvae. Since the end of the nineteenth century this fearful pest has ceased to attack the saiga, probably because by that time the numbers of saiga had dropped below the point where they could maintain the reproductory cycle of this dreaded parasite, and it appears to have died out before its 'host' species. Although the saiga antelope have almost regained their previous numbers, the warble-fly has never returned. In Mongolia, on the other hand, the warble-fly has persisted and continues its parasitic attacks on the saiga there.

Foot and mouth disease is often transmitted to saiga herds by domestic animals. When they catch it the bucks lose the upper part of their horns. The disease kills off the young in masses; in one outbreak there were two dead fawns for every one left alive and altogether forty thousand corpses were counted. However, the loss of saiga from this outbreak of foot and mouth disease was no more than nine per cent of their total number, much less than the havoc caused by a severe winter.

When winter comes the herds, which by now have taken on a very pale, matt grey colouring, move off southwards from the steppes to the desert and if there is snow there too they will dig through it to reach the wormwood herb, which is rich in albumen and other nutrients. All animals that have to dig in the snow have long hooves. Przewalski's horse and the kulan (Asiatic wild ass) with their short rounded hooves lack this facility in digging through snow. Thus when man was added to their natural enemies they were exterminated much sooner than the small but better-equipped saiga.

As creatures of the steppe, saiga are afraid of bushes, even in winter. They will keep at least a hundred yards away from a bush or anything like it and they therefore do little damage to crops. In a field of rye half a square mile in area a whole herd of saiga passing through it did no more than knock down a dozen-odd ears. They had walked with great precision between the rows. As they do not care for such tall plants, saiga will avoid maize fields even in a drought or in high summer, although they may trample its outer edges quite severely. The harm they cause to agriculture is negligible.

The saiga antelope were saved at the critical moment from apparently inevitable extinction. At first the new conservation laws did no more than ensure that the last few hundred survivors remained alive. Then in the 'twenties a gradual increase in their numbers was noted in the area west of the Volga, followed by a similar increase in the 'thirties in Kazakhstan. In World War II, when the stock of cattle was low and men were engaged elsewhere, the process was accelerated. West of the Volga gamekeepers were stationed in every large town, numbering between twenty-five and thirty. They drove around on motorcycles to stop poaching and sent in reports twice a month. Their chief task was to protect the breeding grounds from predatory stray dogs as a great number of fawns were lost every year in this way.

The growth of the saiga herds gained continual momentum: by 1947-48 there were as many in Kazakhstan as there had been a hundred years before. In 1951 there were about nine hundred thousand, by 1960 one million three hundred thousand. Further to the north-east, in the Mongolian Soviet Republic, a protection law was finally passed in 1955. By 1954 the saiga had once more advanced to the edge of the cultivated regions, the limit of territory at present available to them. In Soviet Asia alone this represents one and a quarter million square miles and in European Russia another one and a quarter million square miles, i.e. half the surface area of Europe. But the vegetation on these dry steppelands and semi-desert is extremely sparse and they can hardly support for long more than two saiga per square mile.

In the mid-'fifties, therefore, it was decided to make use of these animals for human consumption and a state corporation, 'Astrakhan Promkhoz', was set up to hunt the saiga. Every year they count the herds at breeding time and again in autumn shortly before the opening of the hunting season. For those with a game licence saiga can be hunted with the aid of a pointer dog from October until November 10, i.e. until just before the start of the rutting season. This method does not produce the amount of meat required, so state 'hunting brigades' shoot the animals on dark windy nights using searchlights – a method which sounds less sporting but is much more humane. Private persons are not allowed to hunt in this way.

A 'brigade', consisting of five men, drives over the steppes in a jeep at ten to twelve mph. Using only headlights, the antelope can be seen at a range of a mile and a quarter, as their eyes reflect. When they are within one or two hundred yards the vehicle stops and a powerful searchlight is switched on. The saiga either stand still in the beam or even slowly approach the searchlight, as we found in East Africa that Thomson's gazelle would do when we rounded them up to mark them. Meanwhile the huntsmen dismount and shoot the animals at the short range of thirty to forty yards. Compared with normal hunting methods this results in very few animals being wounded, running away and dying in pain, besides which at this close range the sex and age can be exactly determined. Young bucks are the principal target. Originally the old bucks were shot, but when their numbers were experimentally reduced to one to two per cent of the stock (the natural ratio of mature bucks being ten to twenty per cent), it was found that in the following year four to five times more does than usual were not pregnant. In five or six hours a brigade can account for one hundred to one hundred and twenty antelope.

Saiga have an incredible capacity for recovering from a blood-letting. When the young are born the herds increase in numbers by one hundred and fifteen per cent at one stroke, thus more than doubling their size within a fortnight. If there are no wolves or marauding dogs, up to forty per cent of the saiga stock can be shot annually without re-ducing their total numbers – even taking into account loss from natural causes. At present two hundred and fifty thousand to three hundred thousand are being shot every year in European and Asiatic Russia. Even so the maximum stock density has not yet been reached; Kazakhstan reckons with a further increase of two to three million. Once dead the animals are used for their meat – which tastes rather like mutton – and for their hide, which is made into patent leather. The horns are exported to China, where they are used for medicinal products. A fully grown buck yields thirty-five pounds of meat, a doe thirty-five to thirty-seven pounds. The Soviet Union thus gathers an annual harvest of six thousand tons of meat and twenty-four thousand square yards of leather, all from desert areas which, if the saiga had been exterminated, would today be completely sterile.

It is curiously difficult to re-establish saiga antelope artificially in regions where they have once died out. Friedrich von Falz-Fein tried to do it on the steppes of Askania Nova, but the animals vanished without trace, even though vast herds of them had lived on the Ukrainian steppes only a century before. Attempts to establish them on islands in the Sea of Azov and the Caspian Sea were equally fruitless, whilst even in zoos they seldom live long and only breed in exceptional cases. In captivity, too, they prefer green fodder to drinking water and are grateful if the water is slightly salted. In the zoo at Alma Ata, in their homeland, I could only find one solitary female saiga in a large enclosure. The only reason why she did not run her head against the railings, said Director Konstantinidi with a smile, was because she was blind in one eye. There are no saiga antelope in the Moscow Zoo and whenever Western zoos obtain any specimens from the Soviet Union these curious beasts soon die in captivity.

The herd on Barsa-Kelmes, a large island in the Aral Sea, was just saved from extinction by last-minute intervention. The island's name, incidentally, means 'Thou shalt never return' in Turkish. Many animals stray there in winter across the ice and then find themselves marooned when the changeable weather melts the ice and cuts them off. Barsa-Kelmes has also been colonised with onager, of which there are now fifty head on the island. The saiga almost died out: in 1929 only five more were left there, all does. Then eight more, including some bucks, were introduced; by 1961 they had increased to two thousand. This herd has the great advantage of being somewhat tamer than their fellows on the mainland. In Kazakhstan and along the Volga they can only be observed from a great distance by car or by aeroplane. Any attempts to catch saiga antelope for experiments or for zoological gardens are usually made here. Originally long nets were set up for this purpose and the herds driven into them by a line of beaters. Ten or twenty head at most would be caught in one drive, but the animals grew more and more cunning. They would turn about just short of the net and race back between the cars and motor-cycles. Since then only new-born or young fawns are caught. It is useless to chase the old ones by car; they only give up when they are completely exhausted and die soon afterwards from oedema of the lungs. In five or six days thousands of new-born fawns can be earmarked. If any of them are to be reared in captivity they are taken to fenced enclosures, but no more than ten

26 *At the end of the tsarist empire the number of saiga antelopes had fallen to less than a thousand head. It was thought that they could not be saved. Today their numbers have regained the three million mark and they are the only form of life with which the vast region of southern Kazakhstan can in future be developed for food production.*

27 *In the bird sanctuary on Amrun Island the eggs of a number of the smaller species of breeding birds suddenly began to disappear and no more young were born. Later twelve hedgehogs were caught in box-traps placed on the narrow paths among the lymegrass, which were brought to the mainland by Herr Ebeling, the bird warden. The first hedgehogs were probably brought to the island with loads of faggots used for building dykes. The hedgehogs were unable to crack open the hard-shelled eggs of seagulls, eider ducks and sheldrake. Their tracks, however, showed that at night they waded far out into the shallows at low tide, where they clearly went hunting for small fauna to be found on or just below the surface of the mud-flats. Here they put their ability to swim well to good use.*

28 *The saiga antelope has re-established itself in more than half the territory of Kazakh-stan. The Kazakhs, whose forebears of only fifty years ago were nomads, now constitute only a third of the population. The old man, whom I met riding his donkey along the road, still wears Kazakh costume.*

are put in one cage, or they rush about so excitedly that their sharp hooves cut the skin of any animals that are lying down. There are now plans to place watering-troughs near the breeding grounds and to provide them with some winter feed, to prevent the herds from moving too far northward and trampling the fields of collective farms.

The saiga antelope have already served the human race well: when our forebears wore skins and lived in caves during the Ice Age they lived almost entirely from hunting. The saiga must then have been the easiest animal to catch and above all the animal which, after a lean year or a hard winter, most rapidly recouped its numbers. Their bones are found in the greatest quantities near the settlements of primitive man.

Who knows what disasters are in store for us and our descendants, what famine and misfortune probably caused by man's own shortsightedness? At this moment there are more people alive on earth than ever before in the five hundred thousand or more years of known human existence, yet the extent of man-made desert is continually growing whilst the human race – two-thirds of whom are already undernourished – increases hourly. The example of the saiga shows what an act of madness it is to allow any form of natural life to die out altogether. An animal species which evolves in the struggle for existence over millions of years often has capabilities of which we are quite unaware. The saiga produces meat and leather from the grim, cold, salt wastes of the desert, something which neither humans nor domestic animals can do. It is horrifying to think that but for the firm action of a few determined and intelligent men forty years ago, these remarkable animals would have vanished from the earth's surface for ever.

29 *Five hundred and fifty thousand roe-deer are shot in Germany in one year; a great deal more than this number are therefore born every year.*

30 *Nowadays foxes have a hard life in Central Europe. Recently the spread of rabies has been due less to dogs and cats than to foxes, for which they are being systematically exterminated in certain districts by gassing them in their earths.*

Modern man, living in air-conditioned caves in concrete mountains, hardly notices any longer whether it is summer or winter out of doors; but our ancestors in their draughty castles with no glass in the windows, as they sat by the flickering light of a piece of pinewood stuck in the wall, deprived of fruit and vegetables throughout the winter, must often have envied those animals which escaped so much discomfort by hibernating. Nowadays surgeons want nothing better than to be able to turn their patients into marmots: before many an operation they cool them down in ice so that the body temperature falls, consciousness fades away and metabolism slows right down. The flow of blood to the brain can then be interrupted for much longer periods than is normally possible.

As I write, the marmots in our zoo are now hibernating in their burrows, as are their relations, the North American prairie dogs. In the autumn they stuff hay into their mouths until they appear to have a bristly moustache and carry it underground, not as food, but to upholster the burrow, make it warm and stop up the entrances from the inside. We have never observed a marmot to lie on its back, pile grass up on its stomach and hold it in place with its paws while its fellows drag it into the burrow like a small haywain. This has been described by those living in alpine districts and has been recorded in several books although there are no really reliable witnesses to this practice.

If we were to dig some marmots out now we should find them cold and lifeless, with a body temperature of only four degrees centigrade. They could be stabbed, or cut, a trumpet blown beside their ears – they would notice nothing. Every few minutes, however, their hearts would slowly contract and they would take a very few scarcely perceptible breaths. They lose from one- to two-fifths of their weight during hibernation, but if they go hungry in a waking state they lose as much weight in twelve days as in five to seven months when hibernating. Whereas the marmots in the Frankfurt Zoo down in the lowlands only hibernate for four or five months, their relatives in the Alps spend seven months asleep, or even as long as nine months in some very remote burrows. They are therefore unconscious for three-quarters of the year and only really live for three months.

Do they forget the past when they wake from their long spell of suspended animation? We know for certain that they do not. When they wake up they are rather bad tempered and inclined to bite for the first few days, but they recognize the members of their family and distinguish between them and other marmots; shy marmots are shy towards humans after hibernation, tame ones are as tame as before. The Viennese biologist Professor Oskar Koenig once rescued a young five-week-old marmot from the clutches of a marten. At first the young animal ran freely around in their apartment and was, as are so many young animals and children, friendly and trusting towards everyone. At the age of seven months it gradually began to be hostile towards strange humans. It only regarded Professor and Mrs Koenig and their large Alsatian dog as being members of its family. It would give them friendly nibbles and invite them to play tag.

Next spring its abilities increased: it climbed all the furniture, gnawed every corner, bit the buttons off cushions and clothes and succeeded daily in its attempt to upset the coal scuttle; it carried stockings, clothes and blankets into its box for comfort and tugged at the towels until they fell off their hooks. To crown all these activities it devoured the indoor plants. Above all it would not tolerate locked doors, insisting that its paths through the apartment should always be unobstructed. The marmot learned to use its teeth and claws to open all the push-doors in the apartment which were only kept shut by a spring-loaded catch and was quite ready to start gnawing through a door if necessary. As soon as someone shut a door the marmot would rush and open it again. When it had marked all the furniture and walls as its own personal possessions by rubbing them with the glandular secretion in its cheeks, its owners were finally obliged to place it in a marmot enclosure along with several companions of the species. Later, whenever they took it out for a few hours and brought it back, its fellow marmots would hurry to sniff at its snout. This was their means of identifying the returned prodigal and of discovering where he had been and what he had eaten.

When a stranger came the marmot, as large as a hare, would waddle up, wag its bristly black tail up and down, whet its teeth, stand up, clasp the visitor's leg and try to bite it. Of course only a tame marmot which regards itself as on an equal footing with humans would behave like this on seeing a human: wild ones give a squeak and disappear into their burrow. In remote regions of the Alps the marmots vanish if a man approaches within two hundred yards and hours will pass before they cautiously re-emerge from their holes. This used to make it far from easy to photograph them in the mountains. One had to stalk them for hours, even days.

In many places this has now changed. Driving southward through the Engadine there is an unusual triangular warning sign to be seen by the roadside; inside the red border is the silhouette of a marmot on its hind legs. This indicates a marmot colony by the roadside and one can often approach within six feet of them. If they are frightened they retreat almost unwillingly to their burrows and once there they immediately turn round again and peep out. Like so many other animals they are not afraid of humans or of the apparatus of civilisation such as cars: they are simply averse to being hunted and killed. If treated kindly they will show confidence.

For some years we kept our marmots at the Frankfurt Zoo in complete freedom. Once they have settled somewhere and dug their burrows they are quite uninterested in running away or even in making reconnoitring sorties. Even in the mountains the 'territory' of a marmot family is little more than an acre. If, as happens in a zoo, they do not even have to forage for their food, they grow even lazier. Our marmots had burrowed under the wire of their enclosure and used to emerge from their burrows outside the fence. This did not worry us at all, but the dogs disliked it. Whenever a dog passed, a marmot buck would leap out, hurl itself at the dog's neck and try to bite it. I was also worried that they might one day burrow under the foxes' enclosure and emerge inside it; the foxes would then have killed them and used the marmot tunnels to escape into the open.

The outcome of a fight between fox and marmot is by no means certain: a few years ago a hunter watched a fox trying to kill a marmot. The marmot defended itself so fiercely that both animals lay dead at the finish. Since the bear and the lynx have long been extinct in the marmot's habitat, their only remaining natural foe is the eagle and even that is now extremely rare in the Alps. But anything moving in the air, even a scrap of paper, will terrify marmots. A century ago tame marmots could still be seen at most country fairs on the Continent, generally led by a boy from the Tyrol or Savoy who played a flute to which the marmot danced.

Marmots have had an easier time since we humans decided to treat them properly, although this cannot be said of many other wild species. By the middle of the last century the few surviving marmots were to be found in the Alps and the Tatra mountains and nowhere else. The reduction of their numbers was yet again a consequence of human ignorance and superstition. Some people had come to the bold conclusion that because the marmot lived in damp holes in the ground, hibernated in winter and never suffered from rheumatism, their fat must be a good cure for human rheumatism. This greatly appealed to simple minds and marmot grease has been in great demand at a high price for centuries. Many are the species which have been doomed because human stupidity has maintained that horns, bones or hairs can arouse love, cure diseases or ward off the Evil Eye. The situation became really serious for the marmot, however, when a druggist from Schaffhausen began to exploit marmot-salve commercially and to advertise it in all the newspapers. The price of marmot grease rose and in 1944 16,000 marmots were shot in Switzerland. Infuriated nature conservationists eventually persuaded the druggist to stop a trade which roused false hopes in his rheumatic customers and was actually robbing them of their money for nothing. Marmot grease contains a high proportion of insoluble fatty acids and Vitamin D. Nowadays marmot oil costs thirty shillings a pint.

Marmots, or 'murmelis' in Swiss-German, have always been cherished by those who value other things beside money. Part of their charm is no doubt due to their fondness for standing upright on their hindlegs and acting like little men and generally being so playful. It can be a delight to watch them from a hide, preferably with binoculars. They play tag with one another, they roll down the mountainside, they stand upright, face each other and strike each others' incisor teeth until the noise rings. They are also fond of boxing, when they stand up and face their opponent. The game consists in hitting the opponent in the neck or on the arms so that he is prevented from striking back.

While the exploiters did their best to exterminate marmots others were striving to re-establish the species. In Germany the only original marmot colonies are those near Berchtesgaden and in the Western Allgäu; all others, as elsewhere in the Alps, have been reintroduced since 1880. Thus the colony at Hohenaschau in the Chiemgau are descended from eight marmots brought over from Berchtesgaden in 1887. The whole present-day marmot population of Styria, with an area of distribution of six thousand, two hundred and fifty square miles, consists of the progeny of a few animals settled there in 1883. The same is true of Carinthia, Lower Austria, Salzburg, the Tyrol and Vorarlberg. In 1963 some *black* marmots were caught in the Zillertal. Around Salzburg there were no marmots before 1912; now they number thousands. In Austria as a whole the total of marmots caught in 1955 was three thousand, three hundred and sixty-nine. Alpine marmots have also been settled in the Carpathians, in the Yugoslavian Karawanken and in the Pyrenees. Europe is now thought to have a marmot population of between fifty and a hundred thousand. The highest known colony is at six thousand six hundred feet, the lowest at two thousand seven hundred feet. In 1947 the French even transferred some marmots from the Alps to the Pyrenees, where they have settled. In 1954 some were introduced on to the Feldberg,[1] after other Alpine species such as chamois had increased in numbers from twenty-one in 1935 to two hundred and fifty twenty years later. Marmots are a particularly rewarding breed to introduce into new areas, as they will gratefully move in practically anywhere, even in lowland country. So far there is no evidence that they do any harm. The Russians, too, have successfully colonised marmots from the Altai.

· There are not many true hibernators in Europe. Hedgehogs, bats, hamsters, dormice and garden dormice hibernate like marmots. Bears, badgers, squirrels and moles do not attain the same depth of suspended animation. When the marmots waken in spring they have a spring-clean: hay, padding and rubbish are thrown out of the burrow. A few days later the mating season begins. Not much is yet known about the mating and breeding habits of marmots, as most of it takes place underground. Only lately has Hans Psenner, in his beautiful new zoo at Innsbruck, been able to construct a marmot enclosure so that the young in the burrow are permanently visible behind glass. It seems that the females are only on heat for one day and on that day they will couple with all the males in their group. The suitors show no jealousy, at any rate there are no fights; brown rats behave in a similar way. Five weeks later the young marmots are born blind and only sparsely covered with hair. After a further three to four weeks they take their first look out of the burrow. One marmot in the London Zoo lived for fourteen years; the life-span in freedom is thought to be fifteen to sixteen years.

Marmots are known for their habit of uttering a piercing whistle. To do so they stand upright and let their forepaws drop. This whistling is not, as so often described in books, a cry of warning but is the invariable response when something excites or disturbs them. The tame marmot mentioned above once whistled for thirty seconds without interruption when it caught its leg in some railings. It even whistled for several minutes on end the first time that it heard the hum of a vacuum cleaner. Whereas squirrels and other related species will occasionally eat eggs and will even kill young birds, the marmot is a strict vegetarian.

This is the reason for the considerable length of this small animal's intestine – twenty-one feet. They will not even eat insects.

Marmots are probably responsible for the belief, held in many Alpine regions, in the 'Tatzelwurm' (one-footed dragon), for when a marmot runs through the snow one of its hind feet steps exactly in the imprint of one of its fore-feet. The trail thus appears to consist of not four but three paw-marks, which has puzzled many observers. All three imprints together look like the mark of one gigantic paw: hence the superstitious belief, caused by one small animal.

[1] Grosser Felding (2,887 feet), highest point of the Taunus range of mountains to the NW of Frankfurt.

Over the last twenty years Kuban cossack choirs have now and again given concerts in the big hall of the Frankfurt Zoo and have sung Russian folksongs in their beautiful manly voices. Under their Hetmans the cossacks first fought for long years against the tsars, then for them, against the Soviets after the revolution and then for them in their army. I never believed that I would ever drive through their proud villages; past castles and old churches built on clifftops and up the Kuban river which pours down from Mount Elbruz, the highest peak in the Caucasus, to the Sea of Azov.

To enable me to do so the kind people from that animal paradise of the Tauride steppes, Askania Nova, first drove me in a new Soviet jeep along endless deadstraight asphalt roads past vast wheat-fields to the isthmus which divides the Crimean peninsula from the mainland, then on between equally endless vineyards as far as Simferopol. There I could have made a short detour to Yalta and to the watering-places along the coast of the Black Sea. But did I want to see fashionable resorts or did I want to see ibex? So I had to step straight into a big jet airliner in Simferopol.

Modern airports are identical everywhere, no matter whether they are in Frankfurt, Cuba, San Francisco or East Africa. I sat with Svetlana Zelkina in the blazing sunshine on a bench like a deck-chair under a long red-and-white striped canopy and waited until we were called for.

Svetlana had been to the Crimea once before, but this time she found it more comfortable and stylish. Last time she had herself saved all the money for the trip and had gone there by train, a journey of several days and nights. Now she was wearing her prettiest dress of pale grey poplin, so we were suitably dressed to be seen amongst these

I

cheerful people who were flying to resorts on the coast or to the Caucasus. If the people here were not talking Russian or the many other languages of the Soviet Union and if the notices were not all in Cyrillic letters I might have imagined that we were sitting in Lisbon or Barcelona airport.

Among the many brightly-coloured leaflets which are handed out to travellers on the flight to Moscow, there was one showing all types of Soviet passenger aircraft and which even carried their descriptions in English. Here I could see them landing and taking off without a break, because it was now the busiest time: old ones with twin passenger decks and four propellers operating feeder-lines from small airports and the big modern jet cruisers. To me they looked little different from the giant jets anywhere else in the world, except that they wore the Soviet star and the designation 'Aeroflot'. What a good opportunity to film a complete selection of Soviet aircraft! Svetlana was immediately taken with the idea. She even began to get my camera out. But I had my doubts. I knew that in many countries aircraft were regarded as state secrets – even in Germany this used to be the case. So I insisted that she should first enquire.

She came back somewhat downcast: no, it was in fact not allowed. I make it a rule in foreign countries to observe as far as possible the laws which govern their citizens; it often saves needless trouble. Jet planes are not worth getting into trouble for – although perhaps ibex are.

With my interpreter Svetlana Zelkina I took off in a Soviet jet from Simferopol airport in the Crimea and flew over the cloud-covered Black Sea, across the peaks of the Northern Caucasus to the region south of Maikop where there is a charming spa town called Minvoda. There the director of the Teberda Nature Reserve came to meet us by car and we drove along the banks of the Kuban river. On the way we stopped to eat, the usual caviar and fried chicken; this time there was no vodka, but Russian brandy instead. Vodka is much better but was presumably thought too ordinary.

Conversation was superfluous during the drive up the Kuban

valley, so I was able to contemplate the scenery. After a drive of one hundred and thirty-seven miles the sun was setting behind snow-covered peaks as we arrived in Teberda, a charming village in the Swiss style, built in 1936, at an altitude of four thousand feet.

The Teberda Nature Reserve – *Teberdinsky Zapovednik* – is in the northern Caucasus, covering an area of four hundred and thirty-two square miles lying between altitudes of six thousand five hundred feet and twelve thousand feet. This sounds a lot, but is in reality little more than half the area of Greater London. Also in the Caucasus is the Nature Reserve in Krasnodar Province which is three times as large and contains some European bison; these are no longer, however, the pure-blooded Caucasian mountain bison, which were rather smaller than the lowland bison from Poland. The Caucasian bison is now unfortunately extinct and the Reserve has been resettled with a cross between mountain and lowland bison.

In 1965 the Soviet Union contained sixty-five National Nature Reserves (*Zapovedniki*) with a total extent of twenty-four thousand seven hundred and forty square miles, equivalent to four-fifths of the area of Scotland. Besides these there are the so-called *Zakazniki* which cover a further nineteen thousand six hundred square miles: these are regions in which most of the animals are protected and which unlike the *Zapovedniki* are not permanent but are allocated Nature Reserve status for a limited period only. In addition there are other *Zakazniki* in which hunting syndicates are restricted to the pursuit of certain animals. Nearly full Nature Reserve status is also given to the five 'Hunting and Conservation Collectives' with a total area of two thousand square miles and the twenty-nine state-run 'Experimental Reserves' (five thousand one hundred square miles). *Zapovednik* and *Zakaznik* are not artificial words of bureaucratic coinage, but are old and familiar expressions in Russian. The Russians have long been used to the idea of nature conservation, above all in forest regions, but all in all these areas are not over-generous in a state covering thirteen million eight hundred and twenty-two thousand square miles. Unfortunately most countries are the same. Man has attacked the earth's surface and its natural inhabitants like a voracious parasite and has only left them tiny areas in which they enjoy a precarious safety.

One of the protected species at Teberda is the chamois. Their numbers were once reduced to two hundred and they have now reached a thousand. There may be more, but they are hard to count as they mainly live in the woods. (In the Alps chamois only retreated to the peaks and cliffs because of constant persecution.) Where they have been resettled in the Black Forest they live as they do here – in the higher wooded regions, and as is the case in the Silesian Altvater Mountains (now known in Polish as *Jesenicky*), where they have also been re-established. Teberda is not so well off for deer. Red deer only live outside the actual Nature Reserve, but they are nevertheless cared for by the one hundred and six workers and the six biologists employed on the Reserve. Four red deer were imported into the National Park and they have meanwhile increased to thirty. In addition fifty-four dappled Ussuri deer were laboriously rounded up in 1938 on the distant Ussuri river north of Vladivostok, where they were already nearly extinct. After three years in Teberda they had multiplied threefold, grown very tame and wandered freely throughout the whole area. During the Occupation the Germans shot them down with machine-pistols, I was told. Nowadays there are only a few small bands of Ussuri deer and they keep strictly to the high ground. There are many bears in the Reserve, but they are rarely seen and never cause any trouble.

But to observe the ibex we had to trek high into the mountains on horseback. Svetlana was nervous, as she had never mounted a horse in her life. A whole cavalcade set off with provisions, tents, and cameras tied in sacks and strapped on the backs of gentle but strong pack-horses. I was put into a kind of overall, complete with climbing boots, which made me almost unrecognisable. The way up the wooded slopes was so steep that the wretched nags were soon flecked with sweat. I felt sorry for them, so I dismounted and walked alongside, but our progress was in any case no faster than my pace.

If I had not been surrounded by kindly, weather-beaten Caucasians I might have imagined myself in the Swiss Alps or the Rocky Mountains. Foaming mountain streams, sunshine slanting through the virgin upland forest, views of snow-capped peaks or down into lush green mountain valleys: but here there is not a house, not a hotel, not a power line and not a chair-lift to be seen. All is as it was a thousand years ago. Where is there a view in Germany or Switzerland without some trace of human habitation or of our ant-like activity? Svetlana too preferred to walk; she did not trust horses.

Just as the sun was setting we came across a mountain hut, lurking among the trees. I was never able to find these huts, so well were they hidden. We as guests were allowed to sleep inside on palliasses, the others spent the night warmly wrapped in the open. In the evening a fire was lit, food cooked and stories told. We were already close to the ibex.

In antiquity the ibex inhabited most of the Alps, and earlier they were probably spread over most of the mountainous areas of Europe. The ancient Romans even caught them and took them to Rome for the gladiatorial games, which accounts for the alpine ibex which was probably the model for a hunting scene carved in relief in the cathedral of Split. Roman and Etruscan buckles in the shape of ibex horns have been found in large numbers along Lake Como and Lake Maggiore. Magnificent fresco paintings of ibex are to be seen in the Egyptian royal city of Thebes. Like the beaver and the marmot, the rhinoceros and the saiga antelope, the ibex fell victim above all to mediaeval superstitition and the weird notions of folk-medicine. They were regarded as a panacea for all ills. As late as the nineteenth century the ibex was a sort of walking chemist's shop. Its blood was said to be a specific against kidney stone (because the animal lived among stones) and rings were made from the horns as a 'protection' against innumerable diseases. Bezoar stones (rough balls of hair, resin, small pebbles, etc. which form in the ibex's stomach) were supposed to be of value against cancer. Even ibex droppings were collected and taken for consumption and gout. The ossified cross-shaped tendons of the heart muscles were alleged to have positively miraculous properties. Anybody who bagged an ibex was practically made for life. The

Prince-Archbishops of Salzburg kept special 'ibex' shops in Salzburg and Berchtesgaden where medicines derived from the animal were sold. Small wonder that the strictest game laws were unable to protect the wretched ibex.

One after the other, from 1712 to 1720, the Prince-Bishop had to dismiss all the six gamekeepers employed to protect the ibex, as there were simply none left for them to protect. The Swiss ibex did not die out until a hundred years after the Austrian herds, although even in Switzerland they were extinct in the northern Alps by the seventeenth century. In the Valais they managed to stay in existence until the early nineteenth century, until there too the last specimens were laid low. Our knowledge of the alpine ibex would be confined to the evidence of crude old wood-carvings had not a forester named Josef Delapierre and a naturalist called Zumsteen persuaded the Piedmontese government in 1816 to protect the last dozen ibex in the Gran Paradiso. This is a mountain chain in Upper Italy north of Turin, along the French frontier in the Graian Alps. Fortunately the ruling house of Sardinia regarded ibex hunting as a royal preserve and protected them with jealous care. From 1854 the Gran Paradiso became the private property of King Victor Emmanuel, who increased the measures for protection of the ibex by detailing a permanent company of Forestieri. The region around the National Park, in the Val d'Aosta for example, is inhabited by poverty-stricken mountain folk; their subsistence in winter depends on factory work away from home and they regard the ibex as fair game. In 1921 the area became a National Park. At first the sixty-four gamekeepers were so badly paid that the best of them also drifted away into industry. The boundaries of the Gran Paradiso National Park are still so badly drawn that they run right across mountain pastures and open fields. Especially in severe winters the ibex and chamois are forced down below the boundaries, which mostly run between altitudes of five thousand and five thousand five hundred feet. Once out of the Park the animals are shot from the roadway using telescopic sights at four hundred yards; in the winter of 1962–63 five hundred chamois alone were accounted for in this way. To judge by the cars' registration numbers, some of these poachers came from as far as one hundred miles away. In the Savaranche valley one thousand one hundred and twenty-five head of ibex and chamois were shot during the winter of 1963-64. One keen shot has built himself a splendid hunting lodge in the San Pietro, just outside the boundary of the National Park, from which he can practically mow down stray game from his bed. Only a sensible redrawing of the park boundary, proposals for which have been disregarded by a heedless government for years, can save this unique natural treasure. The Gran Paradiso is the source of all the ibex that have been reintroduced into other parts of Italy, Switzerland and Austria.

In the Soviet reserve at Teberda (the stress is on the final syllable) the ibex are similar in appearance to our alpine ibex. Further to the east in the Caucasus lives the tur, which lacks the bumps along the forward edge of its horns and has practically no trace of a beard. The tur resembles the ibex, but is coloured reddish-brown. Its big horns curl forwards, much like the spiral horns of horned sheep. There is now a stock of three to four hundred of these turs. All ibex including the Spanish, Nubian and Asiatic varieties belong to the wild goat family as do the markhor with their spirally-twisted horns and the North African arui sheep. How closely they are interrelated is shown, among other things, by the fact that they can be crossbred with each other and with domestic goats. The original wild variety from which they are all descended is probably the bezoar goat, which lives on Crete, on other islands of the Levant and in mountainous regions of Asia Minor and Persia.

To see the ibex in the mountains of Teberda we had to crawl out of our sleeping bags before dawn, at four am, as these shy creatures spend the night well above the tree-line and climb back up the steep cliff-face a quarter of an hour after the sun reaches their early-morning grazing ground; we could not follow them with our clumsy equipment. Even if we had been able to, the ever-watchful ibex would be unlikely to let us approach within range of my telescopic lens, for they are much better mountaineers than we are.

We only had to climb a mile or so from our hut before suddenly freezing to a stop behind some stunted fir trees. After a long delay while I mounted the camera on its tripod, I eventually focused on the herd. Their behaviour showed them to be completely unaware of our presence. They were imposing creatures, especially the bucks with their enormous curved horns; beside them the does with their two small, pointed horns looked incongruous, almost like domestic goats. When a buck stood silhouetted on a peak or an outcrop, turning its head towards the nearest doe it gave the effect of a statue. If the buck is paying court to a doe it jerks its tail upwards. As with the male domestic goat, the ibex buck sticks its tongue out and flicks it up and down with head, neck and ears stretched horizontally forwards. Sometimes it will lift up a foreleg, point it towards the doe and slowly swing it back and forth.

These powerful beasts look as if they could easily kill each other in a fight between jealous rivals but in fact this never happens. In the Frankfurt Zoo, for instance, we have never separated our ibex at mating or breeding times; adult males, does and young all live together in a none-too-large enclosure and we have never had a case of one ibex being killed or even seriously wounded by another. If an ibex threatens a rival it does so by shaking its head, showing its horns and if it wants to make a special impression it stands up on its hind legs. Both forelegs are thrust out at a sharp angle and the chin pressed into the neck. The whole performance seems more of a game than a fight.

Whichever of the two has the uphill position in these boxing matches is halfway to winning, so one tries to run round the other to gain a better stance. The uphill buck then rears up, generally holds its head at a slight angle and gives a violent thrust with the curve – not the points – of its horns against the horns of its opponent, who usually

31 *When marmots are angry they whet their teeth, click them, rear upright and try to seize their 'antagonist' with their forelegs and bite him. In general, however, tame marmots are very friendly.*

32 *The female saiga antelope is the hardier sex. They generally survive even when four-fifths of the males die. Saiga bucks prefer older to younger does.*

stays on all fours the better to withstand the tremendous blow. The noise of the clash is considerable.

Often two bucks will stand side by side like horses in harness, hook their curving horns together and pull at each other. Two jealous ibex bucks may run around like this for days, shoulder to shoulder, as Dr Fritz Walther has observed them to do at the Frankfurt Zoo and else-where. When one finally emerges as the weaker they cease to run side by side but the victor pursues the other for a long while, like an evil spirit. If two bucks start a fight others come and join them for the fun of the scrap and not to reconcile the opponents. In their enthusiasm they will often leap up and turn right round in the air and face in the opposite direction.

Our Caucasian herd was not quite so frisky. Two females lay flat on their side, their legs outstretched. A buck was resting the tips of its horns on the ground, its nose pointing vertically upwards. These enormous horns are obviously a burden; another buck was lying down with all four legs folded beneath it and had lain its chin on the ground to relieve its neck of the weight of the horns. Ibex seem to have no fixed way of getting up, as cows do. One of them raised its forelegs first and sat for a moment like a dog, whilst another pushed itself up on its hind legs first like a cow.

There is a Soviet film about Asiatic ibex, in which a fleeing herd is shown jumping back and forth between two perpendicular and obviously fairly smooth cliff-faces and thus evading their pursuers. People have asked me whether this is trick photography; I do not think it is: ibex can jump with incredible sureness, especially downwards.

At the Halle Zoo an escaped tur buck jumped unhesitatingly from an outcrop of rock thirty feet on to the road below. It then ran off down another road and ended up on the steeply-sloping cliffs above the

33 *Compared with the modest horns of the female, those of the male ibex are large and impressive. The male horns are more for show than anything else and are chiefly remarkable for the noise they make in fighting, whereas the female can do real harm with her short, sharp horns and is well able to hold her own with the big males. These are Asiatic ibex.*

river Saale, from there ran about a mile down the riverside road and finally, cornered, took a mighty leap over the embankment into the river, which is large enough to be navigable at that point. The animal was not so good at swimming and when it managed to climb on to a narrow masonry ledge immediately under the embankment wall, it stayed there and allowed itself to be lassoed by the horns and led back by three strong men to the Zoo. After this unnerving experience it never tried to escape again and spent the rest of its life in the safety of an enclosure. I cannot, however, believe the statement which I have read in a book by an expert that ibex 'can jump several yards into the air from a standstill'; I have never seen it done and think it is unlikely.

Filming animals needs patience. Most of the time they do nothing worth recording. But suddenly as we watched a buck made a fifteen-yard rush at another on its hind legs. The impact as it brought its 170-pound head down on the other's skull was colossal. The thick lumps on the forward edge of the horns ensure that the blow is no glancing one.

These protuberances have little to do with the animal's age. The older an ibex becomes, the longer its horns grow – but they also grow smoother and the swellings on its horns grow progressively smaller. When the young are ready to sprout horns a lump begins to grow under the skin of their forehead which is hot to the touch. Finally the new horn thrusts its way through the skin. The process is not unlike teething. The horns are not of equal size, the right being slightly shorter and thicker than the left. When attacking, most bucks always lead with the same horn. Dr Ingo Krumbiegel made a study of three hundred and seventeen pairs of ibex horns in museums and found that twenty-one of them bore signs of healed wounds; of these seventeen were on the left horn and only four on the right.

Male stags are on the whole aggressive and dangerous when in rut, both to females and to weaker males. Ibex bucks, on the other hand, hardly pursue their females at all. Despite their fierce appearance they are actually rather hen-pecked creatures; the does can inflict much greater damage with their short, sharp little horns. The buck makes a lot of noise and fuss, but the female of the species is more deadly!

The does of our Caucasian ibex had given birth a few weeks before. They do so in the open, but a few hours after birth the kid usually takes refuge in a hollow or small cave; this is often too small for the mother, who then stands guard beside it. For the first fortnight after birth, doe and kid stay very close, as do all mountain-dwelling animals. The kid walks close to its mother's hind legs, so that they constantly touch each other and when grazing the doe will never go further than five or ten yards away from her kid. After fourteen days it becomes more indepen-dent, practices climbing and runs round and round its mother.

The young ibex that we were watching had formed themselves into play-groups. They chased each other, imitated the adults' fighting, stood upon their hind legs and climbed on each other's backs. If one did not want to play, another would scratch its back with a forefoot until it got up and joined in. If two slightly bigger young bucks got into a serious fight, their mothers would watch very attentively, although they paid not the least attention to a battle between old bucks. When that happened they ran up from all sides and stood round watching, but did not intervene.

Even if ibex cannot jump several yards into the air from a standstill, they can reach extraordinary heights if they have only one wall, which can be a very smooth one, against which to jump. Hermann Ruhe, an animal dealer at Alfeld near Hanover learned this when he took delivery of a shipment of Siberian ibex. One of them was put into a small enclosure surrounded by a solid eight-foot wooden fence. The animal at once began jumping from one wall of the fencing to another, going slightly higher each time round, until before the keepers realised what was happening it had worked its way to the top of the fence and was off and away.

An Indian keeper ran after it and found the ibex grazing by the road-side. Being a good hand with a rope, he managed to lasso the animal round its horns, but the ibex was stronger and ran off dragging the man behind it. As they came to the River Warne the buck leaped over the stream in one great jump, dragging the wretched Indian headfirst into the water. The pull jerked the ibex's head round slightly and the rope slipped off its horns. As the incident was reported in the Press, complaints and claims for damages soon began to come in for trampled flower beds, damage to woodland and hay stolen from barns. Finally a farmer managed to shut his barn door while the ibex was inside and it was caught.

Fortunately we Europeans have decided in the nick of time to protect the ibex, so it will not suffer extinction as have the South African quagga, the dronte, Steller's sea-cow, the aurochs, the great auk, the North American passenger pigeon, the thylacine, Burchell's zebra and many, many others. At first attempts were made to preserve the last remaining ibex in zoos. There was, however, a general lack of experience in breeding wild species in captivity and again and again breeders were obliged to mate ibex males with female domestic goats because the ibex does always died. Such crossbreeds are fertile and the Schönbrunn Zoo in Vienna and the Hellabrunn Zoo near Salzburg, which was disbanded in 1866, eventually had little but ibex-goat crossbreeds. Such of their progeny as were subsequently set free in the Alps perished sooner or later. In Bern crossbreed ibex-goats were put into the famous Bernese moat, which for centuries had housed the bears, the city's heraldic emblem. These mongrel ibex could not be kept in their enclosures and soon climbed out and on to the roofs of neighbouring houses; they knocked over a sentry-box and even attacked people, ripping the clothes from their bodies.

In time the Swiss decided to reintroduce the pure-bred ibex into its mountain habitat, where it had once been so savagely and carelessly exterminated. The Peter and Paul Game Park was founded in 1892 near St Gallen, but pure-bred ibex were only to be had from the Italian stock in Gran Paradiso. For years the Italians were not willing to co-operate; the ibex had become an Italian monopoly and with good reason: they were the only country which had taken serious measures to preserve them. It was said that the Swiss were making determined but unsuccessful attempts to poach ibex alive in the Gran Paradiso and smuggle them out. That is to say to use in reverse methods which have so frequently been employed to exterminate game. The first genuine ibex reached the Peter and Paul Game Park quite officially in 1906, generously provided by the Italians. Since then a pure strain has been bred there. All ibex which have subsequently been set free in the Swiss or Austrian Alps originated from there or directly from Gran Paradiso.

Breeding ibex is no longer a difficulty for modern zoologists. At Frankfurt we had by 1963 bred thirteen children and grandchildren from a pair of alpine ibex presented to us in July 1954 by the Game Inspectorate of Canton Grisons.

At first no one at Gran Paradiso was quite sure how to catch ibex alive. It is much more difficult to do than for a hunter or poacher simply to go out with a rifle and bag a good pair of antlers. They began by taking the easy way out – shooting the mother does and seizing the kids. Not only does this method, which has been used with other wild species such as gorillas and orang-utans, have the disadvantage of needlessly destroying the very animals needed to maintain the breed; it is also largely unsuccessful, as it has generally proved impossible to rear the orphaned young. Even when they succeeded in catching the mother with her kid they had many losses; once, for instance, having successfully brought a doe and kid to their new home a golden eagle swooped down and killed the kid within sight of the men who had just brought them.

The first five ibex in the Swiss resettlement scheme were set free on May 8, 1911 in the Grey Horns, a mountain chain near St Gallen. One refused to accept freedom; it kept coming back and would settle down nowhere but in its enclosure in the Peter and Paul Game Park. The others flourished and multiplied. Switzerland now protects them better than their extinct predecessors; when a man illegally shot two ibex in 1953 he was discovered and fined £500.

Meanwhile ibex have been reintroduced in several other places in the Italian, French, Swiss and Austrian Alps, as well as in the German Alps. Many such attempts were successful. In 1964 there were more than thirty ibex colonies in Switzerland, numbering over three thousand head. At the same time the ibex population of Spain had reached ten thousand head, having nearly doubled in the last few years. Only in the German Alps has the ibex failed to settle down. Those which were set free in the Hagengebirge south of the Könnigssee (Southern Bavaria) in 1922 were later infected with chamois-scab and were reduced to ten. They crossed the frontier and joined the ibex colonies on the Austrian side; only occasionally do they stray back on to German soil.

It is not easy to restore the natural balance once it has been destroyed by greed or carelessness. Hunters in particular and even many naturalists make a false distinction between 'useful' and 'harmful' species; they believe that the easiest way to regenerate the antelope or the zebra species in Africa, for instance, is simply to shoot the lions and the hyenas. But beasts of prey have a proper natural function; they weed out the sick and weaklings. Where there are no eagles or lynx lying in wait day and night to pounce on ailing animals, they stay alive and infect one another; in this way mange, scab and other diseases are spread.

In Serengeti about every second or third young Thomson's gazelle and as many gnu calves and zebra foals are killed by leopards, lions, Cape hunting-dogs, vultures, jackals, crocodiles, snakes and many other predators. If this did not happen the herds of peaceful herbivorous animals would soon grow to double, eventually to ten times their size and would finally destroy the land by over-grazing it. Then the hunter must step in, for good or ill, and reduce their numbers by shooting.

Then, of course, the animals grow shy of humans and lose their trusting behaviour which so delights all visitors to the African national parks. There one can ride up to within a few yards of lions, elephants and giraffes or drive through tens of thousands of zebra without the animals even turning to look at the observer. Where we are obliged to hunt them, on the other hand, man is their chief enemy and they fly from him.

In the Soviet Union I was frequently asked about our African method of temporarily paralysing animals with cartridges loaded with drugs in order to catch them alive. In some of the Soviet national parks the deer and above all elk have multiplied to such a degree that they completely prevent the growth of young trees. They must be kept down with firearms and this makes them so shy that they are never seen, at least not in summer. Where this happens the visitors stop coming to the national park, even though the scenery may be as beautiful as parts of the Rockies. For this reason they would like to catch the superfluous deer alive with 'anaesthetic bullets' and transport them for resettlement to other areas.

'Are there no more wolves in the Banff or Jasper National Parks?' I asked them in the Canadian Rockies two years ago, when it seemed to me that the wapiti deer were much too shy for midsummer. The wolves had been exterminated 'because they killed so many elk calves'. Now they were obliged to shoot large numbers of deer to control them, which they were not keen to admit. Exactly the same situation has arisen in the American national parks.

Unfortunately wherever possible the wolf is also vigorously hunted in the Soviet Union. If there are a few left in the Teberda Nature Reserve I suspect that it is only because they have merely not succeeded in bagging every last one. Whereas lions and leopards in Africa confine their activities to fairly small areas and do not stray out of the 'territory', wolves cover great distances in winter. The national parks are simply too small to keep the wolves within their boundaries all the year round, but if they leave the confines of the Reserve farmers in the surrounding countryside start to complain bitterly. This has led to the Russians adopting the same unfortunate policy as the Canadians and Americans of trying to exterminate wolves everywhere; large-scale campaigns of dropping poisoned meat are carried out by aeroplane and the state gives a premium for every wolf killed. The wolf is the only predator in our latitudes which really kills young animals and sick adult animals in large numbers. Where the wolves have been cleared, men must take over the task of slaughter to maintain the natural balance. Besides wolves the only creatures left to perform this function are the lynx, the puma in North America and tigers and leopards in Siberia.

The white man may yet manage with considerable effort to ensure that the last remnants of tropical fauna are preserved in Africa and that

a century hence Africans will still be able to admire the abundance
with which their continent was stocked with elephants, rhinoceros,
giraffe, lions and zebra before European 'order' was introduced. In our
own temperate zones, however, we seem incapable of doing this. To
create true national parks with a correct ecological structure we must
also leave the large predators alive. So far this has nowhere been done.

I had hoped that it was being done in the Soviet Union, but they
have made the same mistakes as have been made in the USA and
Canada. National parks capable of holding wolves must be vast in size
and can therefore only properly be created in the eastern Soviet Union
or the more northerly regions of Canada. Ultimately white men bear
a responsibility towards the human race as a whole – as we so often
preach to the Africans. How otherwise will future generations ever
know what our natural temperate Eurasian habitat looked like before
we allowed it to be consumed and destroyed? Where *will* the first real
national parks be made, beasts of prey included – in the Soviet Union
or in North America?

Thoughts like these arise constantly when one travels. The ibex
alone is not enough, successful though we have been in preserving
and regenerating this breed. During World War II their numbers in the
Gran Paradiso dropped to four hundred and thirteen; by 1963 they
had regained a figure of three thousand one hundred and ninety-eight,
besides five thousand three hundred and sixty-three chamois. Today
there are six thousand alpine ibex in the Alps, a hundred times more
than there were a century and a half ago.

Here in the Teberda Reserve their numbers have increased from
eight hundred to between two thousand, five hundred and three
thousand. They are counted every year on August 20. Students,
biologists and other interested people climb up to the mountain ridges,
where they divide up according to a definite plan and count all the ibex
that they see. This date in late August is chosen because then the animals
climb up to the snow-line to avoid the mosquitoes in the wooded and
bush-covered areas lower down the slopes. According to my friend
Professor Bannikov there are approximately two hundred and fifty

thousand Siberian ibex alive in the Soviet Union today and some twenty-three thousand other varieties.

On my way back from the Caucasus to the spa town of Minvoda, I noticed a number of strips of woodland in the flat lowlands. I had already seen them in the Ukraine, in the steppes around Askania Nova. They are endlessly long strips, a mile or two apart made up of five or six rows of deciduous trees running as straight as a die right through the vast fields of arable. These green strips seem to have no end but simply fade away at the horizon. The trees are young, many of them two years old, some fifteen years old at the most. They have obviously been planted to a plan which was begun during Stalin's régime. Perhaps they should not have been laid out quite so much like the new macadam roads, quite so straight and rigidly squared off.

'These strips have partly been planted by State and collective farms. In many districts the government has been directly responsible for planting them', I was told by Vassily Barabanshchikov, the director of the Teberda Reserve, as he accompanied me back by car. He had lost an arm in the last war but was so skilled in the use of his artificial hand that he completely mended the broken handle of my suitcase which I had been incapable of repairing with my two hands. 'In this way we have planted seven and a half million acres with trees in the entire Soviet Union since the war. The strips begin north of the Caucasus and continue well to the north of Moscow.'

I calculated that this amounted to six hundred and twenty-five thousand miles of timber, if each strip has an average width of ten yards. Coming of farming stock I realised what this entailed: finding the right varieties of trees to suit the differing conditions of soil and climate, growing millions upon millions of saplings in nurseries; but above all there was the task of simply inducing people to plant these strips. They are after all largely unproductive, at least for several decades.

I had read until then virtually nothing about this colossal network of woodland; nothing appears to have been written about it, either in

K

Soviet propaganda literature or in foreign publications. The idea originated from a great Russian scientist, Professor V. V. Dokuchaev (1846-1903), whose special study was the soil and climate of Russia. He was deeply impressed by the ravages of the terrible famines, resulting from drought, which visited Russia thirty-six times in the eighteenth century and forty times in the nineteenth century without anything, except charity balls, being done about it. Many old people had grown blind through sitting in their tiny mud huts crouched over the biting smoke from stoves burning straw, during winters when there was a shortage of wood fuel. Our present era, in Dokuchaev's opinion, was one in which trees were gradually spreading out again over the Russian steppes – at least they would be doing so if man ceased to hinder them. Fir trees and other conifers were, he thought, on the retreat, birches and deciduous trees in general on the increase.

When the steppelands of European Russia were colonised in the eighteenth and nineteenth centuries – especially under Catherine the Great, when many German peasants were settled in Russia, these vast steppes were devoid of fixed human habitation. Tatars and other nomads had passed over, but had never stopped to cultivate them. To the settlers from Swabia and Franconia these great plains looked quite different from their appearance today. There were still woods flourishing between the rivers, for example around Voronezh where the beaver reserve is situated. All the rivers were lined with woodland as they are today in many parts of Africa. These riverbank forests followed the rivers and their tributaries all the way to the Black Sea; along these wooded 'corridors' woodland animals penetrated far into the steppe zones. As has recently been discovered from manuscripts left by a Polish diplomat, who was a keen naturalist, there were bears, wild cats and elk as far south as the Crimea. Similar reports have also come from ancient Greek sources.

All these scattered woods and the long belts of deciduous riverside woodland were entirely destroyed by settlers, exposing the vast steppelands to the danger of erosion by wind and evaporation, like the artificially induced dust bowls of the USA. After the terrible crop-failure and famine of 1892, Vassily Dokuchaev set up three experimental farms on watersheds: between the Volga and the Don at Khrenov, between the Don and the Donetz at Starobelsk and between the Donetz and the Dnieper at Veliko-Anatol. There he began trial plantings of a great variety of trees.

A second great silviculturist and forestry pioneer was Professor Pavel Andreyevich Kostysheyev, who taught at the School of Forestry of St Petersburg University at the same time as Dokuchaev. He had been born a serf on a large estate. Both men gained experience from the success – and the mistakes – of the first experimental forests planted by another silviculturist, A. E. Graff, in 1843 on the bare steppe near the present-day railway station of Velikobnadol. A monument to Graff still stands in the midst of this woodland oasis; he was the first man to prove that trees would grow in the Russian steppes.

The third in this triumvirate was Vassily Williams, the son of an English railway engineer and a Russian mother. When already a father of seven, this tall, strong, broad-shouldered man began studying at his home in Petrovskoe. It was said that he could often have been seen at night reading at the window by the light of a street lamp to save money on lamp-oil. Later he crossed France on foot, worked on bacteriology in Paris under Pasteur and studied soil chemistry in Germany. Vassily Williams is the actual originator of strip-afforestation in Russia, of the countless little dew ponds and all the other measures taken against the erosion which was gradually devouring whole villages; he not only wrote scientific works on conservation but achieved the much greater task of making both government and people actively conscious of the need to preserve the soil of their country.

So these wooded belts were created with the aid of teams of surveyors and engineers, with tree-planting machines, with armies of peasants, factory workers, with students and bands of volunteers; eight million square miles of land were protected from erosion and black dust-storms by the ideas of Dokuchaev, Kostysheyev and Williams put into practice.

To find out the total extent reached by the strip-afforestation project in 1965, I wrote to Professor V. Koldanov at the Institute of Forestry at Uspenskoye. He replied thus:

'According to the data so far published in the Soviet Union, which is not exhaustive, the area of woodland strips on collective-farm land together with anti-erosion plantations in steppe and woodland-steppe districts of the USSR makes up a total of over two and a half million acres. As a rule these strips are between ten and twenty yards wide and lie along the boundaries of grazing and arable land owned by the kolkhoz. Every hectare (approx two and a half acres) is planted with six thousand to ten thousand one- or two-year-old saplings, giving an average per hectare of eight thousand saplings (approx three thousand, two hundred per acre). The total number of young trees planted to date is probably therefore over ten thousand million.

'Naturally in the course of time the original number of saplings gets reduced as growth and thinning-out proceeds. After twelve or fifteen years each hectare contains two thousand or slightly more young trees, which can be regarded as a normal density. The greater part of the strips were planted on kolkhoz land between 1947 and 1953, although large-scale planting was already under way from 1931 to 1941; strip-afforestation is still in progress today in a number of areas in the south-east of the USSR.

'Besides the strips of this type, eight other specially large strips were planted during the same period. These were put down at government expense and are known as 'National Windbreaks'. They are different from the collective-farm strips. Usually they run from north to south and are mostly sixty yards wide; one only is thirty yards wide. The National Windbreak strips cover one hundred and eighty thousand acres and are planted with five hundred and eighty million saplings.

'The kolkhoz strips are distributed over the farmland in a gridiron pattern and occupy between a 100th and a 150th of the usable agricultural land. The eight National Windbreaks act as the major links in this vast network of strip plantations and they cover a total distance of seven thousand five hundred miles. The linear extent of the kolkhoz strips is of course many times greater.

'In years with normal weather the yields per hectare in the areas affected by strip plantation have risen by roughly four to five cwt. In dry years it is entirely due to the windbreaks that the fields in their vicinity can yield a harvest at all. They are of prime importance in combating dust-storms and are the best possible means for protecting arable land from wind erosion.'

Just before I flew back to Germany some Press reporters in Moscow asked me what had most impressed me in the Soviet Union.

'Not the astronauts,' I said, 'not the innumerable blocks of flats which are sprouting out of the ground round Moscow, not your modern hotels and skyscrapers and airports – we have those in the West too. It was something which you city-dwellers probably know very little about.' The journalists were most curious to know. I told them about these strip-plantations, which in my opinion would prove in seventy or eighty years time to be far more significant for the future welfare of the Soviet people than a landing on the moon or any political system. Two-thirds of the world's population are already undernourished. There was still more than enough land to spare in the Soviet Union, but here too the population was growing at a furious rate, here too great cities and industrial complexes were sprouting like mushrooms. It was my belief that one day those three professors, Dokuchaev, Kostysheyev and Williams would take their place in the history books alongside the great generals, the revolutionaries and the dictators.

The menagerie at Versailles was not the first zoological garden in the region of Paris. As early as 1570 Charles IX had ordered cages to be set up in the very heart of Paris, in the garden of the Louvre and in the Tuileries. They housed lions, bears, oxen and donkeys, later augmented by camels and an aviary; the court amused itself by baiting bulls with mastiffs in a bear-pit. A bear-baiting performance took place there in October 1572 – two months after the slaughter of tens of thousands of Huguenots on St Bartholemew's Eve. There were also menageries at the châteaux of Fontainebleau and Chantilly. It was typical of the style of the French nobility of the seventeenth and eighteenth centuries to keep exotic animals. Since France set the tone in those days, many noble houses throughout Europe soon copied them by installing their own menageries.

In 1654 Cardinal Mazarin had a new menagerie built at the entrance to the forest of Vincennes near Paris, to which he transferred among others, the animals from the Louvre and the Tuileries. It was founded over three hundred years ago on almost exactly the same spot where the large, modern zoo at the Bois de Vincennes was recently built.

Nothing, however, has survived of these old zoos. Only two buildings indicate the site of the erstwhile menagerie of Versailles, where it is just possible to trace the foundations of the old buildings in the gardens which now grow on the spot. Although there are no longer any more animals to be seen there, animal-lovers who visit the château should nevertheless take a short walk through the park as far as the old menagerie. Going down the steps from the main façade of the château, go along the left bank of the gigantic cross-shaped artificial lake, then farther along the left arm of the cross until you are facing the two pavilions, and the walls of this famous menagerie. These pavilions were certainly not used to house giraffes as the gardeners who live in them today will tell you; they were small buildings to accommodate guests.

When King Louis XIV decided, at the age of twenty-four, to enlarge and improve the estate of Versailles which had been laid out twenty-eight years earlier by his father, he originally intended nothing like the enormous and magnificent château which later arose there. His first thoughts were for the park itself and the menagerie, of which he was particularly fond. The architect Le Veau designed some extremely bold plans for it. Until then it had been usual for enclosures, cages, ponds and aviaries to be scattered at random throughout an estate. For the first time Le Veau brought all the animal houses together into an enclosed space of about ten acres. Since the menagerie unlike modern zoos was not meant to be open to the masses but only to the king and his noble guests, the architect laid out the cages on a sunray plan like a half-opened fan. From the middle, the pivot of the fan, the privileged visitors could see all the animals at once. This new idea was then copied by practically all the European menageries to be constructed after the example of Versailles and it strongly influenced the Schön-brunn Zoo in Vienna, which is still functioning. At the central vantage point a little château was built, with rooms adorned with paintings and statues of animals.

The king was so delighted with this new and original plan that he insisted on it being built with all speed. The menagerie was begun in 1662 and finished in 1664; it cost 450,000 livres. If this seems relatively little it is because the king relied largely on unpaid feudal statute-labour provided by his subjects. In 1663, after much hesitation, the king even gave the contractor permission for his labourers to work on Sunday after Mass. In 1665 the first exotic animals arrived: ostriches, Egyptian cranes, eagles, porcupines, 'Pharaoh's rats', foxes, a lion, rare doves, a cassowary, an elephant – a present from the king of Portugal – three crocodiles from the king of Siam, camels, deer, gazelles and some Dutch cows, whose milk mixed with egg-yolk was used to feed the flamingoes. There were also pelicans in a special pond. Water for the whole layout was brought via two masonry aqueducts from Saint-Cyr and

Fontenay, which were not completed until 1688. Between 1671 and 1694, according to the still extant account-books, the equivalent of £100,000 was paid for the acquisition of animals. This was a very costly undertaking, as whole expeditions and special ships had to be despatched to collect them. New arrivals in this period included five hundred and thirty-six Allen's Gallinules, one hundred and three ostriches and many other animals. The elephant was specially skilled in untying the knots on its hobbleropes at night. Once it lifted the door of its cage off its hinges without waking the keeper and made its own tour of inspection of the menagerie.

From about 1670 the king allowed the public to have access to the great parks of Versailles, including the menagerie. As a result so many flowers were trampled down, so many statues damaged and so much litter was dropped that in 1699 it was again closed to all except members of the court. Official guests would descend the terraces from the château to the end of the artificial lake where they boarded a dozen or so gorgeous barges, including a number of Venetian gondolas. They were rowed by colourfully costumed 'seamen' to the menagerie and then, generally in the afternoon, on to the Trianon at the end of the opposite arm of the lake. When the once-brilliant Louis XIV had become a disagreeable old man plagued with gout and many ills, he was cheered and amused by an eleven-year-old girl, the rather plain little Princess Adelaide of Savoy who a year later married the Duke of Burgundy. For a caprice he presented her with the whole menagerie and even had

34 *When two male ibex fight, each one tries to gain the uphill position. It then faces downhill at as sharp an angle as possible and brings head and body down on to his adversary with the maximum impact. It is a game, like a tug-of-war with two fingers: no damage is done and the only object is to prove who is the stronger.*

35 *In the Vincennes Zoo of Paris, opened in 1931, there are now as many as seven giraffes. Okapis have been frequently bred here.*

36 *We rode high into the Soviet Caucasus, in the region around Teberda, to see ibex and other mountain fauna.*

it renewed, rebuilt and refurbished before giving it to her. As Adelaide's husband the Duke devoted himself exclusively to mysticism and superstition, she is said to have consoled herself by spending much of her time with her lovers at the little château in the menagerie. When the young woman died at the age of twenty-eight, the king lost all interest in it. His five-year-old heir spent the early part of his reign in Paris at the Louvre and the once magnificent zoo fell more and more into decay over the next hundred years.

When the revolution broke out the Jacobins marched from the town of Versailles with drums beating and flags flying through the park to the menagerie, where they were received by the elderly Director, Monsieur Laimant. The leader of the revolutionaries declared that they had come in the name of the people and of nature to set the animals free; they had been born free by their Creator and had only been kept in captivity for the tyrant's pleasure. Laimant did not object, but reminded them that the beasts of prey would most probably set upon their liberators and devour them. The revolutionaries compromised by accepting from him the keys of all the cages containing dangerous animals. Most of the few other animals still surviving in the menagerie, including a dromedary, five species of apes, some deer and a large number of birds were either taken away, handed over to the knacker or simply let out of their cages into the vast park. Among them were several Javanese rats, whose offspring later did a great deal of damage to the château and the other great buildings. Most of the deer and the birds died during the next winter. Some of them adapted themselves to their new environment and reproduced. In 1840

37 A bird's eye view of the Zoo at Porte de Vincennes, Paris. Top left is the maintenance yard with the two open elephant enclosures in front of it, to the right near the centre of the picture is the stabling for bison, buffalo and the antelope species. The picture shows how only the façades of the houses were sculpted to look like natural rock, whilst behind them are buildings incorporating plate glass and large skylights.

38 A view of Louis XIV's great menagerie at Versailles. Today only two of the pavilions are still standing; all the rest has been torn down and made into gardens.

a zoologist named Jourdain was able to mount a large and extremely interesting collection of exotic fauna which he had shot or caught in the forest of Versailles.

The animals which stayed in the menagerie were a rhinoceros, a lion and a dog to whom it was very attached, a buffalo, an antelope, a quagga, a crowned pigeon, six or seven peacocks and two dozen chickens. After two years of effort the professors at the Natural History Museum of Paris managed to arrange for these animals to be handed over to them and moved to Paris in a cart. The rhinoceros had recently injured itself on its water-trough and died from loss of blood, so only its corpse reached the *Jardin des Plantes*. Around 1809 the buildings of the Versailles menagerie were almost totally demolished. In the 'forties of the last century an attempt was made to rebuild them, with the exception of the little château, in order to set up a stud for breeding Arab horses. Construction was begun, but was interrupted by the revolution of 1848; after that the plan was completely abandoned.

Walking east from the Place de la Concorde along the bank of the Seine one comes to a large park, the *Jardin des Plantes*, in which there is a museum of natural history. Part of the park contains a zoological garden. The *Jardin des Plantes* was laid out by Louis XIII in 1650 as the *Jardin Royal des Plantes Médicinales*. The great naturalist Buffon, who was director of the Natural History Museum from 1739-88 introduced swans, ducks and peacocks into this botanical garden. He also built a bear-pit, which during his lifetime housed only wild pigs, although his ambition had always been to integrate a proper zoological garden into the *Jardin des Plantes*. When in 1783 he finally succeeded in enlarging the botanical garden he intended to ask the court's permission to take over the sadly neglected animals from the Versailles menagerie, but he does not seem to have made a serious attempt to carry this out. It was not until after the revolution that his colleague and successor, Daubenton, was enabled to start the zoo. It covers only thirty-five acres, but for such a small area it exhibits a remarkable variety of unusual animals. The old elephant house was built in 1802, as were a number of the small buildings housing cattle, deer and antelope, some of which are still thatched with straw. In 1927 the old Monkey House, dating from 1841, was replaced by a new one; the galleries that once held the beasts of prey have disappeared and these animals now live in a new building, although they are still surrounded by heavy, old-fashioned iron bars and have no open space. The same applies to the monkeys.

The proliferation of barred cages under the old trees gives the place a thoroughly antiquated look, but zoologically the *Jardin des Plantes* is well supplied: it contains a splendid pair of fully-grown gorillas and rarities such as musk deer, goral, kiangs, Przewalski's horses, bharal or blue mountain sheep, seven varieties of pelican, altogether one hundred and thirty species of mammals in one hundred and fifty different varieties; this is more than there are in the modern Paris Zoo at Vincennes, which has only one hundred and eight species in one hundred and eighteen varieties. Both zoos together form the richest collection of mammals on the European continent, which includes the largest collection of antelopes. Since they are both under one director, Professor Nouvel, they supplement each other's stock.

In the second half of the nineteenth century zoological gardens were founded all over Europe. In 1854 an association of citizens of Paris opened a zoo in the Bois de Boulogne on the western edge of the city in an area of fifty acres. The idea behind it was to discover by experiment whether non-European animal species could adapt themselves to our climate, settle down and be put to use. Unfortunately this original aim has been progressively neglected. Nowadays children ride on an old-fashioned miniature railway through the Bois de Boulogne to the entrance to the zoo where there are huge playgrounds, a swimming pool, swings, slides and an enormous water-wheel which keeps an artificial river permanently flowing. Its rapid current carries visitors in pleasure-boats past the meadows of the park. The naturalist Daubenton, whose statue stands in front of a handsome modern aviary, would hardly approve of the dull collection of very ordinary birds which is housed in the cages – peacocks, domestic pigeons, ducks, bantams and a few pheasants. The unbarred elephant enclosure is empty. In the modern open enclosures for bears, baboons and lions, the bears and the baboons perform ceaseless tricks until the spectators have stuffed them with an excess of sweets and ice-cream from the nearby kiosks. Another enclosure for fallow deer provokes similar behaviour. On a walled-in stage in an arena with seats for over a thousand spectators a circus trainer puts half-grown lions through the hoops. The large dovecote, with its numerous chambers, seems to house no more than birds which have flown there from the city. The seal pond, too, is empty.

Besides the usual tourist 'sights', few visitors to Paris know that it has a beautiful and thoroughly up-to-date zoo. This zoological garden in the Bois de Vincennes on the eastern side of the city was built for the Colonial Exhibition in 1931 to a design by the firm of Carl Hagenbeck. It was often criticised as being nothing but a jumble of artificial concrete cliffs, an 'orgy of concrete'. Visiting it today one realises how much this impression has been altered: for years Professor Nouvel the director has carried out a policy of clothing the lumps of concrete in green vegetation by encouraging climbing plants such as ivy, vines and knot-grass. The trees have also grown and matured in the intervening years and serve to soften and break up the harsh lines of the structures. As the gardens are also beautifully kept, the whole park now has a much more pleasing and natural look than it perhaps had in the first few years after it was built. Only the long frontage of the huge complex of open bear enclosures offers no opportunity for planting with greenery and therefore still gives some idea of the park's original appearance.

The animal-lover should visit both zoos, at Vincennes and in the *Jardin des Plantes*, in order to see the full variety of captive animals in Paris. They include the pronghorn, the only North American antelope, which sheds its horns like a deer its antlers; harnessed antelope, blaauwbok, Thomas' waterbuck, blesbok, Hartmann's mountain zebra and Grévy's zebra; chimpanzees and gibbons, each on an island of their own; a large group of breeding flamingoes, open enclosures for lions and tigers surrounded by enormously wide and deep trenches; large open enclosures for macaques, baboons, spider monkeys, a band of seven giraffes, oribi, Buffon's waterbuck, Sömmerings gazelle, the large yellow-backed duiker, white-tailed deer from America, some okapi which have bred several times, fennec foxes, crab-eating raccoons, Japanese brown bear, a large number of rare lemurs from Madagascar, several varieties of long-tailed monkeys, a monk seal, Siberian wild dogs, Spanish lynx, arctic foxes, lion-tiger crossbreeds, kiangs and kulans. A Przewalski's horse, born in Prague, sent to Sydney, NSW and which returned to Europe, recently died there at the age of thirty.

Neither of the zoos have aquaria, although not far from the Vincennes Zoo there is a fine aquarium and a terrarium for tropical animals inside the Colonial Museum, whilst there is an aquarium for cold-water fish in the former Trocadero near the Palais de Chaillot.

In a weekly magazine which lists all the entertainments and attractions of Paris I found yet a fourth *Jardin Zoologique* under the heading 'Zoos', a private zoo at Ermenonville belonging to the actor Jean Richard; it is about forty miles from the city centre and can easily be reached by car along the Route Nationale 2. Jean-Jacques Rousseau spent the last weeks of his life at this village in the spring of 1778, in the charming moated castle belonging to the Marquis René de Girardin. He was buried there, but his body was later removed during the revolution and re-interred in the Panthéon.

Deep in the woods near his beautiful villa Jean Richard has built a zoo and opened it to the public. Only about a quarter of his park-like garden is devoted to the animals and they are kept in rather small cages and enclosures, but every one of these is kept in exemplary condition, clean and freshly painted. Early on a weekday morning I counted over fifty parked cars belonging to visitors and the little garden was overflowing with people. Amongst others it contains a half-grown elephant, camels, lions, tigers, leopards, llamas, a vulture, macaques and two gibbons. One of these has a belt round its waist and it performs on a wire like a tight-rope walker, its own rope connected by a ring to another parallel wire.

The main pathway through this zoo is lined with caricatures of famous French actors, their heads planted on animal bodies. One of the main attractions are three young trained lions in an arena-like cage, who are occasionally put through their paces by Jean Richard himself. This latest and smallest of Parisian zoos is thus a reversion to the earliest type of private menagerie.

Some readers may object to the *five* Paris zoos mentioned in the title of this chapter, since the oldest and most famous no longer contains any animals. However, Professor Nouvel assured me that plans for a further national zoological garden in the grounds of the Château de Fontainebleau have already been worked out in detail and its construction will shortly begin.

There have been no salmon in the Rhine since death swept away nearly every fish in the river in 1949. Since that time it has been less of a river than one vast sewer for hundreds of thousands of lavatories and billions of gallons of industrial effluent. Today the foot of the romantic Lorelei rock, where bargees are supposed to be entranced by the magical maiden with golden hair, is washed daily by twenty thousand tons of industrial salts dissolved in the water. If this quantity were not borne seawards by the Rhine it would need twenty-four forty-car freight trains to dispose of it. At Mainz a pint of Rhine water contains nearly half an ounce of solid matter, nearer the consistency of soup than river-water. The latest addition to human dung and industrial detritus are detergents, which are not removed from the water by purification plants.

The most critical aspect of this problem is that our rivers not only hold fish but also supply our drinking water. In the majority of West European countries the underground water has long ceased to be sufficient to supply the population's water requirements. Most tap-water nowadays is filtered river- or lake-water. The Institute of Hygiene at Mainz is constantly at work testing the Rhine water. They find that even in water which tastes perfectly good there are frequent traces of benzopyrene and related substances which are thought to be carcinogenic; detergents are constantly found to be contaminating filtered drinking water and both have produced disturbingly high rates of abdominal cancer in experimental animals. These toxic substances are increasing daily. The Bonn government has been obliged to allocate £73 million simply to arrest the deterioration in the state of the Rhine waters and to prevent actual disaster.

What was once a blessing has now become a curse. In 1880, for

instance, seventy thousand salmon were caught annually on the Lower
Rhine, many of which weighed up to 90 pounds and could reach four
and a half feet in length. In the early nineteenth century domestic
servants in Rhineland towns were assured, as part of their conditions of
employment, that they would not be obliged to eat salmon more than
twice a week. Towards the end of the century the Dutch cast nets right
across the rivers forming the Rhine delta and tried to catch the entire
crop for themselves. There was a conference of all the countries involved and the Dutch soon yielded, as they too had come to realise
that the male and female salmon must swim right up the Rhine to its
sources in Switzerland in order to breed. If no young salmon were to
be allowed to pass downstream and out to sea, no more mature ones
would come back, for the salmon's breeding cycle is the reverse of the
eel's. The eel migrates to the open sea to breed whereas the salmon
swim upstream to do so. The Dutch even agreed to take over the costs
of artificially hatching several million salmon and releasing them
annually in the upper reaches of the Rhine.

In many other rivers salmon were so prolific as to be an embar-
rassment. In 1827 over a thousand salmon a day were caught at the
mouth of the River Memel, each fish averaging thirty pounds in
weight. Even at one mark apiece it was impossible to dispose of such
quantities and again and again the only solution was to bury a large
proportion of them in pits. In North America the fishermen used to
build 'salmon wheels', which simply went round and round in the
water scooping out the salmon with nets; one of these could frequently
bring in a daily haul of fourteen thousand fish. Without the migration
of the vast schools of salmon, large areas of Alaska and Kamchatka
would have been uninhabitable; in many places the people of these parts
had only to work at salmon fishing for a fortnight of each year to have
enough on which to live for the rest of the year. When Secretary of
State Seward bought the vast territory of Alaska in 1867 from the Tsar
of Russia for a price of $7,200,000, the Americans reckoned it a poor
bargain and referred to it for a long time as 'Seward's Folly'. But
soon the Alaskan salmon fisheries alone were earning more income in a

year than the total purchase price of the territory. In 1905 one hundred and thirty million pounds of salmon were caught in British Columbia and the state of Washington, but by the 1940s the catch in Washington was down to two million three hundred and fifty thousand barrels per year – a scarcely imaginable quantity, yet a mere sixth of the average salmon catch in the same state between 1910 and 1917. The experts believed that the salmon were only hindered by the numerous dams and hydro-electric stations. The possibility of changing from hydraulic to thermal electricity generation was even discussed, as the salmon catch was economically more important than the current generated in hydro-electric plants.

The young salmon spend about a year in the upper reaches of the rivers and streams; in the more northerly regions of Eurasia and America the period can be as long as two or three years. They look very much like trout and eat the same food: snails, insects and later small fish. Then one day they feel the urge to swim seawards. Once they have reached the sea, salmon do not swim far, as eels do, but remain in the relatively shallow waters of the continental shelf. There they live chiefly on mackerel, sprats and herring by following their shoals, although they are practically omnivorous and grow at a tremendous rate. A marked salmon, caught after four weeks at sea, had increased its weight in that time from twenty-one pounds to thirty-six pounds. It is during this period too that the flesh takes on the reddish tinge known as 'salmon pink'; it is caused by the fat stored up in the tissues.

It used to be thought that salmon could never be caught more than sixty miles from the coast and that they had to stay in the delta region of their home rivers in order to be able to find their way back again later. This theory was disproved, however, when A. Hartt marked thirty-six thousand three hundred and eighty-three salmon in the North Pacific and set them free again. Of some varieties, e.g. red salmon, up to seventeen per cent of the marked fish had been caught again within twelve months. Some of the salmon which had been marked in the Aleutians were found at great distances – in the River Amur in Siberia,

L

for example. Baltic salmon travelled up to six hundred miles from the mouth of their home river, Pacific salmon even further. The longest journey was probably that of a king salmon which was marked in 1956 near Adak, halfway between Alaska and Kamchatka and was caught again in 1957 in the state of Idaho, two thousand three hundred and seventy-five miles from its starting point.

A good half of all salmon spend three winters at sea to build up their strength for the long journey back up the rivers to their sources in the mountains. However, every fifteenth salmon returns after only a year and twenty-five to thirty per cent after two years. Many stay at sea even longer, as do the Swedish salmon. Icthyologists have long puzzled over the way in which these fishes find their way back to the mouth of the same river from whence they came years before, up the same tributary and probably to the same stream and to approximately the same spot at which they were spawned. Of a hundred thousand Swedish salmon marked in their native rivers only about a thousand, i.e. approximately one per cent, were found in other rivers; similar tests have shown the same result in North America.

They apparently find their way by smell. Fish, of course, can not only taste things under water but can also smell. In 1959 in the state of Washington three thousand salmon from two different tributaries of the same river were caught and the nostrils of half of them were blocked with cotton wool. Those salmon which could still use their noses all returned to their native river whilst half of those with blocked nostrils went astray. According to other experiments the salmon have a sensory memory of the composition of the last river water which they smelled before migrating to the sea. If they are put into another river shortly before their journey seawards, they will return to *that* river and not to the one in which they were born. Obviously the water of a particular stream or tributary is being continually diluted the more rivers flow into the main stream and even more by the time it reaches the sea, so the fish must perceive incredibly small olfactory traces. The enormous degree to which river water is diluted when it reaches the sea has been proved by experiments with other species of fish.

It requires a colossal effort to swim so far upstream to the spawning grounds, against the current all the way. It becomes almost incredible when one realises that the salmon take practically no nourishment on the entire trip from the mouth of the river to the headwaters, during which time they must negotiate rapids, waterfalls and weirs, sometimes leaping as high as twelve feet into the air to do so. On the Weser a salmon's rate of progress upstream has been measured at between twenty-two and twenty-five miles per day. Furthermore a major physiological change is occurring within their bodies while they are making this exhausting journey. At the start of migration a female salmon's body consists of 0.3 per cent roe; when it reaches the spawning grounds their body weight consists of from twenty to twenty-five per cent roe, in some cases as much as thirty-five per cent.

Their outward appearance also changes before mating; the older males look specially magnificent. Zigzag lines of flowing red on a bluish ground form on their head. The belly turns purplish-red and a red flush tinges the edges of their fins. A three-feet-long salmon, weighing anything between thirty and forty pounds, can easily injure itself if it hits the rocks when leaping up a waterfall or swimming over pebbles in shallow streams, so its skin thickens as a protection, particularly on the back and the fins; this generally prevents flesh wounds and superficial wounds heal quickly. In many varieties the male salmon also develop a protuberant jaw which serves as a weapon when fighting for the best spawning ground.

When there were salmon in the Rhine they could not be fished on their upstream progress and this was the law on many other rivers. Dry-fly fishing for salmon, however, is a favourite sport on Scottish and Scandinavian rivers and Englishmen will pay high rents for a stretch of salmon fishing. Commercial salmon fishing is carried out with nets, chiefly at the river's mouth. At Aberdeen ten thousand salmon, worth nearly £50,000, were caught by this method in 1952. With such a valuable catch the Scots are very disturbed by the poisoning of salmon as a consequence of the use of chemical weedkillers along the banks of the rivers and streams. Scottish salmon swim up the rivers in single age-groups and each migration is thus uniform in size.

When a female salmon reaches her home waters she examines the gravel bottom and digs a number of 'trenches' by lashing out with her tail and rolling her body forward. The stones are not struck by the fins, but instead are swept aside by water pressure. The males tremble with excitement and fight savagely with each other over the females. When a female has reached the stage of concentrating her digging operations on one spot, the male who has won her will protect this area. When satisfied with her trench, which she tests with her anal fin and then with her pelvic fins, she eases herself into it. The male darts forward, quivering, until he is alongside her. They both expel eggs and semen simultaneously, their mouths wide open with excitement; the male will sometimes bite the female during mating and even females have been known to fight one another.

A particularly good place for spawning is a slit between two fairly large stones, in which the female's fully extended tail fin has space to move without hindrance. Most of the eggs will sink into this slit, whilst the semen fills the whole hollow like a white cloud. Immediately afterwards the female swims a short way upstream, throws gravel on to the eggs that she has just laid and begins hollowing out the next trench. Each of these is between three and six feet long and eighteen inches wide. European salmon spawn between November and January.

One egg is a quarter of an inch in diameter and a female roe consists of six to eight thousand eggs. The time required for the young salmon to hatch depends on the warmth of the water. At four degrees centigrade it takes eighty days, at sixteen degrees centigrade only nineteen days; in very cold water the embryonic fish may need two hundred days to hatch.

Since our rivers have become so built-up and contaminated, it has become general practice to breed salmon artificially, millions at a time, in large hatcheries equipped with tanks of running water. Adult salmon about to spawn are caught very carefully, usually by temporarily stunning them with a slight electric shock. This method has the advantage of allowing the males, very few of which are needed for fertilisation, to be released as soon as they are caught. The females are released as soon as they have spawned. The fish can easily be made to discharge eggs and semen by lightly massaging their bellies; first the eggs are tipped into a bowl of water then the semen is added and the two stirred together. A very gentle touch is needed, otherwise the salmon will ejaculate prematurely. A salmon hatchery in Dorset once produced twenty thousand two-headed young salmon, which all died before they were a month old. In a natural environment such freak specimens would not even reach that age.

As a result of experiments carried out in France it is apparent that the thyroid gland is responsible for making the young salmon swim towards the sea. The gland releases into the blood stream a hormone with an abnormally high iodine content; this stimulates the young fish to swim into the current and to be driven downstream by it – backwards, with their heads facing upstream. When they reach seawater the increased intake of natrium rights the chemical balance in their bloodstream.

The salmon's passage up the European rivers has not only been blocked by detergents, sewage and industrial effluents but also by the numerous dams, weirs and locks. Because the salmon catch is so valuable some salmon ladders have been built alongside the dams, special stepped sluices which enable the salmon to swim and jump upstream in spite of the dam. But they are expensive to build and the hydraulic engineers complain of the water which goes to waste down them instead of making electricity by driving the turbines. Another method is to build fish-lifts, into which the salmon are enticed by an artificial current and then raised to the water-level at the top of the dam by means of a lift. In many cases even this has failed because the water in the dam lake is too warm, so instead the salmon are put into a tanker and driven several miles upstream to points where there is a strong enough current and sufficient oxygen in the water. All such methods can be very costly and are not always successful. Even when the salmon have laboriously worked their own way into the dam lake they often find that conditions there are unsuitable. The lakes are very deep, have steep, almost perpendicular sides, whereas salmon prefer to spawn at depths of no more than ten feet. The streams that feed the lake generally do so from very high waterfalls. These factors have induced the Swedes to pass a law under which hydro-electric stations are obliged to make arrangements for hatching as many salmon as the river produced before the building of the dam. By the early 'sixties these Swedish salmon hatcheries were producing a million young salmon each year, of which every tenth fish was marked.

If breeding in hatcheries can be ensured, then the salmon's passage upriver to spawn is no longer so important. They are now caught in shoals on the high seas with modern nets and all the latest equipment including echo-sounding gear. The markings show that fifteen per cent of salmon caught in the Baltic by German, Danish, Russian and Norwegian fishermen originate from Swedish hatcheries. This does not exactly thrill the Swedes, who would like to negotiate a larger share of the total catch. The rivers which debouch into the Baltic still produce an annual average of between seven and eight million salmon.

Artificial hatching is an effective means of breeding and harvesting millions of salmon, even though most rivers are too heavily polluted for salmon to endure them any longer. We ourselves, however, must continue to drink their waters.

'Who is that gripping my neck?' asked one of the men of Barents' second expedition who had landed on the Siberian mainland in September 1959. A comrade standing near him shouted, 'A bear!' and ran away. The polar bear then killed the man with a bite on the head. When the other Dutchmen attacked it, the bear killed another of them before they finally managed to destroy it.

A friend of mine, the Copenhagen biologist Alvin Pedersen (who has survived many winters in the Arctic, is the foremost living authority on polar bears and who has read everything that has been published about them since AD 890), could find in all these one thousand one hundred years evidence of only one other case in which a polar bear made an unprovoked and fatal attack on a human being. This happened a few years ago on the north-eastern coast of Greenland. A fur hunter left his hut one evening to find a spot on the ice from which to make a sketch of the landscape. When he did not return by late evening, his friends set off to find him. He lay stretched out on the snow with his skull smashed in and the surrounding tracks in the snow left them in no doubt that the culprit was a polar bear.

These bears were probably unaware of what it was that they had killed, because they made no attempt to eat their prey and have indeed never touched human corpses even though the graves of eskimos or fur hunters give them frequent occasion to do so.

Polar bears are very selective in their prey. In Greenland they very seldom attack a musk-ox, they practically never go for reindeer and in lemming years they seem merely to amuse themselves by turning over stones and making farcically clumsy paw-swipes at the little rodents as they scuttle away. Their chief prey is seal and of these they prefer the ringed seal.

The polar bear has always hunted seal in a particular way. It crawls slowly up to the sleeping seal, if possible under cover of icefloes or snowdrifts, choosing for preference seals which are in moult and therefore abnormally inert and tired. The bear kills it with a colossal blow with its paw – always with the *left* paw, it has been claimed – or by a bite at the head. If the seal is lying on another icefloe the bear slips quietly into the water and then swims backwards towards it, the last stretch under water. When close to the seal it jumps out of the water on to the ice and cuts off its line of retreat to the sea. It will also lie patiently in wait by the air holes which the seals make through the ice. If one comes up for air the bear crushes its head against the edge of the ice. Many varieties of seal have caves scooped out of the three-feet thick layer of snow above the ice, in which they give birth to their young. The entrance is from below, through an enlarged air-hole. Up above on the snowfield there is no trace to be seen of these chambers, but polar bears can scent these seals' lairs through a layer of snow three or four feet thick. This is considerably better than dogs or wolves, which can only scent them at a depth of eighteen inches to two feet. The bear digs its way through with lightning speed and is particularly fond of eating young seal. In the arctic summer the bear prefers eating the red meat, whilst in winter it touches practically nothing of the seal's carcase except the blubber, which it tears off with the skin in great strips. But summer or winter the greatest delicacy are the entrails.

Animals which concentrate on one particular prey and one method of hunting it find it very hard to adapt to another environment and are not, as we understand the word, very intelligent. Thus polar bears have still not learned the lesson of the last few centuries that man is their only really serious enemy and that they should run away from him whenever

39 *Alaska now supplies half the world, including inns along the Rhine with 'Rhine salmon', even though huge bears devour enormous quantities of this fish.*

40 *Hares are solitary animals. Where they are forced into each other's company, such as a place where food is still available in winter or in rivalry over a female, quarrels easily break out.*

they spy him even from afar. 'Hunting polar bears, as conducted today, is neither dangerous nor particularly demanding of much skill on the hunter's part,' declared Pedersen. Recently enterprising Norwegians have been inviting international tourists to go polar bear hunting in the Arctic as the latest thrill. One party of four hunters and a five-man crew set off on a polar bear and seal hunt towards Spitzbergen. They did not sight a bear until they were off Franz-Josephs-Land and the hunters drew lots for it. The bear took no notice of them although they took a boat to within a hundred yards of it. Other bears were enticed with lumps of fried seal-blubber or shot while unsuspectingly at play. One professional hunter who had spent the winter of 1958 or 1959 on a small island north of Spitzbergen told that during that time he had shot and skinned one hundred and twenty-nine polar bears.

Mr M. Schein, a biologist from Pennsylvania State University, tried out the technique of catching polar bears with anaesthetising shot on the east coast of Spitzbergen. He wrote: 'The bear – a female – fooled us. She swam to a big ice-floe and then at the safe distance of a hundred yards she completely ignored us. The animal devoured the remains of a small seal while we watched and took photographs. Amazingly enough she still paid no attention to us when we approached her across the ice, even though we made no attempt to conceal ourselves. Only when our shots grazed her back from a range of fifty yards did she get up and go away.' It was then a simple matter to drug the three or four year old four hundred pound beast with an anaesthetic bullet, tie her up and bring her back to a cage on the ship. The bears caught in this way were later released with coloured bands round their necks as a means of checking on their seasonal migration. Personally I fail to see what sport there can be in shooting such harmless, trusting animals.

Often polar bears will retreat cautiously on encountering the strange phenomenon of man. They do not do so with any great speed – an

41 *When hand-reared, hares can become trusting domestic pets. They are not at all cowardly but can hold their own against cats and dogs.*

energetic bear runs at about the same speed as a man. If the hunter has dogs the bear can never get away. They quickly catch it up, bark at it and worry at its hind legs until it stops and sits down. The hunter can then approach and shoot it from five yards range. Even a bear that has been shot at will not attack a man if flight is possible. If the hunter's gun misfires he has only to throw it down and run away, the bear will not usually follow. Only in rare cases can a polar bear escape when hunted by man, by escaping to the sea and swimming away or by climbing up a high cliff.

Polar bears often approach men out of simple, unsuspecting curiosity. Eskimos can quickly spot a bear that is merely being inquisitive. As soon as it turns away they shout, wave their arms or throw pieces of clothing into the air to attract its attention again. Polar bears will even approach on the ice quite close to ships and stare at them and will take pieces of blubber handed to them on the ends of poles. Once a barrel, left behind on the ice, attracted all the bears in the neighbourhood; they approached it cautiously, poked it and started playing with it. Finally they rolled it for nearly a mile. Once a man who was pushing a sledge towards his ship was unaware that he was being closely followed by a polar bear until warned by the cries of his companions. When seven Dutchmen spent the winter of 1633-34 on Jan Mayen Island (the first Europeans to do so) they had constantly to ward off inquisitive polar bears. During the long arctic night seven of them were killed close by the hut before the others learned to be shy of firearms. These experiences were only learned from their diaries: the last of the seven men died of scurvy on April 30, 1634. Eskimo women when out gathering berries frequently encounter polar bears without ever being attacked or pursued.

Fully mature, self-confident male bears are particularly inquisitive and can often only be discouraged with shots. Payer, writing in 1876, described how 'on the second German expedition to the North Pole, whilst they were wintering on Sabine Island off the coast of north-east Greenland, it happened that a sailor left the ship unarmed to take a walk to Mount Germania, and as he was resting on the peak of the mountain he noticed a large bear standing near him and watching him attentively. Horrified, the sailor ran down the mountainside, but on turning round as he ran he saw that the bear was following him and rapidly catching up. He shouted, but this did not frighten the bear off – on the contrary, it seemed only to arouse its interest. To distract its attention the sailor threw off his jacket. The bear examined it carefully, but then resumed its pursuit at an increased speed. The sailor cast off more pieces of clothing, but although the bear looked at them all it still came nearer until finally it was so close to the sailor that the man was able to throw his very last garment, his scarf, at the bear's head. The animal was now so close to him that the man stopped. The bear came close beside him and sniffed his hands, so that he could feel its cold nose. Meanwhile the other explorers in the expedition's winter quarters had heard the sailor's cries for help and hastened to his aid. When the bear saw the other men approaching over the ice it turned away from the sailor and fled.'

One of Fridtjof Nansen's companions was surprised by a hungry polar bear in the dark and was bitten in the hip. As soon as the man hit the bear on the head with his lantern, it made off. Worse befell another member of the expedition, a scientist named Dr Börgen, who went out one night not far from the ship to watch the stars. As he was returning a polar bear struck him to the ground and bit him in the head – Dr Börgen could actually feel the bear's teeth grinding against the bone of his skull. His cry for help only deterred the beast for a moment, after which it came back and bit him again in the head. When Dr Börgen's companions came to his assistance the bear was dragging his victim away by the head; they fired a shot and it dropped him, but then it seized him by the arm and dragged him further. Only when the explorers had almost caught up did the bear drop its prey and vanish into the darkness.

When explorers' or trappers' huts in the polar regions are left uninhabited for more than a year they are certain to be broken into and ransacked by polar bears. They are most probably animals which have grown hungry in the arctic winter because they reject nothing which is edible or which even looks edible, preferably things which are heavily salted. Boot-grease, fur clothing, rubber and glue have all been eaten by bears. In one case seventeen sacks of hay were dragged far out on to the ice and laboriously stuffed into water-holes.

Bears will examine tents with great care from the outside, but are curiously shy of going into them. When this did nevertheless happen once during the Kane expedition, the explorers held lighted matches under the nose of the intruder, which drove it to wild flight. During Pedersen's first winter spent at Scoresby Sound a young female polar bear broke into the stores hut. She liked it so much that she lay down to sleep on some sacks of flour. Another young bear walked quite calmly into a hut occupied by Pedersen and one of his fellow-explorers. The bear, wandering quite unsuspectingly through the half-open door, was so terrified when it saw the two men reach for a weapon that it stood for a moment as if petrified. Then it tried to rear up on its hind legs, but was hindered by the low door frame. For a second it stared at the men, its anxiety clearly betrayed by a helpless expression in its eyes. It backed out of the doorway and ran off towards the beach with such speed that Pedersen only managed to catch sight of it diving into the water as he came out of the hut.

It is in fact easy to detect a bear's intentions by the way it approaches. If its motive is not curiosity but hunger, it crawls along using every piece of cover and advances practically flat on its stomach. A bear that is merely inquisitive will approach quite openly and with apparent disinterest.

At the request of Roald Amundsen, the Norwegian polar explorer (1872-1928), Carl Hugenbeck succeeded, without great difficulty, in training twenty-one polar bears within nine weeks to pull a sledge. Their trainer, Reuben Castang, was unwilling to go on a polar expedition and since it was doubtful whether they would obey anyone else, the trained bears were put through their paces in the circus instead.

The polar bear is always on the move. There are no polar bears at the North polar ice-cap. They move round the Pole with the great masses of drift-ice and into the seas north of Siberia, Scandinavia,

Greenland, Canada and Alaska. Every bear is a solitary beast living in a state of 'armed neutrality'. They do not harm each other, but stay at a respectful distance apart. They do fight over food and female bears, but such encounters are never fatal.

When the female bear gets on heat in spring, three or four male bears follow her, but at a good distance from one another. The fertilised eggs seems to remain latent in the womb for months until the bear crawls into a snow-cave to hibernate. No female polar bear has ever been shot in summer with a detectable embryo in the womb. There are not even any reports of new-born polar bear cubs having been seen in the Arctic; all our information on them comes from zoos. They are tiny, about equal in size to rats, weigh only just over a pound and are born blind. Unlike brown bears, polar bears very rarely breed in captivity. A marked exception to this rule is the Nuremberg Zoo; there, as I learned in correspondence with the director, Dr A. Seitz, thirty-seven polar bears have been born between 1945 and 1960 and of these nineteen have been successfully reared.

The cave which every bear digs for itself at the start of the long Arctic night is just high enough for it to stand inside. As the walls turn to ice, a temperature of something over zero centigrade builds up, as it does inside an eskimo igloo. The entrance is soon covered by snow. When the female bear emerges from her warm winter quarters, her cubs follow her in single file to tread in her footsteps and thus to avoid having to slog their way through deep snow. They keep warm during hibernation by sleeping between their mother's legs and never enter the water until they are eighteen months old and have survived their first winter.

The cubs' favourite game is tobogganing at which their mother joins them. They lie down on their bellies at the top of a slope and slide down again and again, hind legs stretched out behind them. The mother suckles her cubs for at least a year and nine months and they remain with her for a long time: it is not unknown to find a female polar bear with male cubs that are already bigger than her. Three years pass before another mating period and the female cubs only reach sexual maturity after four years. The males continue growing until they are eight years old. A fully grown male measures eight feet from its nose to the tip of its tail, a female just six feet. A male weighs between eight hundred and nine hundred pounds. An Italian expedition once reported having shot one which measured nine feet and six inches overall and weighed one thousand six hundred pounds, but dimensions of this order have never been confirmed from any other source.

During the Arctic summer polar bears are extremely fond of eating bilberries and cranberries. From the blue stains round their mouths and anus and from the contents of their stomachs when shot it is obvious that bears often subsist on nothing else for weeks. They will also eat juicy grass and herbs and many bears have been observed diving for marine algae and seaweed. Like brown bears, polar bears will position themselves at the mouths of the great northern rivers when the salmon arrive in their myriads to swim up-river. They catch them by scooping them out with their paws, but they are much less skilled at it than brown bears.

Like pigs, polar bears sometimes harbour trichinae in their muscular tissue. Many a polar explorer has died a painful death from trichinosis after eating insufficiently cooked polar bear meat. The liver of the polar bear is even more dangerous, as its extraordinarily high concentration of Vitamin A renders it toxic. Eating it produces headaches and vomiting and after a few days the entire skin peels off.

There was a time when polar bears inhabited all the seas and coasts wherever drift-ice reached. Over a century ago they were still to be seen in Labrador together with the native brown bears and both species co-existed happily. They were to be found as far south as 52° North, i.e. on roughly the same latitude as Liverpool. In 1497 Cabot landed on an island off Newfoundland which was 'full of white bears'. They have occasionally reached Iceland on drift-ice and for lack of their natural prey they usually attack cattle there; the last occasion when polar bears drifted to Iceland was in 1932. Bear Island, north of Spitzbergen, was given its name because Barents, the Dutchman who discovered it, killed a polar bear on the island on June 8, 1596.

Polar bears only settle on land in winter in order to sleep in their caves. They do this not because of the darkness but because there is no more food for them; they do not hibernate in the true sense, because if they are disturbed in their lair they are wide awake in a moment. As they spend the summer circling the pole with the drift-ice in pursuit of seals, they find themselves in the company of the sealers, who are also on the track of these aquatic mammals. Bears therefore fall easy prey to the seal-hunters on board these ships; there are at present no legal means of protecting them since they never remain in one national territory or territorial waters for long but are in permanent migration. The only solution to their gradual extinction would be an international agreement. In the past hundred years they have been wiped out in all the more southerly regions of their area of distribution.

The situation has grown really serious since the discovery of Spitzbergen and Novaya Zemlya, when the hunters began to penetrate into the actual breeding grounds of seal and bear. The rate of decline in the number of polar bears can be judged from statistics provided by Norwegian seal-hunters: in the period around 1925 their annual toll was seven hundred to eight hundred polar bears, which were brought back for the sale of their skins, whereas shortly before the last war the number had dropped to three hundred and fifty. This gives us grounds to assume that the global polar bear population has been halved between 1924 and 1945, a process which is accelerating from year to year. One of the most damaging factors has been the establishment of polar weather stations and military bases by the USA and other nations. Crews are regularly changed by transport aircraft and every man's motto is: 'You can't come back from the Arctic without having a shot a polar bear.' The various national authorities seem unaware that they are in danger of allowing the destruction of an irreplaceable natural treasure.

Mr C. Harrington, a biologist who has spent long periods in the Arctic and has specialised in polar bears, has calculated the total stock of polar bears in the Canadian Arctic at between six and seven thousand head, the global stock at something over ten thousand. He claims that about two hundred are killed annually in Alaska, six hundred a year in Canada and between one hundred and fifty and three hundred in Greenland and the Norwegian Arctic. Until 1956, when a policy of strict protection was introduced, at least one hundred and twenty were shot yearly in the Soviet Arctic. At present, therefore, about one thousand three hundred polar bears are destroyed every year. They are virtually devoid of protection in Norwegian territory; anyone can hunt and kill them, except on King Karl Land, an island east of Spitzbergen much used by polar bears for breeding. Since 1956 on Soviet territory polar bear cubs may only be taken alive to supply zoos; this amounts to thirty or forty cubs per year. For a limited period, initially for five years, polar bears are completely protected on Wrangel Island (north of the extreme eastern peninsula of Siberia).

On land the polar bear is the dreaded and invincible foe of all seal species, with the possible exception of the walrus, toughest of the breed. In the water the situation is reversed. The polar bear is not a good swimmer. It only paddles with its forelegs; its hind legs merely trail in the water. It therefore swims fairly slowly, only dives to a depth of six feet at the most and cannot stay under water for longer than two minutes. When the air is cold and windy it puts its eyes and nose repeatedly under water.

When they are in their proper element the ringed seals, which are normally the bear's chief food, swim along behind it and bite its hind legs; the walruses stab it in the back with their tusks and grip it from behind with their pectoral flippers. No polar bear will venture into the water if there are walrus swimming in the vicinity. In winter bears are very reluctant to take to the water at all, a fact which constantly surprises people who work in zoos and who are unfamiliar with the behaviour of polar bears in their natural habitat. However, a polar bear which climbs out of the water dripping wet is soon dry again without shaking itself. Its fur fills with air, which keeps it warm and repels the water.

Polar bear skins are for this reason specially prized by the eskimos as winter clothing, heavy though they are. The hairs on the belly are about eight inches long. The only spots of black on a polar bear are the nose and the claws, although there are frequent reports of people seeing polar bears with 'blue feet'. These arise from the animals being obliged to walk for long periods through hard, crusty snow, which gradually tears off the hairs from their legs; the dark skin then shows through. Especially in summer, polar bears living in captivity often lose patches of hair, particularly on their neck and shoulders. This is very noticeable and looks extremely ugly. Its cause is not clear. Generally the hairs reappear after prolonged treatment with insecticide and ticks are therefore thought to cause this loss of hair, but there are practically no means of proving this. Adult polar bears are never tame enough to allow themselves to be closely examined without drugging them and narcosis is usually lethal for many wild animals.

The polar bear is completely defenceless in water. With a rowing boat, or better still with a motor boat, a polar bear may be easily pushed through the water and guided in any direction with a boat-hook or an oar. In this way eskimoes bring swimming bears close to their encampment before killing them, to save themselves the trouble of dragging the heavy corpse over a long distance. A polar bear which had been driven through the water like this for half an hour was so exhausted that it collapsed gratefully on reaching an ice-floe and allowed a photographer to approach within a few feet without getting up or making any attempt to defend itself.

Polar bears can scent carrion at a range of up to twelve miles and wherever a whale is stranded the polar bears will come crowding round. When they are on the scent they wag their heads from side to side, which is probably the reason for the slow, monotonous head-shaking exhibited by captive bears. They may, incidentally, live for as long as thirty-five years in captivity.

Alvin Pedersen has described an unpleasant experience which happened to him while chasing a polar bear with dogs. The animal fled on to some newly-frozen ice which was still fairly thin and swayed under the pressure. Pedersen was not deterred, knowing that even thin sea-ice will carry a considerable weight. Suddenly the bear began to

M

do something extraordinary: it stopped, jumped into the air and went on jumping until with one great leap its hind legs broke through the ice. The ice cracked over a wide area, the dogs fell into the water and Pedersen too fell in, even though he immediately lay flat. Fortunately he was quickly able to climb on to firm ice and go straight back to his hut where he ripped off his soaking clothes and crept into his sleeping-bag. If the incident had occurred further away from the hut he would undoubtedly have frozen to death in his wet clothing.

In most of western Europe the hare is one of the commonest and least known wild animals. Until fifteen years ago we were ignorant of vital facts about the breeding of hares which were known to the ancient Greeks. The most ridiculous nonsense is still believed about hares: that they sleep with their eyes open, that they interbreed with domestic rabbits and that hares have been seen with horns on their heads. In German the hare is even synonymous with cowardice.

In general it seems that hares, at least in West Germany, are gradually on the decline; this is true of all species whose habitat is the open field, whereas woodland animals are increasing. This probably has less to do with the depredations of foxes, cats, dogs and men than the growing use of chemical pesticides, rat poisons, etc. The hares have compensated for this, however, by spreading into regions to which they are not naturally suited. The hare is an animal of the open, treeless plain; it is to be found in the greatest numbers in the fertile plains of the Lower Danube. Lately, however, colonies of them have penetrated the forests, have climbed mountains and displaced the alpine hares, with which they interbreed. Since 1825 hares in Russia have spread northward and westward over vast areas, partly as a result of planned translocation by humans, until they have occupied two and a half million square kilometres. In addition to penetrating south-western Siberia, they have moved into the Friesian Isles, Ireland, southern Sweden, where they were previously never found, North America and South America, including Argentina, where they have also partially displaced the native species of hares. In Yugoslavia tens of thousands of them are caught annually, as they are in Hungary and Poland; they are then sold abroad in large quantities for breeding purposes. Thus a large proportion of the hares found in Germany are descended from stock brought in from Bohemia, Hungary and Yugoslavia. One hundred and thirty-two hares, which were set free in 1933 on the upper reaches of the river Yenisei in Siberia, multiplied so fast that in the hard winter of 1945-46 their descendants were to be seen in villages and round haystacks in places at vast distances away from their point of origin; the only difference in the species was an average loss of one-third in weight, due to the rigours of living in a cold environment.

Hares spread themselves and defend themselves against their many enemies by breeding. The bucks fight over the does on heat; they stand up on their hind legs and box one another with their fore-feet, jump up and kick their opponents until great tufts of fur go flying – which many birds find very useful for building their nests. Rutting bucks will jump right over the does in their wild enthusiasm, squirting them with urine as they do so, or throw up their hindquarters, take aim and deliberately cover them with a jet of urine. Because ten or twelve bucks may fight over one doe, people still firmly believe that there are many more bucks than does, but this is not so. A doe drops four litters a year, each litter averaging two or three, although a litter of one is not unknown and they can contain as many as five. The young born in the spring are not yet sexually mature by the autumn. The mother only suckles her young two or three times a day, otherwise she stays away from them. Suckling does take the greatest care to hide the place where their young are kept. In thirty years service one gamekeeper only twice came upon a doe hare with her family. The leverets weigh only four ounces, i.e. three per cent of the weight of the mother, but if necessary they can be weaned at three weeks. Family life does not play much part in the hares' existence. After coupling, bucks pay no more attention to does; even when old the animals live solitary lives. When a large group of hares, as often happens, is dotted over a field they never assist each other with a common warning signal for the approach of an enemy, as for instance do marmots, rabbits and jackdaws. Among hares the rule is every man for himself.

Bucks can be so silly with love that they may come right up to a man's legs if he stands still by a tree. It once happened that a buck mistook a dog for a doe, ran after it and caught up with it – to their mutual amazement. Nevertheless they cannot successfully interbreed with domestic rabbits. All 'leporids', as such assumed crossbreeds are called, have always turned out on closer anatomical investigation to be pure domestic rabbits. The two species are not nearly so closely related as might be supposed from external appearances. Wild rabbits live in underground burrows, hares do not. Young hares are born with sight, with all their hair and physically independent; rabbits on the other hand are born blind, naked and helpless. The so-called hare-rabbits are a breed of domestic rabbits with occasional specimens coloured hare-grey.

Since leverets are always found without their mothers, those who find them usually think that they have been orphaned and feel obliged to take the little animals home. This can cause a number of problems, which will be mentioned later. It is also untrue that does will refuse to accept their young once they have been touched by humans; nevertheless people should not pick them up. It can happen that a family of leverets will defend themselves and even attack a man.

The ancient Greeks hunted hares with clubs, nets, arrows and spears. They regarded the animal as a symbol of love and they cherished it to such an extent that they introduced them to islands where hares were hitherto unknown. There they developed into a pest and ate the land bare, much to the amusement of neighbouring islanders. The Greeks, and indeed all the peoples of the ancient world, observed and described animals with far greater insight and accuracy than did the men of the Middle Ages. Herodotus, for instance, reported that a doe hare could give birth to young while already pregnant with her next litter. For a long time this was thought to be nonsense until Professor Hediger demonstrated with captive hares that it was true. In the Chorzelow Research Institute in Poznan hares have been bred in cages for several years and it has been established that does more or less regularly couple and are fertilised five or six days before giving birth. Whilst the nearly mature embryos remain in one part of the womb, new ones begin developing in another. Although the normal gestation period is forty-two days, does can produce litters at shorter intervals. It is incredible that such an unusual and interesting biological fact has remained undiscovered for centuries – and this in an animal of which man has hunted and eaten millions.

The ancients also claimed that the most hideous man would become handsome for nine days after eating roast hare, so the Romans bred hares in enclosures with high, smooth walls which no predator could enter and from which no hare could escape. Nero introduced them into the circus and had them chased by lions for sport. He was specially keen to get white hares for this purpose, which were said to come from Arcadia. They were probably bred specially to furnish this demand. Albino hares with red eyes do occur now and again; one was caught in Germany in 1955, another in 1956.

Hares stay on their home ground. The whole life of a hare is generally lived out within an area of not more than one thousand two hundred acres. When one hundred and sixteen hares were marked as an experiment and then set free, sixty per cent of them were later shot within a radius of one and a quarter miles, ninety per cent within a radius of three miles. Only one had moved twenty-five miles from the starting point. Animals imported from other countries and then set free may well travel further; but the story told of one hare sent from Hungary to Germany and then being shot in Hungary, i.e. several hundred miles away, seems to me rather improbable.

Because so many hares are shot by sportsmen, very few of them reach old age. Among the marked hares which were shot, two-thirds were less than a year old and only three per cent were aged between four and seven years. The number of sexually mature females constituted no more than a fifth of the bag. If they were only left alive, they could live much longer: Dr Erna Mohr, a zoologist, had a hare which lived in captivity to an age of nine years and one hare has been shot with an earmark which had been attached twelve years before.

A hare makes itself thoroughly at home and secure in its 'territory'. It does not run back and forth across the countryside at random but makes paths, along which it always bites the vegetation short; country people call these 'witches' paths'. Also characteristic of hares are their 'setts', in which they sit and sleep. Setts are about eighteen inches long and dug deep enough to allow very little of the hare to be seen from outside. All the hare's enemies, including humans, easily overlook it in its hide. One can pass very close to a sett without noticing it and without the animal running away. If one does see a hare, its wide open eyes are very striking. Hence the legend that hares sleep with their eyes open. With their natural protective colouring hares have very strong nerves: one is known to have sat regularly in its sett only a few paces away from a railway track. Express and freight trains thundered past daily without disturbing it. If, however, things do get too threatening, the hare positively 'explodes'. It leaps up in a flurry and pelts off. This has the effect of surprising, even terrifying, an unsuspecting man or dog to such an extent that several fractions of a second pass before they set off in pursuit, by which time the hare is well away; they can, after all, easily reach speeds of forty mph, as has been proved with the help of cars.

If the pursuer keeps on the hare employs a number of tricks, which are, of course, purely instinctive and not proof of any particular intelligence or cunning. One is the well-known method of doubling-back: when the hare has just enough distance between itself and the dog it runs back along its own track, takes a wide leap sideways – it can jump eight feet six inches – and starts a new track. This may be repeated several times. The dog follows the trail with its nose, finds that it suddenly comes to an end, has to run back again and then cast around until it finds the new track. This gains the hare much valuable time. It can then take cover, lie low and observe its enemy's movements. When doing so, a hare will often stand upright on its hind legs and may even take a few paces forwards on two legs. Other tricks are to leap on to a fork in a tree or a wall and survey the situation from there. Even experienced hunters can be foxed by acrobats of this kind. One hare jumped over a four-feet-high churchyard wall, another in despair leaped on to a hunter's shoulders – a man of six feet. Another landed on the petrol tank of a motor cycle, from there on to the driver's shoulders and away over the back wheel in a flash. A hare has even leaped clean over a large car and in another case over a horse.

In hotels which cater for shooting parties one can sometimes see stuffed hares with little antlers on their heads and some have even been displayed in natural history collections. These are clever hoaxes perpetrated by skilled taxidermists who have fastened small roedeer antlers to the hare's forehead. It is not true that hares are water-shy. No animal that has a thick undercoat of fur likes getting wet, but hares have been observed amusing themselves by bathing in brooks and repeatedly going into the water. When pursued they can swim across wide rivers, sometimes for as far as 600 yards. Hares will swim daily out to offshore islands where the grass is particularly juicy.

If a hare feels safe and well fed it can indulge in the most extraordinary behaviour. Seated in a raised hide, Dr T. Zwiesler watched a hare hop up to within six feet of a starling where it leaped into the air from all fours, waving its hind legs as it did so. In between a series of these leaps it rolled on its back like a dog and bowed to the starling by bobbing its head to the ground from a sitting position. This remarkable

42   *Unlike brown bears, polar bears are seldom born and reared in zoos. This one was hand-reared by two scientists, Dr and Mrs Faust, after it had been abandoned by its mother. Called 'Novaya', this animal has lived for years in the Frankfurt Zoo.*

43   *The stork has a very flexible gullet, essential if it is to swallow a diet which includes frogs, snakes and mice.*

44   *Our European stork, which nests on the housetops, sees more of the world than most human Europeans. This picture, taken in January, shows one of them walking among zebras in the Ngorongoro Crater, Tanganyika.*

45   *The polar bear is not a good swimmer and is helpless in the water; the seals, which it hunts and kills on land, can bite its hind legs in the water. Anyone with a canoe can push a polar bear along in the water and steer it in any direction. In winter polar bears avoid the water.*

46   *A group of pack-elks on the march at the Experimental Station of Pechora-Ilyichsky.*

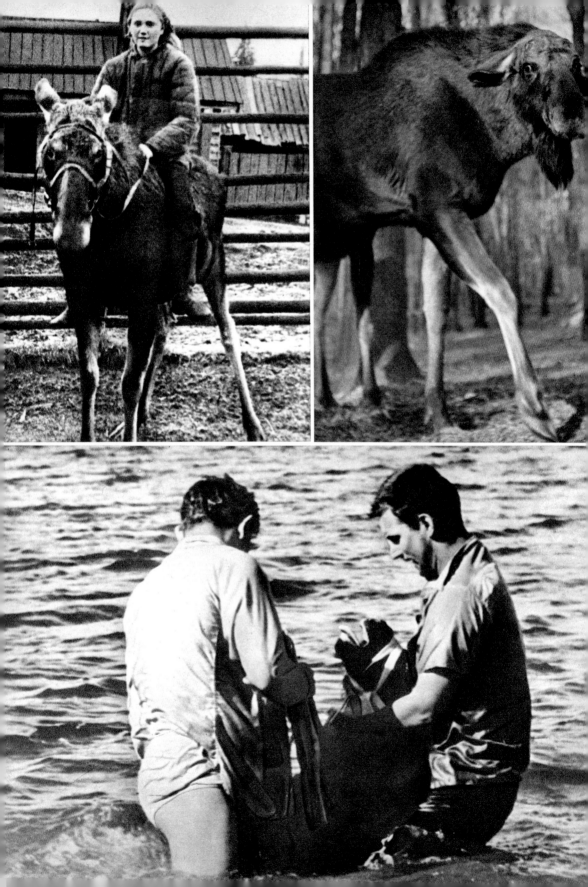

dance continued for about five minutes in a semicircle round the starling, which followed the performance with its head cocked to one side.

To Europeans the hare is something of an archetype of a stupid, timid animal. African hares, on the other hand, which are smaller and have longer ears than ours, play very different and much more artful and cunning roles in native folklore. They fool other animals, as Reynard the Fox does in our stories. To run away from a dog or a man is no more 'cowardly' than for a man to show a clean pair of heels to an elephant or a lion. Hunters who are interested in more than shooting and enjoy observing the animals on their 'shoot' have often noticed with amazement how brave hares can be. It is not so uncommon for them to defend themselves against cats and even dogs. A hare has been known to jump at an attacking cat and pepper it so hard with its hind legs that the cat fell over; this happened three times in succession until the cat ran away. Another hare, a female with young, defended her leverets all day long against two predatory crows.

When Professor Hediger was engaged in breeding hares at the Basle Zoo he had great difficulty in preventing them from running their heads against the sides of their cages whenever spectators came too near. He was obliged to put up barbed wire fences to keep visitors at a suitable distance. We originally had no intention of keeping hares at the Frankfurt Zoo, but as so often happens at zoos we were often given tame hares that their owners wanted to get rid of. Animals which have grown so accustomed to humans cannot simply be set free, because they will be immediately killed. From necessity we put them into cages designed for small animals, which could not be more unsuitable for creatures such as hares. We tried to find new owners for them, but

47 *Elvira Lebedeva, a keeper, training a two-year-old elk cow to be ridden.*

48 *When an elk has shed its antlers its appearance is completely changed.*

49 *Like the elk, young musk oxen are best caught by driving the whole herd into the water. They can then easily be seized from a boat or by wading in after them.*

before we could find any several of the does produced litters and started to rear the young. Similar experiences have frequently been reported elsewhere. Hares are capable of adaptation, can modify their 'explosive' natural behaviour and can even live in small enclosures without smashing their skulls provided they have been brought up from young with humans.

Once I had a hare called Theodore, who ran around in our apartment and was anything but shy. He ordered the dogs about, drove them out of their baskets by drumming at them with his forepaws when he wanted to lie down and had his fixed paths round my room, under the desk or along the bookcases, exactly like a wild hare living in the fields. Theodore was very fond of sausage and mincemeat, as are many captive hares, although animal remains have never been found in the stomachs of wild hares. They presumably satisfy their need for albumen by eating very young plants and shoots that have a high albumen content, which they cannot get in adequate quantities in captivity. Tame hares can master all kinds of tricks. There is a broadsheet of 1689 in which an artist by the name of Charlos Legrand illustrates hares marching along upright on their hind legs and beating drums.

The late Freiherr von Boeselager once possessed a similarly tame hare. He kept it indoors for five months then let it run free whenever it wished to. If guests came in the evening, he had only to open the French windows, switch on the light and call the hare by name. It would run into the house, jump on to its master's lap and was quite undisturbed by a dozen strangers sitting about the room. One of its ears had been cut off to prevent it being shot by mistake, but this did not save it from falling victim one day to a predatory animal.

Storks are like me; when winter approaches we set off for Africa. They do, however, take slightly longer to get there. A stork, ringed for identification, has been known to cover four hundred miles in two days, but in general they make a fairly leisurely journey southward. If they leave Germany in August they do not reach Africa until November. Being averse to moving their wings, they fly by gliding and need thermal up-currents to maintain altitude. Since there are practically no thermals over large expanses of water, storks do not fly over the Mediterranean. The West European varieties travel in a south-westerly direction via Spain and Gibraltar, then across the Sahara and thence to South Africa; the East European storks come through the Balkans, over the Bosphorus and through Turkey to East Africa. Many of them spend the whole winter in East Africa and I have photographed them strutting about among rhinoceros and zebra just as in Germany they walk the fields behind a farmer at the plough. Hardly any storks fly over Italy; there as in England and nearly all of France they were exterminated long ago and no longer breed. The dividing line between the storks which fly by way of Spain and those which travel via Turkey runs from South Holland, through the middle of Hesse and on to western Bavaria.

Naturalists have tried their best to discover why some fly southeast and others south-west. Working in East Prussia at a time when storks were still very prolific there, Professor Schüz sent young fledgling storks to the Rhineland, where storks are rare and had them reared there. 'Native' Rhineland storks set off south-westward for Spain in August, but the young East Prussian storks, which were only released long after all the adult storks had left to migrate, turned south-eastward, as was proper for their breed. They flew over the Alps and reached the

Po valley. Their instinct to fly south-eastward was thus inherited and not learned from their parents. A few years later a large number of baby storks were collected from farmhouse rooftops in East Prussia and reared in the Rhineland in an attempt to build up the stork population in that part of the country. These storks flew off with the 'native' adults – south-westward. In this case the example of transmitted experience was stronger than inherited instinct.

Storks only fly to Africa at a certain time of year, in late August. In 1939 the Polish ornithologist Wodzicki sent a number of young storks by aeroplane from Lvov to Palestine two months earlier than the usual start of the autumn migration. Within twelve days these storks had flown back under their own power to their nests in Poland. A few weeks later they made the journey again in the opposite direction.

One day I received a letter from Myles Turner, a game-warden at Serengeti in East Africa, saying that they had found a dead stork there with an aluminium ring around its ankle. The ring was marked: MOSKWA 6069. Whenever a ring like this is found it should be sent to the nearest ornithological station, which will transmit the information to the ornithologists who ringed the bird – in this case almost certainly Moscow. This particular find is evidence that many of the storks which winter in East Africa were born in Russia. Fifty or a hundred years ago this would have been impossible. There were no storks in the Moscow region then. They have only recently settled in that area, whilst they are growing scarcer and scarcer in Germany. At the turn of the century there were one hundred and fifty breeding pairs of storks in Switzerland; today there is not one. The decline of the stork population is also causing disquiet in Alsace. There they have always been proud of their numerous storks; every other village had a 'Stork Inn'. In 1947 there were still one hundred and seventy-seven breeding pairs in Alsace, by 1958 only one hundred and thirty-five. This situation prompted an industrialist, M. Waldvogel of Rappolts-weiler, to found a 'Society for the Preservation of the Storks of Alsace' in 1956. The members built twenty-five new nests, even bought fields and made two large and three small artificial ponds into which schoolchildren put frogspawn and tadpoles. The following April the storks came back from Africa. They are incidentally much quicker on the return flight and cover about sixty miles in a day, presumably because they are driven on by the mating instinct. The stork couples inspected the friendly welcome which had been prepared for them, but the majority flew on northwards. Nevertheless three extra pairs stayed there and this example, which was quoted in all the newspapers, encouraged many more people to build nests, buy up fields and take other measures to encourage storks. The king of Morocco even sent twenty storks to Alsace by aeroplane.

For the second time a stork couple in South Africa has been observed to have saved themselves the long journey to Europe and has bred there; this occurred in South West Africa in November 1961. My friend Myles has also written to me to tell me that among the many storks at large in his part of the world there was one with a native arrow stuck in its wing. In spite of this it could still fly. One hundred and forty years ago there was another stork which proved in the same way that storks migrate to Africa in winter. An African arrow had passed through the length of its throat, with the end sticking out of its breast and the iron tip lying alongside its head. Even in this condition the bird completed the return journey to its home at Wismar, a small seaport on the Baltic, where it was shot by a hunter on May 21, 1822. The stuffed bird, with the two-feet-eight-inch-long arrow still in its body, stood in the museum of the Rostock Zoological Institute for over a hundred years. The stork's instinct to return to its birth-place must be extremely powerful. Even though many young storks stay in Africa for their first summer – they are only sexually mature after the age of four – eight per cent of them nevertheless settle down in their home village, forty-one per cent settle within a radius of six miles and a further twenty-one per cent at distances between six and fifteen miles from the spot at which they first crept out of the egg.

They are, it appears, more attached to their nest and their home district than to their parents. Of sixty storks thirty-seven were found a year later on the same nest, eleven after five years and after seven years only one. In this connection one should remember that the maximum age reached by storks is about twenty; in Natal a dead stork was found in 1961 which had been ringed at Rossitten, East Prussia in 1942. But very many perish on the journey. A little while ago several hundred dead storks were found in the region of the Drakensberg mountains in Natal; they had all been struck down by a hailstorm. When a factory chimney was demolished in Alsace which had been out of use for fifteen years, inside it were found the skeletons of more than fifty storks which had fallen in. Young storks have frequently been killed by bees.

The notion that young storks feed and care for their old and weak parents is a myth. The ancient Greeks, however, believed it so firmly that they gave the name 'Pelargonia', to a law which obliged the citizens to care for their parents, from the word 'pelargos', a stork.

There are a multitude of other legends which are still believed about storks. All over Roumania, for instance, people will swear that storks exact the most terrible revenge on anyone who destroys their nest. They are said to carry glowing coals out to the thatched roof and fan it into a blaze with their wings. Only recently I read in our biggest newspaper devoted to hunting and field sports an absolutely serious report about an incident which was said to have occurred in a village in Courland (south-western Latvia). 'A boy had climbed on to the roof, had removed an egg from the stork's nest and substituted a turkey's egg. The young birds all hatched at the same time. When the father stork saw the one alien fledgling in the brood he was horrified, flew off and in no time forty to fifty storks had gathered. They made such a clattering with their beaks that people stopped work to see what was happening. Then the storks all disappeared except the father stork and one of his companions, who flew to the nest and killed the mother stork and all her young, throwing them all out of the nest. Having circled round the nest once more the two guardians of morality flew off and never returned again.' In another case the storks were described as having assembled in a meadow before the migration. 'Among them was one stork with diseased legs, which the storks'

"Health Tribunal" thought would leave him unfit to make the journey. Two storks seized him by the wings and dragged him to a tree whose trunk was riven to ground level by a split. His head was forced into the cleft and the poor young stork left there to die. The other storks made ready to fly away.'

The myth of the substituted egg and the innocently executed 'adulteress' can be read in a book dating from the year 1220 written by Calsarius von Heisterbach and entitled: *Dialogus magnus visionum et miraculorum*. In 1954 it was retold in *Reader's Digest*, this time with a goose egg and the locality moved to West Germany. According to Professor Konrad Lorenz the male stork does not protect his 'wife' but simply 'the female on the nest'. It may well be another female. Stork couples are by no means so magically and inseparably wedded as are pairs of cranes, jackdaws, geese or crows. The male and female of a pair of mated storks even migrate at different times. In spring the male returns much earlier than his mate, or rather, than the female belonging to that nest. Naturalists know of many such old wives' tales which live on for centuries, even millenia, and which crop up again from time to time in the guise of a genuinely new and true story. The one I like best is the little anecdote told by a forester which was reproduced, presumably as a joke, in a sporting magazine. 'The storks simply fly up and up,' the man said, 'higher and higher into the sky and stay up there for twelve hours. In the meantime the earth has revolved underneath them and when they come down – they're in Africa.'

There are also a number of quite newly-coined and positively breathtaking stories about storks. It is to the credit of Rudolf Kuhk, an ornithologist, to have firmly nailed one of them with a great deal of sound sense and persistence. In the autumn of 1953 several major German daily newspapers ran a very detailed story with big headlines, according to which a four-engined Indian passenger aircraft, registration no OZ14, with forty-four passengers on board under the command of Flight Captain Dadim Thelum had run into a swarm of twelve to fifteen thousand storks somewhere between the northern tip of Crete and the island of Kasos, at an altitude of 3,217 feet. 'The propellers mangled dozens of storks until finally their bones and feathers brought all four airscrews to a standstill. Before this fearful incident the aircraft had already altered course, due to a storm, for Heraklion airport on Crete, to which it now flashed an SOS signal. The airport's instructions to effect an immediate forced landing somewhere on Crete were not carried out. The critical situation produced the most disturbing scenes on board the aircraft: four Indian industrialists radioed their last will and testament. The aeroplane made a forced landing one and a half miles east of Heraklion and touched down with a tremendous impact; it burst into flames, but everyone on board escaped alive in spite of numerous injuries, some very grave.'

Kuhk traced this report and ascertained that it had been put out by a news agency in Lübeck, which in turn had received it from an Arab agency in Cairo. Enquiries addressed to the Cairo agency were never answered. The German Embassy in Athens, the management of Heraklion airport, the Greek airlines, the Indian airlines and every official body concerned were brought into the investigation. Result: in all Greece nothing had ever been heard of any such dramatic incident and neither the pilot nor an aircraft with that number existed. The whole event, which I have already described in my book *Twenty Animals, One Man*,[1] was in every detail a complete fabrication.

In old textbooks one can still read that adult storks show their young how to fly and that the young have to learn from them. One only has to rear some orphaned young storks – which is not difficult to do – to convince oneself that this is not so. That famous couple of ornithologists, Dr Oskar and Mrs Magdalene Heinroth, did it several years ago and described it exactly. The young storks were very friendly towards Mrs Heinroth, the person chiefly concerned in looking after them, but they would lunge at Dr Heinroth's face with their beaks. He would give them a sound box on the ears, at which they stopped attacking him; this behaviour was maintained even when they were much older: they recognised a form of authority without resenting the slaps on the head. Their attitude towards Mrs Heinroth was never anything but affectionate.

Young storks are also quite willing to take their food – meat, finely chopped fish, etc – from a feeding bowl. They are used to their parents depositing it in the nest in front of them, whereas many other young birds are fed by having the food put directly into their beak or gorge. For this reason it has always been possible to feed young orphaned storks by passing their food up to them on the roof in a basket on the end of a long pole. Other baby birds, which sit waiting for their parents with wide open beak would simply starve to death if anyone tried to feed them in this way. Incidentally, as an instance of the care needed when feeding birds (even young ones) with such powerful beaks, with two blows of its beak a young stork once smashed the lens of a reflex camera held by an erstwhile colleague of mine, the late Professor Karl Schneider, director of the Leipzig Zoo.

One day in Esslingen there was a short electric power cut. Later a male stork was found lying dead on the ground, having flown into the high-tension lines. Its mate continued to incubate the eggs alone for three days on end, during which time she only left the nest for a very short while to look for some food. This was remarkable, because normally male and female storks take it in turn to sit on the eggs. In the case of domestic pigeons, for instance, if one of the parents dies the other one will only remain sitting on the eggs for the 'regulation' number of hours. When the usual time comes for the change-over the bird gets up and flies away. Unaware that in the meantime the eggs will cool off and die, it comes back again at change-over and starts brooding again. The female stork hatched out her brood alone, presumably because the accident occurred only a few days before they were due to hatch. But a week later the young had disappeared; they had probably died and been eaten by their mother, as has been observed to happen in other cases. Once in another village when a soldier of the occupation forces shot the female stork, the father reared the young single-handed; fortunately they were already two or three weeks old when they lost their mother. Young storks such as these, who are brought up by only one of their parents, are usually a few weeks late in being ready to fly.

N

Adult storks have to forage for food in considerable quantity and variety. Professor Schüz once noted that a stork which was following the plough caught forty-four mice in an hour. Another time a stork's meal consisted of: seventy-six cockchafers, six hundred and seventy-four small ground beetles, seven hundred and thirty saw-fly larvae and one thousand three hundred and fifteen grasshoppers. In South Africa the Zulus and many other native tribes simply call the stork 'locust-eater', which is the best evidence of its feeding habits.

During the mowing of winter-sown mustard, Andresen once observed a stoat crawling out of a molehill. A stork which was following the mowing-machine immediately attacked the animal. Whenever it tried to defend itself and made a rush at the stork, the bird flew about three feet into the air. When the stoat had been jabbed and thrown into the air by the stork about five times, the stoat was dead. With some difficulty the stork then ate it. Often storks, which can grow very tame and walk about the farmyard, will so far forget themselves as to catch chicks and carry them up to their young on the nest.

In the Münster Zoo a pair of storks, which had already lived there for eight years with clipped wings, reared two young, while the keepers reared a third young stork artificially. Storks are quite white, with the exception of their wing-pinions, which are shiny black. These great pinion feathers grow three-eighths of an inch per day between the thirty-first and forty-eighth day of a young stork's life. At two and a half months the young storks are capable of flight. At this age the young storks of Münster began flying over the town and settling on roofs and towers – excellent publicity for the zoo. Unfortunately the young stork which had been artificially reared insisted on regarding humans as its friends and was made to suffer for it. Even when he was far from Münster with his two companion storks and walking in a field he would joyfully greet any human who approached. He would squat in a perching position, flap his wings and make hissing and miaowing noises. Children and stupid adults poked the bird with sticks, threw stones at it and made its life such misery that the people at the zoo would have done it a kindness by clipping its wings. When the storks flew away they were first spotted at the Dutch frontier and a fortnight later one of them was shot in the Marseille region. Another hand-reared stork, when later set free to fly with other storks, would come down to the ground to its foster-parents when summoned by clapping hands and calling 'Hansi'.

Kludskj Circus of Czechoslovakia once bought fifty young storks in Roumania and allowed these birds, which could not yet fly, to walk around freely in the fenced-in area round the circus caravans. They were well fed, but when the time came to cage them as the circus was moving on, they all took off and flew away. The circus folk had forgotten that they had in the meantime grown big enough to fly. At the circus' next stand at Košice in Czechoslovakia, several hundred miles away, suddenly there they all were again, perching on the guy ropes of the big tent. Only when the white fence was placed round the circus grounds would they come down and let themselves be fed. When the circus moved on once more they vanished again and re-appeared in Brno.

A stork in the Skansen Zoo at Stockholm has proved that they are also good swimmers. Two storks lived on an island in the zoo's pond; a third stork, who did not get on well with the other two, lived on another island. Twice the lone bird, which could not fly, swam across the forty-foot stretch of water between the islands. In the Basle Zoo a black stork, which had been made incapable of flying, mated with a free-flying white stork. The pair of them produced a mongrel chick which managed to stay alive for as long as fifty-three days. There are throughout the world seventeen different species of stork.

As soon as a stork crawls out of the egg it lays its head on its back and makes snapping movements. People who bring up young storks have thought that this was some kind of cramp; it is however a pre-liminary stage in the characteristic clapping of the stork's bill. The little birds are trying to clap their bills but it is inaudible because they are still soft. A slight noise can be heard after six weeks. Heinroth has said – 'One has the feeling that they would rattle their bills while they were still inside the egg, if only there were room.' This is a sign that they do not learn it from their parents but that the behaviour is instinctive. Young storks clap their beaks whenever they are fed, at least in their early days, however hungry they may be. It almost gives the impression that they feel the need to prove to their parents that they are 'real storks'. This can be a nuisance if one is in a hurry and anxious to feed one's foster-brood as quickly as possible.

When adult storks clap their bills it simply means, 'I am excited'. Whether the emotion is anger or love or something else can only be determined by what the stork does next. Sometimes a newly arrived stork is so shocked as to forget even to clatter its bill. In the village of Rajen a farmer noticed that a stork which had come back from Africa had flown into the air as if horrified by the sight of its nest, settled on the roof of a neighbouring house and kept looking back at its nest, which in the course of years had grown to be six feet wide and to weigh many hundredweight. Finally the farmer fetched a ladder and climbed up – and a mallard practically flew into his face. In the nest were ten blue-green eggs, which the farmer put to hatch under a broody hen. As soon as these squatters had been evicted the stork, 'visibly relieved', re-occupied its old home.

What is happening to those attractive and popular birds, our European storks? From the end of the last century until 1928 their numbers were steadily decreasing. Then they rose steeply until 1937 and since then have been on the decline again. A questionnaire was sent out by the Radolfzell ornithological station to all European

VI At one time the North American trumpeter swan was almost extinct. With great difficulty the world stock was raised to 451 head in 1950; by 1960 its numbers had increased in Canada and the USA (including Alaska) to 2,262. In addition there were 36 of them living in various zoos throughout the United States. In winter trumpeter swans fly as far south as Southern California and Texas.

VII The North American wapiti is larger than the European red deer but its mating call is higher-pitched and more grating in tone. The wapiti are growing in numbers in every region where the wolf and the lynx have been exterminated.

countries, from Portugal to the Soviet Union: in 1958 the total was sixty-eight thousand four hundred and twenty-three breeding pairs. In Germany there were four thousand eight hundred pairs compared with nine thousand and thirty-five in 1934. The place with the greatest number of storks in Germany is Bergenhusen in Schleswig, which in 1939 had fifty-nine occupied nests; in 1950 there were twenty-six. The Bergenhusen storks fly to South Africa via the Balkans. A ring from this village was sent back to Europe from a village near Capetown, a distance of six thousand five hundred miles. Bergenhusen is surrounded by large tracts of marshland.

The Japanese storks are in a much worse state. They are nearly extinct. In 1964 there were only thirteen of them compared with twenty-five in 1960. Since they no longer breed in freedom, probably due to the use of toxic pesticides, huge aviaries have now been built to house the very last few pairs.

Are our storks dying out because we drain all our swamps and dry out the ponds? Because our great cities are pumping the ground-water into their pipes, the ground-water level is consequently dropping everywhere and the countryside therefore growing steadily drier? Or are too many West German storks shot on their way across France? Another possible explanation is the mass destruction of locusts in Africa carried out with chemicals from aeroplanes. However, the fact that their numbers are declining in Germany does not necessarily mean that they are dying out. Great quantities of storks are now breeding in

VIII   A mountain goat stares calmly at its adversary. Not even dogs or wolves put them to rout.

IX   In spite of their name the small North American black bears (ursus americanus) are by no means all black in colour. They are found in all shades from brownish-grey to cinnamon brown. Especially in nature reserves, the human spectators' unfortunate habit of offering them food has often made them tame enough to be fed by hand. When the supply of tit-bits runs out or the visitors wish to stop feeding them, these bears may then turn angry and bite savagely.

North Africa and as we have seen they have moved into new territories in Eastern Europe. Nevertheless we must ask ourselves whether German children, just as the Swiss, the French and the English, will soon be deprived of the chance of ever seeing a stork in their lifetimes.

[1] *Twenty Animals, One Man* published by André Deutsch, London (1963).

Because criminals could easily escape from the Russian police across marshland by riding on elks, Catherine the Great made it unlawful to break in and train these huge stags for riding and driving. Even the University of Dorpat was not allowed to drive vehicles pulled by elk because the horses were shy of them. So at least by implication it should be possible to train elk to be ridden or as draft animals.

In fact they are not nearly so shy and disagreeable as they are often made out to be. During the work on the canal between the White Sea and the Baltic, elk would often stray among the grazing cows kept to supply the workers and would often be found wandering between the rows of huts and the village streets. Even in winter they were not simply driven there by hunger. Once ten years ago a yearling elk leaped through a classroom window in a school on the outskirts of Stockholm, to the delight of the children. When Baron von Tiesenhausen was lying in wait for capercaillie, a bull elk began to show a great interest in him. The sportsman was only partly successful in driving off the beast with a flaring match, as the little flame in the darkness attracted the elk all the more. It drew so close to the baron that he was finally obliged to light a whole box of matches at once and throw them into the elk's face. Only then did the great beast make off with cries of terror.

In recent years elk have frequently been seen in districts from which they had disappeared centuries ago: for example in Czechoslovakia near such towns as Usti nad Labem, Znojmo and Olomuc; in Germany in the Spree Forest, the Oberlausnitz, Saxon Switzerland and in the district of Anklam, New Brandenburg. None of these solitary animals were particularly shy; most of them were bull elks. Nobody has a good explanation of where they came from – probably from the elk reserves which have been set up in Poland since the war.

Germany too was an old home of the elk; we have, however, succeeded in exterminating it. As has been proved by the spades made of elk antlers which have been dug out of peat bogs, about a thousand years ago elk abounded in Upper Swabia and the Allgäu; the Roman occupation troops knew about them and drew pictures of them. Three thousand years ago they lived in Austria, e.g. around Mariazell, and they may have been there for very much longer.

Elk belong to the deer family and are the largest and heaviest species of the genus. Bull elks can weigh up to sixteen hundredweight and the points of their antlers may reach a span of six feet. Others are often seven feet high at the shoulder and produce much the same massive effect as an elephant. In general deer are not to be trusted. Tame red deer which have been hand-reared by humans invariably turn savage and dangerous as soon as they are mature and in rut. Having lived with humans when young, as adults they regard men as fellow members of their species and subject humans to attack as they would other deer. The human foster parents are always indignant at the 'ingratitude' of the creatures they have reared. Only recently two old ladies wrote to tell me that they had been attacked by a roebuck while on a walk through the woods. One of the two was just able to grip the animal by its sharp horns and so they both retreated, half pushed by the animal, their clothes torn, until they managed to escape into an inn and slam the door behind them.

The biggest and strongest deer, the elk, does not generally behave like this. It may be connected with the fact that bull elks also behave much more calmly in rut. They are not concerned, as are red deer and the big American wapiti, to collect dozens of females and protect them against rivals. They behave much more sedately. A bull elk pairs with a cow (sometimes with two at once) for ten or fourteen days; then they separate and the bull seeks a new mate. It is particularly easy to handle elk when they are swimming. D. W. Simkin, a biologist, used a helicopter to drive them into lakes in Ontario, brought the machine down close beside them and marked the animals' ears with a special punch. This enables them to be traced and helps to provide such information as how old they grow and where they migrate. In July the heads of several of the elk were almost completely covered with gad-fly, although the powerful breeze from the helicopter must have blown many of the pests away.

In the countries round the Baltic, in Sweden and in Russia countless elk calves have been reared by hand. Elk brought up in this way by humans move freely about indoors and even climb stairs. They are said to have a revulsion against mirrors and are fond of smashing them with their forelegs. Harry von Walter, a senior forest warden who died in 1937, kept in Livonia an elk called 'Chuk', who would leap in and out of the room through the open window with astounding skill, would lie down in the living room at mealtimes and followed his master everywhere in the forest like a dog. Horses and dogs got on well with the elk. It let itself be ridden, but would not tolerate a saddle. Unfortunately it learned the easiest way of finding its favourite food, mushrooms: it attacked the peasant women who came to gather mushrooms, chased them away and devoured the contents of their baskets. It was frequently locked up to keep it out of mischief whenever its master went away, but the elk's nose is so good that it could follow the trail of its master's horse, even half a day after he had left. Unfortunately someone poisoned the animal when it was five years old – it had made too many enemies.

Why has the elk, a tame, strong and trusting animal, never been domesticated? So far this has only been done with one deer species, the reindeer, and then with less than complete success. The Lapps drive their reindeer in herds over the tundra and use them, unsatisfactory though they often are, to pull their sledges. They are such aggressive and quarrelsome beasts that this can only be achieved by castrating all the full-grown males and only using the half-grown young stags for breeding purposes. Elk are not only strong, they can also, at least for short periods, run at a speed of forty mph. Unlike reindeer they do not eat moss but find part of their winter food from the shoots of conifers and although their main diet consists of leafy branches, they will if necessary kneel down and crop the grass. These mighty deer

o

can also jump well. In the animal enclosures in the Neandertal valley near Wuppertal they once jumped nine feet six inches from a standstill over the fencing – and over the Head Keeper who was standing behind it – because the newly-introduced bison came too close for their comfort.

Elk are easily exterminated as they are apparently only afraid of wolves, bear and lynx, but appear unwilling to learn that their worst enemy is man. Over a century ago there were about a million of them in North America, but now the stock has fallen to almost exactly one hundred and ninety-five thousand and is kept at that level by state conservation laws. During World War I they were almost wiped out in Eastern Europe and as a result Lenin, himself a hunter, issued a decree prohibiting elk-hunting throughout European Russia. The Soviets even started an elk farm south of Moscow in which as late as 1937 elk were trained to be ridden and driven; evidence of this in the form of photographs was found by German troops who occupied the area during the war.

In World War II also the elk were almost exterminated in East Prussian and Eastern Poland, so the Poles instituted an Elk Reserve of about four hundred and ninety-five thousand acres in the eastern part of the country at Czerwony Bagno ('Red Swamp'), where the bearded giants have increased to over two hundred head. A second Reserve, only sixteen miles from Warsaw, was started in 1951 with one male and two females. This colony has now grown to eighty head of elk. Where these animals are protected, it is clear that they grow and multiply at a considerable rate. In Sweden, for instance, elk hunting has been forbidden for a long time, although in the last few years a short annual open season in elk has been declared. By this kind of careful control the elk population of Sweden has grown by ten times since 1929. Each year about half a dozen hunters shoot each other dead, whilst the total bag of elk slowly increases. Although this figure has been well over thirty thousand, in the past few years, people complain that they are still far too numerous. They ravage the woods and the elk themselves that are shot grow smaller and lighter from year to year.

About ten years ago the biologist Peter Krott, who was living in Finland at the time, experimented with two tame elk calves to see how they would react to being ridden and driven. When they were nearly full-grown he was astonished to find that they allowed him to put on the specially made harness, bit and bridle without the slightest resistance. No young horse, however trusting, will allow one to do this, because horses are far more sensitive and ticklish. They chewed with enthusiasm on the rubber bit – an iron bit seemed much too cold for wintertime – rather like Americans with a piece of chewing-gum. They were not in the least disturbed by the empty sledge which they were made to pull. 'Jussi' and 'Magnus' as the two animals were called simply walked about with their harness and sledges as if they were grazing normally. They followed wherever their owner led them, but every twenty minutes or so they would stop to graze from bushes and after half-an-hour at the most they lay down and spent three-quarters of an hour resting from their efforts. They had no trouble in jumping, sledge and all, over a six feet-wide stream and three feet-high fences were no obstacle.

But as soon as Krott put a load on their sledges, even if it were only branches and greenery, the animals soon chafed themselves raw on the harness, however carefully it was padded. The tame elk that belonged to Walter, the forest warden whom I have already mentioned, would let itself be ridden without any trouble. It never attempted to throw its rider, as any young horse would. But on the other hand it simply took its rider where *it* wanted to go and stopped when it felt so inclined; it could not be guided by the reins or by leg pressure and would not tolerate a saddle.

Peter Krott later took 'Jussi' and 'Magnus' to a number of Finnish towns to demonstrate them as draught animals. 'The show was a failure,' said Krott. Certainly the two great animals, enticed by a cabbage-head, followed their master up a ramp and on to a lorry, allowed themselves to be tied up at the front end with a halter and calmly lay down throughout the journey. Whenever they turned their heads their dangerous antlers often only missed Krott's eyes by millimetres as he stood between them – evidence of the precision with which they controlled their movements.

Having reached a town and spent the night in the lorry, when they heard the familiar voice of their master next morning as he approached the vehicle, they simply sprang up and leaped through the canvas sides of the truck ten feet down on to the roadway – at which the crowd fled. When called, however, they at once stuck their noses under the arms of their human friend and let themselves be led like dogs. During the demonstrations they were quite undisturbed by the crowds of people, the numerous cyclists, the cars and buses. Only at the railway station did they take fright, when a train roared past them, but they calmed down again as soon as it was past and returned to the showground without incident.

To the joy of the many children the animals simply lay down amidst the crowding spectators and refused to be disturbed as they rested and ruminated. They were not even moved by a private aeroplane circling low over them. Every attempt at making useful draught animals out of them having failed, 'Jussi' and 'Magnus' were sent to zoological gardens, one to Hamburg and one to Denmark.

At the state Nature Reserve of Pechora-Ilyichsky in the USSR they have had more success in riding and driving elks than did Dr Krott. There they have recently found a number of rock-drawings showing elk being herded by men or harnessed to sleighs, indicating that by the start of the New Stone Age the inhabitants of Siberia must have kept elk; they were presumably superseded later by horses and reindeer.

In 1938, at the Serpukhovsk experimental station near Moscow, thirteen tame elk were kept and were put daily into sledge harness. They pulled between one and one-and-a-quarter cubic yards of wood ten miles in an hour, once even covering a record stretch of fifty miles in one journey. Unfortunately this experimental station was destroyed during the German occupation, but it was re-opened later in Siberia, where there are ample supplies of the elk's chief food – leaves and twigs. In summer only it will also eat grass and mushrooms. In many mountain forests it lives chiefly on pine branches in winter, but the animal can adapt itself to a completely new environment, e.g. in summer it will go as far as the sea-coast to escape the horse-flies and is to be found in the sunflower fields of the Kazakhstan steppes.

In the Siberian breeding farm elk show practically no fear of dogs and beasts of prey. A big male elk can smash a bear's skull with its huge spade-like antlers. These are obviously used chiefly as a kind of jousting weapon in fights against other male elk during the rutting season. Young elk, on the other hand, can fall prey to bears. In the summer of 1962 two bears broke into the elk farm in broad daylight and killed two young elk before the eyes of the farm workers. In deep snow a glutton can also overcome an elk. With its broad paws the glutton hardly sinks into the snow; it follows pregnant elk cows or crouches on a branch and jumps on to their backs.

Between 1946-48 the practice at the elk farm was first to catch the young elk when they were between one and three days old; they would then drink cow's milk from a bottle without difficulty. These animals grow extraordinarily tame and affectionate towards humans. The stomach of an elk calf holds about three pints of milk and it will consume up to four pints a day. A wild elk cow gives on an average forty gallons of milk in a year, but by regular milking over a number of years the lactation period can be extended from four to six months. After six years the best cow, Maika, was giving nearly twelve pints a day and one hundred gallons in a year.

When they are two or three months old a halter is put round the animals' necks and they are tethered to a post with a leading-rein. After a few weeks they learn to run on the leading-rein. It is important that they learn not only to follow the call of their keeper but also to obey the sound of a horn, otherwise they will only run after one man, whereas anyone can summon them with the horn. At a signal from the horn the whole herd marches behind the herdsman into the farm where each one is given a few pounds of potatoes or turnips as a reward for obeying the horn.

The young elk on the leading-rein follows its keeper exactly as it would its own mother. This only begins to present difficulties when the animal comes to be taught to pull, as it must then go in front of its keeper. The best way to begin this training is when the animals are called back to the farm from pasture; then they naturally move off in the familiar direction without the keeper walking in front of them.

As soon as the elk reach a weight of about three hundred pounds – this can often be at six months old – they are trained to carry weights and pull loaded vehicles. The most difficult part is when the animals have to leave the herd – just as it is with horses. During the second winter the sledges are loaded with two or three hundredweight and the elk are made to travel five or six miles at a speed of five mph. At the age of three they are completely broken in and capable of acting as draft animals. They can be ridden and can pull several hundredweight. Fully grown elk will carry up to two and a half hundredweight on their back, which is about a quarter or a third of their live weight.

A six-year-old castrated male elk called 'Ural' weighs nearly half-a-ton (an elk called 'Akvi' has pulled a sledge with a total weight of one and a half tons). Unlike the horses on the farm, the elk are not afraid of aircraft and will pull their sledges right up to an aeroplane on the ground. They show equally little fear of cars and lorries with running engines.

So the elk may yet prove to be a useful worker in the northern taiga. It needs no fodder supplies as horses do, no fuel supply as cars do; deep snow, swamp or fallen trees are no obstacle to it. Even in the Siberian winter its needs no stable but lies down to rest in the snow and after a heavy snowfall only its head is showing by the next morning. Perhaps in Siberia at least the elk will come into its own before long and more and more men will ride them and glide over the snow in elk-drawn sleighs.

'With a coat of musk-ox fur no one need freeze, even at the North Pole,' so claims Alvin Pedersen – and he ought to know, because he has, as I have already mentioned, spent several winters in the Arctic. One day when the temperature was minus twenty-seven degrees centigrade, he hung a skin, freshly stripped from an old bull, over a plank and stuck a thermometer into the fur. The watery sun was just on the horizon. After ten minutes the thermometer showed plus two degrees centigrade. So musk-oxen never freeze – although the heat of summer must cause them some trouble. There is even a compensation for this, since with their thick fur they are largely spared (except for their eyes) from a plague of flies and mosquitoes which make the Arctic spring and summer into sheer hell and drive elk and reindeer to despair.

The musk-ox has the longest hair of all wild animals. The hairs on the back measure six and a half inches in length, whilst they can grow to lengths of two feet and even three feet on the neck, breast and hindquarters. When they moult in spring and get their new coats, the old fur hangs in tufts on jutting rocks and bushes or simply lies around in heaps on the ground. Musk-oxen in zoos generally have this 'moth-eaten' look, so that when I saw wild musk-oxen in Canada for the first time in my life I did not recognise them. They were magnificently smooth-coated animals, dark brown to black in colour and much bigger than I had thought. A musk-ox bull's back is only four feet three inches high from the ground, but with its thick fur it gives the impression of being much bigger, and above all much fatter, although they only weigh between four hundred and fifty and eight hundred and fifty pounds. Many people must have wondered why these small Arctic wild cattle, which almost look like a transitional stage to a large sheep, have not been domesticated and their wool used for spinning. But it is not so easy to get their wool: if a musk-ox is shorn, it almost invariably perishes soon afterwards from inflammation of the lungs. Besides this, the warm woolly hairs are thickly interspersed with long and hard bristles which are difficult to remove.

During the Ice Age musk-oxen lived in North Germany, Mongolia and in the northern parts of what is now the USA, but as the ice withdrew northwards so did the musk-ox and they were only dis-covered in 1869 by the 'Second German Expedition to the North Pole' under Captain Koldewey when they wintered on the island of Sabine-Üya off Greenland. Here the expedition had a very hard time, which almost led to their extinction. When one reads the exciting descriptions of it, one does not realise that these great polar expeditions carried out a fearful blood-bath among the musk-oxen. They are about the easiest Arctic animal to kill. Not only did the explorers and their companions live off their meat, but they were largely killed to feed the expedition's many sled-dogs, employed to pull their heavy equipment and their supplies over the ice.

Ultimately the musk-ox was saved by the invention of the auto-mobile and, above all, of the aeroplane. Modern polar expeditions no

50 *Wolves are essential for maintaining the natural balance of wild life. Like lions, hyenas, leopards and Cape hunting dogs in Africa, in our latitudes wolves are practically the only animals which ensure that the grazing herbivores do not over-multiply and thereby destroy the vegetation.*

51 *The curlew* (mimenius arquata) *can put even the powerful bustard to flight by stabbing with its pointed bill in the region of the anus, as the zoologist Wolfgang Gewalt observed on a number of occasions. From England and Western France these curlews have spread over all Europe and Asia as far as Siberia and they spend the winter in southern Europe or throughout Africa. One of these curlews was once shot at thirty-one and a half years of age, as was proved by the ring on its foot.*

52 *In spring mating couples of the long-eared owl* (asio otus) *sing to one another with a muffled, groaning 'oom' sound. When disturbed they puff their feathers in and out. They live almost entirely off mice.*

longer used sled-dogs; instead they are flown in comfort direct to their camps. Incidentally there is no such thing as the stink of 'musk' which might prevent people from eating musk-ox meat. The bulls may smell rather powerfully during the rutting season, but musk, which is an ingredient in all good perfumes, actually comes from the musk-deer, a small deer, about as large as a dog, which is native to the mountains of Central Asia. No one knows how the musk-ox came to be given its misleading name.

They are extremely brave, tough beasts; they run away from nothing, be it wolf or bear. If they are attacked a herd of musk-ox will form up into a circular 'laager', like a wagon-train attacked by Indians: the fully-grown bulls and cows face outwards with the calves in the middle and they never weaken or give way. If a dog or a wolf ventures near them it will be hurled into the air with a lightning thrust of sharp horns and trampled by hooves. The bulls even make surprise sorties, rushing out of ranks at the attackers. It is then that their long-haired fleece provides them with protection from being bitten on their undersides. Having made a sally they gallop back to the ranks and push themselves backward into the front line.

However their long belly-hairs also enable snapping dogs to get a grip on the animal and bring it to a halt, after which the hunter can approach safely to an easy range without endangering himself. Even then, thanks to their tactics of communal defence, the hunter must kill

53 In England a toad (bufo bufo) once lived for thirty-six years under some steps leading to a garden and allowed itself to be fed by hand and even stroked. These creatures are strongly attached to their home area. Around the Teufel-See near Potsdam some toads were marked on their hind feet, removed from the lake area and let loose. One toad covered nearly a mile to return to the lake, which also included climbing a three hundred feet high hill. It did, however, take two years to make this journey whereas all the others, who had been released nearer to home, made their way back after a few days.

54 Animals are naturally more interesting to children than any inanimate toy, but must this be a reason for the hundreds of thousands of tortoises to die a miserable death every year? Anybody who buys one and brings it home should ensure that it is properly looked after.

the whole herd in order to lay hands on his prey. The hunter – if this kind of slaughter can be called 'hunting' – can sit in safety and take careful aim. He will need to take *very* careful aim. The Arctic traveller Vitalis Pantenburg, for example, once shot at the forehead of a bull with a 9·3 mm steel-coated bullet at a range of thirty yards without it making the faintest impression on the animal. The two horns are joined above the eyes by a slab of bone. It is elastic and as hard as steel; it is about four inches thick and easily withstands the impact of a modern high-velocity projectile.

Anyone who wants to catch musk-ox calves must also slaughter the entire herd. This hardly disturbed the sealers and whalers of the turn of the century if they could earn a few extra hundred pounds by bringing back a deck cargo of a few musk-calves. In this way zoological gardens unsuspectingly contributed to the extinction of the musk-ox in Greenland during the first quarter of this century. Between 1900 and 1925 at least two hundred and fifty musk-ox calves reached the zoos and it is fair to reckon that for every calf taken five or six adult beasts were shot. The New York Zoo alone acquired twenty-six musk-calves between 1902 and 1939. Generally these animals never lived long. Coming as they do from regions which are virtually free of bacteria, they have almost no resistance to the diseases rife among cattle and sheep in our latitudes, to say nothing of the strain of the change of climate. However, if they do survive the adaptation they may live longer in a zoo. At the Boston Zoo, which acquired an acclimatised pair of musk-oxen in 1925, the bull died after eleven and a half years whilst the cow was still alive after fifteen years.

When zoo directors realised how these animals were caught they resolved to buy no more. This rule has generally been kept for the last twenty-five years and the seal-catching crews can no longer carry on this trade on the side.

Knowing that the musk-ox is so extraordinarily resistant to winter weather, has such good meat and such good wool, many have thought of trying to settle them in other parts of the world. However, every animal soon died when transplanted to Iceland. Even the first six calves which were let loose in Sweden quickly succumbed to inflammation of the lungs. In Southern Norway a total of thirty-eight calves were set free on Dovre Fell. Five were soon killed by an avalanche and not many of the others survived. The young bulls left their heifers, vanished and then re-appeared in the middle of some herds of domestic cattle at Sundalon, where they terrified the women who came to cut hay. However, it was apparent that cows, humans and musk-oxen soon grew accustomed to each other. Gradually the musk-oxen even went into the byre at night with the cows. Out of doors they were always docile; the bulls of domestic cattle are often more dangerous. A wild musk-ox has never attacked a human being. These animals from Dovre Fell then discovered for themselves a romantic and completely isolated little valley called Stolsdalen and are living there today; the herd is, however, very small.

In the past the mistake has probably been to leave the young calves to themselves too early and to bring them too far south. The distinguished American biologist Hornaday acted with greater fore-thought and caution. His object was to settle musk-oxen in Alaska to provide a source of food for the undernourished Eskimoes, for which Congress voted him an appropriation of $40,000. In 1930 a total of thirty-four musk-oxen – fifteen bulls and nineteen cows – were caught in Greenland and shipped via Oslo to New York, thence after four weeks in quarantine by rail to Seattle, onward by ship to Seward in Alaska and finally by rail again to Fairbanks in the Alaskan interior.

The animals stood up well to their journey of twelve thousand seven hundred and seventy-five miles. Travelling in the care of experts is a different matter from being hi-jacked by whalers. Furthermore they were not simply let loose as soon as they arrived in Alaska but first kept in pens. The following year six of the musk-oxen were killed by bears and three more died from other causes, but apart from these there were no further losses. In the meantime, however, reindeer had already been introduced into Alaska and proved to be much more suitable as semi-domesticated animals for the Eskimoes. The musk-oxen, which had multiplied, were rounded up five years later and transported to Nunivak Island, which lies in the Bering Sea off the coast of Alaska. By 1943 their numbers had increased to one hundred and not long ago an airborne observer reported that the herd had grown even larger. The resettlement was therefore successful.

A similar result was achieved on Spitzbergen. Of the seventeen musk-oxen that were brought there one fell over a cliff to its death, but the others stayed alive and settled in the area round Advent Bay. By 1942 they had increased to seventy head. Musk-oxen multiply relatively slowly. A herd of twenty animals seldom includes more than three or four calves. They are born in April, at a very cold time of the year when the nights are longer than the days. They often freeze to death before they are dry after birth. Most of the musk-oxen on Spitzbergen were shot during World War II, but by 1960 the stock had reached one hundred and fifty head. Lately the Canadian government has authorised the export of herds of musk-oxen to the Soviet Union, where they are to be settled on Wrangel Island in the Arctic Ocean off the coast of Siberia.

A small country town of eleven thousand inhabitants probably contains more people than there are musk-oxen alive today. Alvin Pedersen has calculated that the world stock stands at around ten thousand. The Canadians are rather more sanguine. They have placed these tough, black-brown animals under very strict legal protection. The mere possession of musk-ox hide attracts an extremely severe penalty. They reckon that in Canada proper, on the mainland and the islands of the ice-ridden northern seas there are altogether thirteen thousand and another eleven thousand on the northern and eastern coasts of Greenland. No information is available on developments in recent years. Weather stations and military bases in the Arctic contain, as I have already mentioned, crews who get easily bored up there and amuse themselves by banging off all around them. Taken all in all, however, the outlook for these stalwart northern beasts has improved.

17 WHAT IS TO BECOME OF 300,000 PET
TORTOISES?

In the autumn of 1963 the House of Commons held a debate on the length of the shell of young tortoises. A bill was tabled to prohibit the import of small Greek and Mauretanian tortoises if their shells were less than four inches long. In 1959 eighty-eight tons of these unfortunate little creatures had been imported into England and sixty tons in 1960, chiefly from Morocco. This averages out at 250,000 tortoises a year. In 1961 the Moroccans reduced the number exported by a half, but others came in their place from Tunis and principally from the Balkans, whence the Germans import similar quantities. The bill was withdrawn from the House of Commons as the British importers voluntarily undertook to buy no more small tortoises.

The members of Parliament did not spend so much time on this matter from sheer love of animals. Tortoises are, as we shall shortly see, naturally tough and long-lived. In northern European countries they are dealt with exclusively by pet shops and stores, because they cannot be eaten and the famous soup is only made from their marine cousins the turtles. When so many hundreds of thousands of 'toy' tortoises continue to be imported this simply means that the same number of tortoises die every year.

It is not so noticeable, however, because they die very slowly. Like toys which children forget to wind up, they sicken and slowly pine away on cold balconies or concrete kitchen floors until they end up dead in the dustbin. Or one gets bored with them and tries to dispose of them to the nearest zoo, whose demand for small Greek tortoises is strictly limited. We at the Frankfurt Zoo get so many enquiries about the care of tortoises that we have long since arranged for the reply to be printed by duplicator. In particular it is the small baby tortoises which have very little prospect of survival in our cold regions.

They are of course nice animals, by no means unintelligent and they can provide a lot of enjoyment, provided that one observes a very few rules for keeping them healthy and happy. First of all they need warmth, for preference twenty-five degrees Centigrade (77 degrees F.). Being cold-blooded, i.e. adopting the temperature of their surroundings and hardly generating any heat of their own, it is as pointless to wrap them in a blanket as it would be to wrap up a snake. In our rooms it is colder on the floor than at the level of our head and hands. If they have the chance of moving into the sunshine, the rays of an electric fire or a small heated floor-tile, then they immediately liven up. Only they should not be kept exclusively in the sun or near a radiator – they must have the choice of going where it is cooler.

If they are comfortably warm they will start exploring the room and when they have been moving about for a few days they will tend to keep to certain fixed paths, as they do in the wild. They are very stubborn: if a chair leg is blocking its usual route to the wall, the tortoise would not dream of making a detour round it but instead will make desperate efforts to push the chair aside with its shell – which it often succeeds in doing. If it is too heavy the tortoise will stop after a while and fall asleep.

They soon find their way about the house. If the weather is fine out of doors and the door to the garden is shut they will walk up and down in front of it. If their feeding bowl is empty they will waddle to the nearest human, place themselves beside his chair and stare fixedly up at him. H. G. Schmitt, a scientist who studied tortoises all his life, kept some tortoises who enjoyed climbing mountains of folded carpets, the steeper the better. One of his tortoises even battled its way past three hedgehogs to its feeding bowl. The tortoise bit them so relentlessly in the face that the hedgehogs retreated in terror to the far side of the feeding bowl. Eventually whenever this tortoise heard the characteristic lip-smacking sound which hedgehogs make while they are eating it would hurry over to claim a share in the hedgehogs' prey.

One of Herr Schmitt's tortoises even learned to open a door when it was ajar by standing upon its hind legs close to the opening and pressing on it with its torso until it gave way. The zoologist Professor Otto Koehler was once camping out in Anatolia and had put a number of captive tortoises into a box. Hearing them making a lot of noise in the night, he switched on his flashlight and saw an extraordinary sight. Four tortoises were standing on each others' backs in the corner of the box and the topmost one was just about to climb over the edge.

Greek tortoises are pure vegetarians, unlike our native swamp tortoises and other turtle species. They are satisfied with lettuce, cabbage leaves, dandelion leaves, strawberries, cherries, plums and any other sort of fruit. They also like eating white bread softened in water or milk. In their homeland they are said to be fond of eating human and animal excrement.

If a pet tortoise will not eat this is usually because it has been kept too cool. Often a lukewarm bath does wonders, if the water is shallow enough for the tortoise to hold its head out of the water with comfort. It should in any case have a bath once a week. The Moorish tortoises, which mostly come from North Africa, need even more warmth than the Greek tortoises from the Balkans. These Mauretanians are more brightly coloured; a frequent colour is olive-green. The two varieties are easily distinguished as the Mauretanian tortoises lack the horny tip on the end of their tail and have only, at the rear end of their carapace, a simple marginal plate over the tail, whereas the Greek variety has two marginal plates there. Besides this the Moorish tortoise has two horny warts, one on each side of the tail root. Oddly enough the North African tortoise has the Latin name of *testudo graeca* (i.e. Greek tortoise), while what we call a Greek tortoise is known scientifically as *testudo hermanni*.

When the summer weather grows really hot the tortoises begin mating. One is amazed by the speed with which the male tortoises then run round the females or chase them, often with their small legs fully extended to keep their plastron from touching the ground. If the female rejects the male, the disappointed suitor draws in his head and violently batters his shell against the female's hard posterior, making a great deal of noise as he does it. Finally he has to climb half-way up her back, which is by no means simple with such a rigid carapace, so male tortoises are provided with a concave plastron – the only means of quickly identifying their sex. When coupling, male tortoises utter noises which sound like the soft miaowing of a cat.

Greek tortoises soon grow so tame that they no longer withdraw head and limbs into their shell when picked up. Most of them can be fed from the hand. They have a considerable capacity for learning and gaining experience. One which had fallen off the table several times learned to crawl round it and avoid the edge. If, however, they are determined to go out into the garden they will obstinately climb down the steps, even if they fall head over heels at every step. Tortoises have the same faculty for distinguishing colours that we have.

In the Balkans the favourite season for catching tortoises is when the melons are ripe. At other times they must be caught individually up in the hills, but then they descend on the fields in absolute armies. Where there are a lot of them they can eat everything bare. In a single day one tortoise-catcher was able to pack and despatch seven thousand two hundred Greek tortoises in sixty-five crates. Several years ago near the capital of Albania people organised tortoise races for fun. Because all the spectators had put their money on the favourite and it had lost, the race ended in a terrible fracas after which five wounded and three dead were left on the field – not tortoises, but people.

If the winters are not too severe, escaped Greek tortoises may survive in our latitudes. H. G. Schmitt, whom I mentioned above, acquired his tortoises from a gamekeeper on the Amper, a tributary of the River Isar. They had lived wild there for years. As many as ten years previously the gamekeeper had seen young tortoises which had 'undoubtedly hatched from eggs laid in the wild and which had survived the raw winter of the Alpine foothills'. However, it only needs one specially cold year to wipe out a tortoise colony living so far in the north.

Pet tortoises give most trouble in autumn and winter. If it is very warm, particularly if the floor is warm, they do not necessarily need to hibernate, but it is better for them if in autumn they are put into a wooden box which is filled to a depth of eight inches with leaves and moss (not with peat mould and not with sawdust – these dry the animal out). The box should then be put into a dark, cool place which is safe from rats and mice, in which the temperature is no higher than five to seven degrees centigrade (41-45 degrees F.) and not lower than three degrees centigrade (37 degrees F.). If necessary the moss can be dampened from time to time. When spring returns and the temperature reaches twelve to fifteen degrees centigrade (54 degrees F.), the hibernating tortoise should be gradually brought out again. It should first be given a bath in lukewarm water, which it usually drinks greedily. Tortoises which have hibernated are often much more lively than those which have spent the winter awake in our rooms.

A pet tortoise may see the children of a family grow up and live on to see them have children and grandchildren of their own. It is not known how long Greek tortoises live in the wild, but we know of a lady who was given one in 1930 when she was a child: the creature then weighed slightly less than ten ounces; in 1964 it weighed three pounds. Dr Eugen Görk wrote to the magazine which I publish, *Das Tier*, describing how he had acquired his tortoise in 1911 when it was no larger than a half-crown. The shell was still soft and yielded to the pressure of a fingernail. This animal lived with the family for half a century. In 1958 it laid its last eggs, but continued none the less to grow. In November 1960 it weighed five pounds four ounces, a year later five pounds five and a half ounces. Unfortunately it died of a chill in 1961.

This is nothing compared with the proven age of a wild Eastern 'box turtle', a land loving species from the region of New York. A farmer found it in 1953 on his farm in Rhode Island and brought it to the New York Zoo. The Keeper of the Reptile House, Mr James Oliver, was extremely interested in this otherwise fairly common species for one reason: engraved on its plastron (belly armour) were two inscriptions – 'EBK 1844' and 'GVB July 22, 1860'. With the help of the local newspaper and radio station he started a search for a person with the initials 'E.B.K.' who could have carved that date. His grave was actually found – in a village cemetery in Wyoming. His name was Edward B. Kenyon and his headstone was marked with no more than the three initials 'E.B.K.' which he had scratched on the tortoise-shell. When he did this he was 19. He can hardly have expected the animal to survive him for so long. By 1953 it was already 129 years old!

They do not, on the whole, breed often in captivity. It is certainly not uncommon for female Greek tortoises to lay eggs in spring. Even tortoises kept singly do it; like hens they do not have to be fertilised to lay eggs, only of course infertile eggs do not hatch. These eggs are soft-shelled and white. The tortoise digs a hole with her hind legs and tail, lays the eggs in it, then fills up the hole again and crawls back and forth until the place can no longer be seen.

The eggs of tame tortoises can be put into a flowerpot full of earth and sand, moss laid on top and occasionally watered. Stemmler-Morath did this once and put the flowerpot on the radiator to keep it at a constant temperature of twenty-two to twenty-five degrees centigrade (73-77 degrees F.). After the pot had stood there from October to January, a young tortoise hatched out. Recently a lady keeper at the Dresden Zoo told me that she had put some tortoise eggs in a cupboard drawer and forgotten about them. The cupboard stood in a damp, permanently heated corridor. Later baby tortoises were found crawling about in it. But these were lucky flukes; breeding in captivity is generally unsuccessful.

Never buy little tortoises for your children thoughtlessly instead of toys; but if you do buy one, please make sure that the little creature is treated as tortoises deserve to be treated. It is not much trouble.

Nobody knows why pronghorn antelopes so seldom breed in zoos, nor why they usually die after barely a year in captivity. Although they live wild in the American west they cannot even survive long in the zoos of the eastern United States, to say nothing of Europe. Since no one likes keeping animals in zoos if they are unable to stay alive, pronghorns are seldom seen in our zoological gardens. Now and again someone renews the attempt, using a new foodstuff or a new way of keeping them. Thus I saw the first pronghorns of my life in one of the Paris zoos, but shortly afterwards I was able to observe and photograph them in Canada.

Pronghorns are not even particularly rare animals. Around 1800 there were probably more than forty million head of them on the American prairies; they were as numerous as the herds of buffalo which people slaughtered for fun. On the new railroad track just laid between Denver and Cheyenne whole carloads of dead pronghorns were brought to town daily during the winter of 1868-69. There were three or four million of them to be found alongside the track. In those days three or four of these dead antelopes were sold together for twenty-five cents; a quarter was then the smallest coin in circulation in that region.

People are now beginning to realise that these hordes of buffalo and pronghorn on the prairie could well have been the most efficient way of exploiting certain kinds of terrain to provide food for human consumption. Admittedly, once all the wild animals have been shot, meat can be produced by a combination of arable cultivation and keeping domestic cattle, but never in the same quantities per acre. Above all the wild herds never damaged the soil, whereas after a century of agricultural exploitation there are now large areas of the United States which have been turned into dusty deserts. And we are just about to make the same mistakes on a large scale, with our development aid schemes, in East and Central Africa; the only difference is that under the tropical sun the soil degenerates much faster into wilderness.

Anyone who thinks of antelopes tends to think in terms of Africa and India. This sole species of American antelope is unique in being the only animal in the world which sheds the horny sheath of its otherwise permanent horns every year. As we know roe-deer and stags shed their bony antlers annually and grow new ones in the spring. Their antlers are pure bone without the horny sheath common to goats, sheep and antelopes. The pronghorn only keeps the bony stumps on its head, but the sheath of horn loosens every year and falls to the ground where it is eaten by mice, chipmunks and hares. Before the sheath is cast the new horn has formed beneath it; it first emerges with a fur-like protective layer and hairs growing at its base. Four months pass before the new horny sheath is really hard.

Long before us the pronghorns 'invented' the heliograph. If one of these antelopes sees a wolf, a coyote or anything else unusual in its neighbourhood it raises and flattens the long white hairs on its rump, so that they flash like two great chrysanthemums and reflect the light. Other pronghorns can see this for miles and they at once pass on the signal. Like lightning the alarm is given to the whole herd. At almost the same moment scent glands underneath these posterior hairs give off a sharp smell which even humans with their inefficient noses can detect unmistakably at 100 yards and more.

These 'flash and stink' antelopes are the fastest mammals of the American continent. For about a mile they can keep up a speed of fifty mph. This means that no wolf, no coyote, not even a greyhound can catch them up. Only a thoroughbred horse can maintain a comparable speed for longer, yet the pronghorns were quickly slaughtered in their millions. Originally their curiosity was their downfall. The old settlers used to tell how one only had to lie down on one's back and shake one's legs in the air or wave a red rag on a stick to entice the animals back into rifle-range. By now at any rate they have learned better but it used to happen that they would trot along parallel to ox-drawn or horse-drawn wagons at a mere hundred yards distance and unsuspectingly run through tented camps at night.

Of all animals pronghorns seem to have found the most effective answer to barbed wire fences. They do not jump over them but simply through them. Without slackening their considerable speed they fly between two horizontal strands of barbed wire that are only fourteen inches apart, even though they are at least as large as goats. Now and again they play a game of galloping along beside a car, then accelerate, overtake it, cross the road in front of it and once on the other side slacken their speed as if satisfied at showing off their paces.

In exactly a hundred years we men have reduced these curious and beautiful American animals from forty million to nineteen thousand head. It looked as if they were finally due to disappear from America and thus from the earth, but at the turn of the century the Americans realised – largely due to articles and books written by the celebrated American author and naturalist, Ernest Thompson Seton – what a shameful episode in their history had been perpetrated by the sadistic annihilation of the great buffalo herds. There was a general movement to protect threatened animal species again and the National Parks were founded. This has led to the gradual re-establishment of this antelope with the brilliant white stern-patches. By 1924 they totalled forty thousand; now there are four hundred thousand at large on the prairies. To prevent the farmers from shooting pronghorn on their land as 'vermin', many states pay them a premium. In Wyoming any hunter must pay five dollars to the farmer on whose land he has shot a pronghorn; in Texas the premium is from thirty to a hundred dollars. These fleet-footed animals have virtually no other enemies but man.

During the rutting season pronghorn bucks are content with a small harem of three or four does, although a particularly bold male may have up to eight. The females generally give birth to twins. Like roe-deer the mother leaves her young during the daytime and only returns for short periods, chiefly at night, to give them the udder. The two fawns always lie apart, often as much as eighty or a hundred yards away from each other; in addition they have virtually no scent. If a predator does come across a young fawn, the other one usually goes unnoticed. The mother will attack coyotes, foxes and even eagles with her fore-hooves and almost always succeeds in driving them away.

These antelopes have more right to call themselves Americans than the Americans, even than the Indians and most other animals of the continent. Pronghorns are scarcely related to any other American species and they are not even very closely related to the antelopes of other continents. Unlike most other ungulates they have only two toes on each foot and no dew-claws, the short stunted vestigial relics of other toes, generally found higher up the leg, which buffaloes, stags and other cloven-hoofed animals still retain. The forebears and relations of the pronghorn are to be found in America itself, where they lived a million or two years ago. Whilst their contemporaries of that era, the big giraffe-camel and the hornless stags, have long since died out, the pronghorns have maintained their breed. They have been true Americans for millions of years, whereas the other large cloven-hoofed animals, the bison, stags, elk and wapiti were later immigrants to the continent – not to mention such latecomers as the Indians, horses and white Americans.

In my nature-study book at school there was a beautiful illustration of a mother opossum which I shall never forget. She carried her tail arched over her body and on her back sat her children, who had all hooked their little tails round their mother's tail which was stretched out above them. Like this, they could never fall off her back. I have only recently learned that this picture is factually incorrect and that it was a pure invention first put out over two hundred and fifty years ago by a German artist, Anna Maria Sybilla Merian (1647-1717). She was in Surinam from 1699 to 1701 and there she drew pictures of flowers and insects which to this day continue to charm all who see them. These pictures were published by her daughter after her death. On the last page of the book, among the ground-insects, there is a mother opossum carrying her children on her back. Their tails are pointing to the rear and entwine the backward-stretching tail of the mother. In later illustrations one can follow the sequence in which this picture was repeatedly copied and gradually 'improved', until finally the mother's tail is turned round over her back and made into a sort of guide-rail for her young. There are even photographs of this phenomenon, but they have been taken from stuffed animals in museums that have been 'doctored' to conform to the picture.

Since the opossum first became known to Europeans – which was in 1500 – it has continually stimulated our imagination and provided the raw material for most incredible stories. Of recent years in America its life has been more thoroughly studied than that of any other marsupial in the world. In the course of these studies facts emerged which at first sight might appear to be fables. When the explorer Pinzon returned to Spain from newly-discovered Brazil, bringing with him a female opossum with her young in her pouch, King Ferdinand and Queen

Isabella, astounded, put their royal fingers into the pouch and expressed amazement at such a wonder of nature. For there is not a single marsupial to be found in all of Europe, Asia, Africa, Java, Sumatra and the Philippines. They only occur in North and South America, in Australia, Tasmania and a few neighbouring islands, but whereas there are a hundred and fifty species of marsupials in Australia, the opossum seemed to be fighting a losing battle, even among the many other 'backward' species in America. It continued to grow rarer and was on the point of disappearing from most regions.

People thought that it was simply not intelligent enough in comparison with other mammals. If an opossum is compared with a cat, which is about the same weight, it is true that the opossum's brain is only a fifth of the size of the cat's brain. Nevertheless the opossums have been progressively re-establishing themselves in North America since 1920 and have moved northward on a considerable scale. The American fur trade now deals annually in about two or three million opossum pelts.

The first bad mark awarded to the opossum in books about the newly-discovered continent of America was its evil smell. The stink was said to penetrate wood and stone and to be lethal to Indians who smelled it. A village had to be evacuated if approached by an opossum. Then it was supposed to catch little birds, kill them, put them on the ground and suspend itself by its tail over the corpse. When a bird of prey arrived to claim the dead body the opossum would drop on it and thus catch two birds with, as it were, one blow. Opossums were said to copulate through their noses and the mother would *blow* the young into her pouch.

The only element of truth in the story of their evil smell is the fact that most animals do not care for the taste of opossum. Opossum

55   *A female tortoise digs a hole in the ground and lays her soft-shelled eggs in it.*

56   *This fox terrier took part in the expedition to catch young musk-oxen for Al Oeming's farm in Alberta, Canada. Here he makes a playful rush at two eagles.*

remains are scarcely ever found in or around foxes' earths. If a dog catches one it may perhaps shake it once and leave it for dead, whereas it would probably half eat a woodchuck and bury the rest for later. Yet people do eat opossum, particularly in the southern states of the USA where in some parts they are regarded as a special local delicacy and are eaten with sweet potatoes; many people, however, recommend one to stick to the sweet potatoes and leave the fried opossum on the plate.

The opossum's powers of survival are due not only to its unpleasant taste but chiefly to its physical toughness. Examining a collection of opossum skeletons in museums one finds remarkable numbers of well-knit bone fractures which other mammals of equal size would never have survived, especially not in such numbers. Its other great talent is feigning death – hence the American expression 'playing possum', which has become synonymous with 'pretending to be dead'. This form of behaviour is of course widespread among animals; birds, reptiles, amphibians and anthropoids are capable of it, but none of them are as familiar or popular as the opossum. Even so opossums, in common with other mammals, cannot really 'play dead', i.e. it has no nervous mechanism inducing instant immobility as a protective reaction. With mammals it usually takes the form either of unconsciousness or of temporary paralysis of the area of the brain controlling respiration, induced by the pressure of a predator's tooth or by blows. An opossum will lie on its side, its mouth half open and its tongue protruding. A boy once carried a dead opossum around with him for two hours, dangling it by its tail, until he climbed over a fence and noticed that the 'dead' animal was clinging fast to the fence.

Even though the opossum does not use its tail as a strap-hanging device for its young, it does use it for transporting leaves and grass into its lair. It bends the tail forward underneath its body, pushes the padding material between tail and belly by using its mouth and thus is

57 *Around the year 1800 there were forty million of these handsome pronghorns living on the American prairies.*

able to carry six to eight mouthfuls at once into its burrow. These marsupials never use their tail to grip branches, as do, for instance, capuchin monkeys. The opossum uses it almost exclusively to secure a loose grip while climbing; if it were to hang by its tail alone it would quickly let go and fall.

In previous ages of geological history marsupials were distributed over practically the whole world. In 1820 Cuvier found traces of them in the gypsum used to make the streets of Paris. When Dr Barnum Braun excavated the skeleton of a horned dinosaur, a reptile, in the Canadian province of Alberta in 1915, he also found the remains of an extinct marsupial of the same period. Its tiny bones aroused much more interest than the enormous bones of the dinosaur. As the little marsupial belonged to the first mammals to appear on earth in the era of the great reptiles, it was given the name of 'Dawn Opossum' – Eodelphis, as it was an opossum of the sub-class of marsupials. The present race of opossums has not yet reached the latitudes of Canada. As natives of the south they do not hibernate like other North American fauna such as the marmot, the prairie dog, the skunk or the raccoon, or European animals such as field mice, hamsters and marmots. The tips of the opossum's tail and ears freeze easily in winter, but this seems to cause them no concern.

Whereas the gestation period of a horse is almost a year, of a goat five months, dogs and cats about two months, the rabbit one month, the coypu more than four months, the opossum needs no more than thirteen days to bring its young into the world and their short gestation is very obvious from their appearance. Six new-born opossums weigh ·035 of an ounce, twenty-four would fit on to a teaspoon and one of them weighs a mere ten-thousandth of the weight of its mother; they are born blind, naked and with no more than rudimentary hind legs; one might therefore be forgiven for mistaking them for embryos. Even when an opossum gives birth to the unusually large number of twenty-five young, the event may last no longer than five minutes.

For centuries no one knew how these tiny, unformed little creatures reached the mother's pouch from the cloaca. Numerous theories and guesses have been put forward, as they have about the kangaroo. Many people claimed to have seen the mother pick up the young in her teeth and put them in the pouch, whilst others imagined that she bent herself into such a shape that the cloaca was brought into immediate proximity with the wide-open aperture of the pouch and the young needed to do no more than grip the teats in the pouch with their teeth.

In the case of the kangaroo the procedure was explained by a certain Mr Goerling who observed his tame animal on February 25, 1906, as the three tiny young spent half an hour laboriously climbing up the fur of their mother's stomach and then disappeared into the pouch; the mother gave them practically no help on their way. In 1933 a visitor to the Halle Zoo saw the same thing, although in this case the mother calmly licked a smooth path in the fur for the infant on its way up. As far as the opossum is concerned, birth was first witnessed on February 6, 1920, by Dr Carl G. Hartman of the University of Texas. He was able to watch how the minute embryonic opossums climbed the three inches along their mother's belly to the pouch, unaided by the mother but using their well developed fore-feet. In this state they look more like worms than mammals. They must reach the pouch or die; apparently no more than half of them succeed. Dr Hartman has thrown more light on the life of the American opossum than any other scientist. He published a book about them in 1952.

When a baby opossum finally reaches its mother's pouch it has overcome the first and greatest obstacle of its life. The pouch contains thirteen teats and the mother can fully close it at will. The air inside it then becomes very foul, with a six per cent carbon dioxide content. It is in fact almost a miracle that the baby opossums can survive in such an atmosphere. Finally after ten weeks they are independent of their mother and move clumsily about; in three to four months they are ready to stand on their own feet. Two-thirds of their food is of animal origin – insects, mice, cockchafer grubs, earthworms and even toads, which are shunned by many other small predators. As opossums only have about two years to live they must breed fast: a female has two litters in a year. A few years ago Glen Sanderson in Illinois achieved the remarkable feat of marking the young while still in the pouch so that they were distinguishable as adults. Using a magnifying glass he cut out a small portion from one of the ten toes of their hind legs, marking a different toe for each animal. This enabled him to make a number of observations on their life and habits; the male-female balance, for instance, is roughly equal among opossums. They are, it appears, distributed at a density of about one hundred and thirty-five opossums to the square mile.

Whilst marsupials as a whole have a reputation for not being particularly clever, the opossum seems to be even less gifted in this way than most of them. Gerd-Heinrich Neumann succeeded in teaching a great grey kangaroo and an opossum to look for food in only one of two boxes, over which a certain pattern of dots had been painted; the other box was marked with a triangle. The kangaroo learned to distinguish between seven different pairs of patterns and wherever necessary to take the food from one box only. The opossum on the other hand could only manage two pairs of patterns. Whilst the kangaroo remembered for five months which marks meant food and which did not, the opossum had forgotten after four weeks. In Professor Hediger's menagerie an Australian opossum obstinately spent the whole winter on a very hot radiator pipe, although branches were close at hand for it to climb. The animal suffered severe burns on its feet and on the naked tip of its prehensile tail. The reason must have been the animal's preference for the heating pipe as a hiding place, as it ran close to the ceiling.

However, radiator pipes and black and white symbols on sheets of cardboard are not things which play a very big part in the opossum's normal life. As they have proved in the last forty years in the USA and more recently in New Zealand, these marsupials are well adapted to survive in this world. From the earliest days of European settlement in New Zealand the New Zealanders have exhibited a passion for introducing the most varied animal species into their country and the American opossums that were brought there were only allowed to be shot from 1947 onwards. Now they have reached a figure of twenty million head and they are said to be increasing at an annual rate of six or seven million. Their density of distribution is about one hundred and thirty-five per square mile as in the USA. They are supposed to do a lot of damage to trees. It appears that in nature, as in politics, one can survive without much brains.

Until some years ago the only keepers at the Frankfurt Zoo to receive
danger-money were those in charge of the big cats, the bears and the
elephants. When considering the likelihood of accidents in a zoo, one
naturally thinks first of lions, leopards and polar bears – animals which
in their wild state live by killing others; and yet these animals cause less
injuries or fatalities to their keepers than any others. They are always
housed in double enclosures: if they are to be fed or their quarters
cleaned the beasts of prey are first let into the other enclosure, so that
no one ever has to be shut up alone with them. If in spite of these
precautions they injure someone, it is generally due to carelessness or
the result of an attempt to train the animals.

On the other hand many have needed surgery after attacks by
anthropoid apes, zebra stallions, camels, bulls or wild pig. The worst
hand-biters are guenons (long tailed monkeys), martens, foxes and
similar small mammals, especially when they are being rounded up or
transferred. A few years ago at Frankfurt a wart-hog nearly killed one
highly experienced keeper and a year later a keeper in Duisburg
actually was killed by another equally tame wart-hog. Deer are
notoriously dangerous. Tame roebucks have put many people into
hospital. Twenty years ago a red deer gravely wounded one of our
keepers; he was just able to climb over the railings. A keeper in the
Basle Zoo was gored to death.

Not that red deer in the wild, with their magnificent antlers, ever
attack humans. They only lose their fear of bipeds in zoos where they
are kept in highly unnatural conditions. With us a stag spends the whole
year in the company of a small troop of hinds and young stags. We
build dividing fences across their enclosures with small gaps to enable
hinds to make a quick escape from vicious or importunate stags. Their

spreading antlers prevent or at least hinder the stags from following them. In the woods, on the other hand, the antlered deer only spend a twelfth of the year in the company of mature females during the rutting season in September and October. For the rest of the year the stags keep together in troops, without there being a leader among them. They do not pay much attention to each other, but neither do they fight often. If there are any antlered stags among the troops of hinds these are well-grown young stags, two- or three-year-olds. They still retain an attachment to their mother, although if they have been well fed they will already have developed a handsome set of horns. They have no authority in the herd, which looks for guidance to an experienced older hind – at least as long as she is still leading young of her own. Deer live to be about twenty years old, sometimes considerably more.

A set of stag's antlers, which can weigh over thirty pounds, is an astonishing thing. It can hardly be comfortable to carry this contraption around on one's head for a large part of the year until it is finally cast, generally in February – a month which used to be called in German 'Hornung'. Well before February it has become dead bone, a process which begins in July or August when the stag sloughs off the dried-up skin from its horns. Then special cells between the top of the scalp and the fluted roots of the horns cause the bony structure to break up and one day both halves of the pair of antlers fall off. Remarkably enough, both generally fall off on the same day. The loss of this fearsome weapon must be quite a shock to its owner. He is suddenly made aware of his own vulnerability or inferiority. A stag in the zoo, until then the terror of all who beheld it, is suddenly given a tremendous drubbing with the fore-hooves and is sent packing by some old hind. The stag could of course defend himself in the same way; stags which have just shed their horns or are 'in velvet' (the sensitive stage of growth when the immature antlers are covered in soft skin) settle their differences by rearing up on their hindlegs and slashing at each other with their forelegs. The discarded antlers are soon eaten by mice, squirrels and other rodents; in Scotland the deer themselves are said to eat them.

A deer's body has to store up a mass of nutrient in advance in order to enable another massive set of antlers to grow again within a few months. They first sprout from the head as two bumps. When they are half grown, with rounded ends and covered in a velvety skin, they feel warm, indeed almost hot to the touch. Growing bones secrete much greater quantities of unstable elements than mature bones. That is why larger quantities of toxic radioactive strontium are found in children's bones than in the skeletons of adults. The antlers of a Scottish stag which were examined in 1957 contained twice as much radioactive strontium than others dating from 1952. Stags' antlers are thus a peculiarly sensitive indicator of the increase in atmospheric pollution by atomic fall-out from nuclear bomb tests.

For centuries the inhabitants of Siberia, Kazakhstan and the Altai have been selling the immature antlers of the striped East Asian sika, Dybowski's red deer or the big plain-coloured maral deer to the Chinese, neatly crated in bundles. This was one contributory cause of the red deer's disappearance from large areas of Russia. Peasants supplemented their income by keeping the stags in enclosures and sawing off their antlers 'in velvet' every year at the season when the blood was still coursing through them. Nowadays this is done on a large scale by state farms in the Soviet Union. After being sawn off the antlers are held in almost boiling water, the process being repeated at regular intervals. When they dry out they lose between forty and sixty per cent of their weight.

Owing to the great demand from Chinese druggists for such useless junk as rhinoceros horn, the teeth of extinct animals and bottled snakes, the Soviets cashed in on this business with a superior smile. The Academy of Sciences in Moscow then made some clinical experiments with stags' antlers. It transpired that they really do contain a large concentration of sex hormones and nutrients. They are effective against symptoms of senility and promote healing of wounds. The Chinese also buy up dried unborn baby deer and other organs of the stag.

In Germany there have been deer for at least six to eight hundred thousand years. Once they were so numerous that one of the earliest periods of human settlement in Switzerland, the first lake-dwelling period, has been referred to as the 'hartshorn period'. Around 1900 there was not a single red deer left in Switzerland; the Switzers had completely wiped them out. This is possibly due to their excessively democratic government: in other European countries dynasts and nobles took care to preserve some of these handsome beasts for the pleasure of hunting them. The woods and the wilderness were originally common land, where all cottagers and peasants had the right to hunt for meat and gather firewood. The noble lords of the Middle Ages, however, soon annexed them to their property, or at least maintained the sole right to hunt deer, bear, pig, wolves and other beasts of the woodland. The chase was a kind of substitute for warfare, a hearty change from the boredom of court life and yet another pretext for the display of pomp and splendour. First hunting lodges then hunting castles were built in the woods; these buildings, such as Schloss Moritzburg in Saxony, were often gigantic.

These knights, counts, princes, kings and prince-bishops hardly treated the wretched quadrupeds in what we would call sporting fashion. They hunted the stags for hours on end with packs of hounds until they were exhausted, then wounded them in order to round off a strenuous day by following a trail of blood. To make it easier they arranged for the game to be driven into large enclosures from which it could not escape and despatched it with spear, crossbow and musket. As part of their feudal labour-dues peasants were made to build walls of many miles in length to ensure that there were always troops of stag available in 'deer parks' for the lord and his guests. The antlered beasts were chased into long hedges whose gaps concealed snares and nets, as the Ikoma tribe do to this day around the Serengeti National Park in Africa. The longest stretches of fencing required vast nets, into which all game was driven. To keep these nets properly ventilated and free from mould when not in use, special 'net-houses' were built. The 'net-house' at Waldau in the Hessian Forest is over seventy-five yards long, i.e. half as long as the full length of the net when hung up inside it.

Q

The hunt servants of the nobility soon turned their craft into a kind of occult science, as was common practice in the guilds of the Middle Ages and later. About one thousand five hundred huntsman's expressions, of which many are over a thousand years old, have been retained to this day and have enriched the German language and many others.

The well-to-do of Europe and elsewhere still turn to hunting for pleasure. Often the motive is not only the joy of wandering through woods and fields that makes such a pleasant change from the drab routine of money-making – the modern equivalent of dancing attendance at court – but because hunting still has a slightly aristocratic, upper-class cachet. Anyone who can invite people for a shoot or to come stag-hunting finds it slightly easier to forget that he has come by his money in the wholesale gut trade or by selling refrigerators. This has always been so and a very good thing too; otherwise who would pay the farmers for their shooting rights, compensate them for damage to crops caused by game and feed the deer in winter? Without our field sports devotees farmers would long since have exterminated partridges, hares, foxes and deer as 'destructive vermin'.

If only some of these sportsmen would learn a little less about blowing hunting horns and the etiquette of the hunting field and a bit more about natural history: that, for instance, animals of prey are not criminals fit for nothing but the death sentence simply because they (like the hunters themselves, be it noted) kill non-predators, but that lynx, wildcats, eagles, foxes, eagle owls, buzzards, falcons, otters and martens are merely fulfilling their natural purpose in killing the sick, the weak and the superfluous progeny of herbivorous animals. They do not just go hunting at the weekend but at night too, in driving snow and in drizzle and have a much better eye for the animal that is sick and weak than the most experienced sportsman.

In bygone days hunting rights were owned by the man who was both landowner and judge; he was therefore not disposed to treat with much leniency those who competed with him for his own game. Outlawry or running the gauntlet were the least of punishments for a poacher. Other princes might have his hand chopped off, have him blinded or stoned. Keepers ruthlessly enforced the game laws. Many of them were themselves ennobled; their origin is often still traceable from the antlers in their coats of arms. Often it was not the joy of the chase which drove the peasants to poaching, but sheer despair. Nowadays in Germany a square kilometre of mixed woodland is reckoned to support one red deer, coniferous woods half as many. The red deer population of West Germany is no more than sixty thousand, compared with ten times as many roe-deer. But the grandees of old Europe wanted to see more and more acres given over to agriculturally unproductive woodland, at the inevitable expense of the peasants' arable land. Since they were under no obligation to compensate the peasantry for trampled fields and ruined seed, they were delighted when the numbers of the red deer increased.

Many a noble sportsman would first have the game collected in pens and then mowed them down one after the other as they were driven past him, preferably sitting in the window of his hunting lodge. In this way the heir to the Austrian throne, who was later murdered, would sometimes bag over a hundred stags in a day and the last Kaiser, Wilhelm II, would indulge in this sort of hunting in Upper Silesia with two personal loaders to keep handing him an endless succession of loaded shotguns. In his *Chronicle of Nassau in the Year 1848*, Wilhelm Heinrich Riehl wrote: 'Who were the instigators of the revolution in Nassau? The deer, which grazed in the cornfields at night. They were the real demagogues, and agitators. It was the deer which first bred liberal ideas in the poor peasant.' The little man was all too prone to regard game as belonging to 'them', to the nobles. It was doomed to vanish with the nobility, as happened in Switzerland.

I had been afraid that the same thing would happen in Africa, and for this reason I objected when rich tourists, well protected by 'white hunters', could go shooting lions and tigers on so-called hunting safaris, whilst the wretched African was imprisoned as a poacher. I was worried that the Africans would remove the Cape buffalo, rhinoceros and giraffe along with their European rulers. That is why in the 'fifties my son Michael and I attacked this indiscriminate slaughter of game in the book *No Room for Wild Animals*[1] and in the colour film of the same name. This form of destruction has nothing to do with shooting rights and sportsmanship as we understand them in Europe. Together with a group of like-minded people who appreciated the nature of the crisis, we succeeded in changing the views of the African politicians in these new states at the eleventh hour before independence.

I wanted wealthy European sportsmen to rent large shoots in East Africa, to maintain their own gamekeepers, to shoot the game in accordance with the needs of the Game Department, combat poaching and pay the native tribes as much for their shooting rights as they pay the farmers in European countries. I do not go shooting myself, but I find a certain form of the sport perfectly justified – *outside* national parks and nature reserves, of course.

There are even red deer in Switzerland again and in fair numbers. In 1914 the Grisons National Park was founded and only a year later nine deer crossed over from Austria. By 1939 there were three hundred and fifty of them and today there are if anything too many of them because there are no predators to keep their numbers in bounds. Anyone can go there in the autumn to hear the stags in rut, for only then do the stags begin to court the females. Their mating-call is part of the romance of the forests of Europe. Often its value as a tourist attraction is so great that inn-keepers pay a few forestry workers to lurk in the thickets and imitate the mating-call with watering cans! The visitors are impressed and the gamekeepers are delighted, because it keeps the flood of sightseers away from the real rutting grounds of the red deer. A rutting stag will often collect as many as fifty young and mature hinds around himself. This is not a real 'harem', as the stag does not act as their leader or guardian and quickly runs away if dogs or hunters approach. His only care is to see that no other stags trespass or that none of his hinds desert to another stag.

When two stags fight it is obvious that their antlers are more suited to a formalised duel like fencing than to lethal combat. The proliferation of points on the antlers ensures that the opponent's thrust will be intercepted before any vulnerable organs can be damaged. Once they are face to face with antlers enmeshed it is more a question of pushing and shoving, a trial of strength comparable with a tug-of-war between men. It occasionally happens that both antlers become so hopelessly interlocked that the duellists are inseparable and die a miserable death from starvation. It can be dangerous when instead of the normal branching antlers a stag grows only two long, sharp horns. The stag with plain horns can easily penetrate its opponent's branches and stab it. Young stags which grow their first pair of plain horns are no danger. They lack the courage to be aggressive, but old stags with plain horns are feared as murderers.

The points of the antlers do not grow progressively symmetrical and more handsome with the years as people often imagine – in the first year a 'yearling' with single horns, in the second year a 'knobber' with forked horns, in the third year a six-pointer 'staggard' and so on. The size, weight and even the degree of ramification depends in no small degree on how well the stag feeds. In its second year many a stag grows into a six-pointer or even an eight-pointer. When a stag is past its prime – in about its fourteenth or fifteenth year – the spread of its antlers begins to reduce; it grows fewer and fewer points until it finally reverts to the same two plain spikes of youth, although they are much stronger than those of an immature stag.

In Schloss Moritzburg in Saxony hang the antlers of a red deer weighing forty pounds and displaying sixty-six points. King Frederick I of Prussia, when he was still the Elector Frederick III of Brandenburg, exchanged these antlers with the King of Saxony for a specially tall young recruit for the famous tall grenadiers of the Potsdam garrison. The Elector had shot the stag by having it driven within range by a gamekeeper's daughter riding on a tame elk.

During the rutting season, and probably at other times too, stags frequently exhibit the most extraordinary behaviour. In the Giant Mountains of Silesia one of them took a fancy to a certain grey mare that pulled a shooting-brake. Whenever she whinnied he replied with a bellow and vice versa. He used to haunt the bushes near the brake, was eventually enticed out into the open and shot.

Hinds are usually two or three years old before receiving the attentions of a stag in rut. During this period the stag is quite meek and peaceably behaved towards the females. The fawns are allowed to remain in the breeding herd and many hinds are fertilised during their first breeding season.

After eight and a half months, at some time during May or June, the hind will break off one day from the troop and retire alone to give birth, having first chased away her last year's fawn. The birth seldom lasts longer than ten minutes, to the accompaniment of gentle groaning and bellowing from the mother. Until the fawn can walk, i.e. during the first two to four days, she leaves it hidden and only returns twice a day to crouch over it and suckle it. As soon as it can follow her about it sucks every few minutes. The previous year's calf, which will have rejoined them, is often also allowed to suck.

As long as young hinds have no young of their own they remain with their mother. Only the young stags leave the female troop sooner and join up into bachelor troops. Von Asseburg, a keen hunter, had occasion to observe how they helped each other. He had shot at one of eight stags. The animal went limp and started to collapse, but the others crowded up to it to support it and hustled the weakening animal first into a field of rye and then into a forest. Similar instances of help to wounded companions have been frequently observed among elephants and kaffir buffaloes. Speeds of 42 mph have been recorded for stags in flight.

Where deer are not being hunted, particularly at feeding-places in winter, they grow very tame and one can approach very close to them. One hunter would feed deer twenty yards away from his house. Summer and winter they would come at night-time, undisturbed by an electric light burning in a tree twelve feet above their heads. The lamp could even be switched on from indoors by a switch on a desk, allowing the inhabitants to see at once when it was time to go and watch the deer.

At about seven pm on Easter Sunday 1943 a herd of about twenty deer paid a somewhat startling visit to the town of Zahna in Saxony. They leaped over the little Zahna River, swam across a pond and invaded the town centre. Frightened by the numerous pedestrians, some of them fled towards the railway station whilst others leaped over various garden fences. One smashed a plate-glass shop window and injured itself badly, some even went into houses. Altogether they did over a £100 worth of damage.

Deer having always been regarded as a regal game, it has long been the custom to present them as gifts. In 1661 and 1662, one hundred and fifty-nine stags were caught in north-eastern Brandenburg and shipped to London. Today European red deer have greatly multiplied in Argentina, Australia and especially in New Zealand. In return German game breeders thought at one time that they might produce bigger and more handsome stags by introducing strains such as the wapiti from North America or maral from eastern Russia. Those species are certainly bigger, but German sportsmen quickly lost interest in the wapiti as they only utter high, piping tones in the mating season and lack the much-admired neck mane of the red deer. Scarcely any trace of these imported breeds remains; they probably lacked the necessary resistance to European diseases and parasites.

Five hundred or a thousand years ago, hunters in Germany could expect to bag much larger antlers than is usual today. This may be partially due to the fact that our present-day stags have perforce become creatures of the woods, although by nature they are more suited to open, sparsely-forested downland. Between 1934 and 1954 many relics of the past, starting with the early Middle Ages, were excavated at the little Pomeranian town of Wollin. This town had once been very important, with a population varying between five thousand and ten thousand, which by mediaeval standards was almost a metropolis. In the Middle Ages the Wolliners manufactured large quantities of bone combs and sold them all over the world. These combs were chiefly carved from the horn of red deer's antlers. The rosettes at the base of the horn were cut off as superfluous. The excavations showed that the size and weight of the rosettes declined over the years. The most powerful stags in Europe today are to be found in the Carpathians, in East Prussia and in the Balkans, the easterly regions of Europe.

Princes who loved pomp frequently attempted to harness stags to their carriages. The Emperor Aurelian was the first to be pulled by a four-in-hand of tame stags in a triumphal procession after the Roman victory over Queen Zenobia of Palmyra; the Emperor's coach was said to have previously belonged to a King of the Goths. Afterwards the stags were sacrificed to Jupiter on the Capitol. Prince Pückler once drove down the Unter den Linden in Berlin drawn by six stags. In such instances the animals used are always castrated stags, which are much more amenable. When castrated they cease to shed their antlers every year, provided they are already formed when the castration takes place; if they are gelded before their new antlers have grown, they are incapable of growing any more.

Jerome Bonaparte, brother of Napoleon and king of Westphalia who ruled in Kassel, had all the parvenu's fondness for costly and exaggerated entertainments. On August 15, Napoleon's birthday, he ordered stags to be harnessed in a four-in-hand for his amusement. The animals bolted, raced along the avenue and the passengers leaped out in terror. When they returned to the stables on foot, the deer had already returned before them, attached to no more than some tattered harness and the shaft. In 1813 the Russian general Chernichev captured the town of Kassel by a surprise attack and took the stags back to Russia as spoils of war.

[1] *No Room For Wild Animals*, Bernhard Grzimek. Thames and Hudson, London, 1956.

58   This picture has been a source of error for two hundred and sixty years. It was drawn in 1700 by a woman artist, Anna Maria Sybilla Merian, who specialised in painting insects. It shows baby opossums riding on their mother's back and gripping her tail with their own. In the course of centuries the picture was repeatedly 'improved'. Even in modern books on natural history baby opossums are shown riding, with the mother's tail arched right forward over her back in such a position that the young could hang from it.

59   During the Ice Age musk-oxen lived in North Germany and the northern regions of the United States, but they retreated so far northwards with the ice that they were not discovered until 1869.

Imagine yourself taking a lift past countless floors to the roof of a New York skyscraper. On the eaves, the pinnacles and mouldings of the Woolworth Building, the Empire State Building and all the other mammoth tower blocks of Manhattan you see white shapes climbing about – goats, improbable goats, walking along cornices, standing on gutters, clambering up the mouldings or calmly sitting on the window-ledges and staring down hundreds of feet into the canyons of New York. This would be something like the impression you would get from gazing through binoculars at the mountain goats in the cloud-hung perpendicular cliffs of the Rocky Mountains. (This was roughly how they were once described by the great American zoologist Ernest Thompson Seton, whose books I devoured as a boy.)

'One day Mother Nature decided to make a creature which should live happily among the towering, deserted peaks which crown the stone cathedrals of the Rocky Mountains. As raw material she took a hoofed animal from the plains, endowed it with a fearless heart, nerves of iron, sinews of steel and a coat of warmest wool fortified with long, rough bristles. Then she bleached her newest plaything until it was pure white and ordered it to go to the Promised Land which was to belong to it without dispute.'

The North American mountain goats are not merely brave; they are remarkable animals. To begin with they are not even goats, although they look very much like goats and behave like them. Their shoulders and neck are much more powerful, their horns smaller and

60, 61 The North American opossum, a pouched mammal, which for a century seemed in retreat before the more highly developed mammals and threatened with extinction, has made a strong come-back in the last twenty years.

not twisted in a spiral as goats' horns are. They are more closely related to asiatic mountain antelopes such as the goral and the serow and to our European chamois, although their appearance is different. Besides this mountain goats are surely the only ungulates in the world which normally sit back on their hindquarters, with torso erect and their forelegs dangling, rather like a dog sitting up to beg. A mountain goat buck sitting in this attitude and gazing with dignity at the landscape looks rather like a professor staring over the top of his spectacles.

My heart thumped in my throat when I first saw these famous beasts, about which I had read so many thrilling stories. They are not even particularly difficult to see in the Banff National Park area of the Canadian Rockies. One only had to stop one's car on the macadam road which curves so elegantly through this super-Switzerland and by following a sign walk to some railings at the edge of a precipice. Here, with the aid of fieldglasses, one can see them grazing below on the green fields, looking like snow-white sheep which have just been washed for shearing. I had expected to see them only after days of hanging around and cunningly stalking them from crag to dizzy crag. In reality things are quite different. There are indeed very few mountain goats left – twelve hundred at the most in the USA (in the two national parks of Montana and Washington) and perhaps a few thousand in their real homeland the Canadian Rockies; but the territories of the various herds are known, the animals do not wander about in the mountains but stay for weeks and months, often the whole year in the same restricted areas, usually above the tree-line. There they have no real enemies, least of all in winter when every other animal has fled from this terrible icy wilderness. Then the hooves and horns of the mountain goat turn blue-black, whereas in summer they are whitish-grey. Often all that can be seen of them are their dark eyes, their black lips, their hooves and horns against the brilliant white background. What they do in winter, up there in the freezing storms of that mountainous waste, nobody knows, because no human beings have ever dared go after them in winter to watch them.

These bold mountain beasts do not leap nimbly about the rocks like squirrels in a tree, but move slowly, in a rather dignified and circum-spect manner like the experienced mountaineers that they are. Going uphill a man can almost keep pace with them. No one has ever seen a herd of mountain goat dash off in wild flight when surprised or frightened as lowland antelopes do, but instead one suddenly finds them in places, on steep slopes or rocky ledges, which one would never imagine that any four-legged creature could reach without wings. Again and again one finds it hard to believe that they are animals and not a deceptive heap of snow.

A mountain goat does not jump very high into the air, seldom more than three or four feet, but it will not hesitate to jump twenty or twenty-five feet down a cliffside on to a tiny ledge which may be covered with ice. Mr W. Seymour, the mayor of Seattle, once saw a mountain goat perform an almost incredible feat, the description of which he prudently had signed by four other men in whose company he witnessed it. 'Last August we saw a mountain goat which was working its way up the practically smooth face of Little Big Chief. At an obviously impassable point I involuntarily shouted: 'Don't go on, you fool – you'll never do it!' But the goat went on. At a number of places it jumped the whole length (not height) of its own body up to the next ledge. Finally it tried a leap and failed. The ledge was more than a goat's length above it. Its forefeet just reached the rim of the ledge, but were unable to get enough purchase to pull it up. We thought that the goat was bound to fall and be smashed to pieces; instead it pushed off from the ledge with fore and hind feet simul-taneously, did a complete backward somersault in the air and landed safely on all fours on the ledge of rock from which it had just tried to jump.'

Although at first sight they look like woolly sheep, these goats have hearts like lions. Charles Chapman and a companion once set off to capture young mountain goats for the Bronx Zoo. They hit on the idea of draping themselves in mountain goat fleeces and camouflaging their faces with handkerchiefs. On hands and knees they crawled up to a mother goat with her kid as they browsed at a spot where the snow had slipped away and uncovered the soil. Quiet is not always essential when approaching them. Many people claim that mountain goats are deaf at times. In fact the ears of dead mountain goats have frequently been found to be full of ticks, gorged on blood, right into the inner ear. Sometimes there are as many as twenty ticks in one aural passage – small wonder that the animals hear badly. In this case, though, finding herself being encircled the goat simply attacked her pursuers. Knowing how sharp those horns were, there was nothing for them to do but get up and run for it. As soon as the goat realised who her enemies really were, she turned and ran herself, over crags and clefts which looked completely impassable. Her kid could not follow her and the two men seized their first prize for the zoo.

In other cases the story has ended less happily for the attackers. At the end of the last century, when mountain goats were not protected throughout the American continent as they are today, Enos A. Mills described how some hunters and their dogs drove an old mountain goat buck into a defile at the head of a glacier, in the region which is now Glacier National Park. The buck was poised on an outcrop at the very edge of a steep precipice, looking for a chance to escape. It made two attempts at flight, but the dogs surrounded it. It jumped at one of them and with an amazingly quick movement of its head spitted the dog on its sharp horns. Then came a second sharp jerk and the dog flew into the air and over the edge of the gorge. In rapid succession the buck despatched three dogs in this way and the rest of the dogs withdrew. Finally it set off on its way over ledge and scree with calm assurance, as if quite unruffled by the whole episode.

Mountain goats are seldom found on the prairies. Nobody knows why it is that now and again single animals or a small troop will resolutely set off in a certain direction across the flat, open plains. Arthur Fenwick, a farmer from Fort Steele, B.C., once came across a mountain goat buck in this situation: 'Old Chief Isadore, who was camping nearby, saw him first. Isadore and two other Indians thought they could catch the animal alive with horses, dogs and lassos. Altogether fifteen dogs set off from the camp to catch him. A while later an Indian woman noticed that there was a terrible scuffle in progress somewhere and she ran off with a rifle to have a look. One of the men shot the buck dead. All the dogs had meanwhile been killed by the goat or died soon afterwards. The Indians had the greatest difficulty in preventing their horses, too, from being gored by those terrible little horns.'

High in the mountains the puma or mountain lion is the only enemy which the Rocky Mountain goat has to fear. The idea that eagles attack them is obviously based on a similarly false belief that European eagles carry off lambs and roe-deer fawns in the Alps. Both sorts of eagle are attracted to carrion, but the presence in eagles' nests of bones and scraps of hair from mountain goat kids or young roe-deer does not necessarily mean that the eagles themselves have killed these young animals. As far as I know there is only one piece of first-hand evidence of such a case. Two men on a trip to catch mountain goat had separated a kid from its mother, when the kid quite unexpectedly escaped by climbing along a nearly perpendicular rock-face. At that moment, when it was out of its mother's protection, it was seized by a bald eagle (the original of the American national emblem). Normally a mountain goat has little difficulty in warding off an eagle attacking its young; its tactic is to rear up on its hind legs.

Even when a mountain goat has gone badly astray and is stuck out on a ledge too narrow for it to turn round or go back, it still has a trick up its sleeve. The animals have often been seen to stand up on their hind legs alone and to work their way back like this, their backs to the cliff-face.

Mountain goats are only in real danger when they go down into the valley or through woods. In many regions they are regularly to be seen grazing in meadows on the valley floor, whilst in other areas they seem to avoid the valleys. They must cross valleys and traverse woods when they move from one mountain chain to another or go to look for a new salt-lick. It is then that they are occasionally attacked by grizzly bear, by the slightly smaller black bear, by wolves, wolverine and even the powerful mountain coyote. They are, however, quite

capable of defending themselves; at least if a mountain goat does die
after such an encounter it does not often die alone. The horns of the
buck are normally a mere ten inches, sometimes perhaps one foot long,
but very sharp and handy. The same Arthur Fenwick, who witnessed
the scene described above, one day found a strong mountain goat
lying dead, obviously killed by a grizzly bear to judge from the
numerous paw-prints and the fact that the mountain goat's neck had
been broken. 'I wondered why the bear had not dragged the mountain
goat away and buried it, as they generally do. So I looked around and
found a large grizzly bear, dead and covered in blood. When I examined
him I found that the mountain goat had twice stabbed the bear immediately behind the heart. The bear had just managed to kill the
goat before going off and dying in turn.' Predators have often been
found killed by jabs in the heart, lungs and belly from mountain goats.
The commonest cause of death for the goats themselves is probably
avalanches.

Incidentally, even rain has its dangers for them. In zoos they need
some kind of shelter, at least a roof, otherwise their woolly fleece gets
soaked full of water and they can then easily die of inflammation of the
lungs. In the wild they look for shelter under overhanging rocks or in
caves. Their wool is actually finer than cashmere. In many places the
tufts of their discarded wool can be gathered by the pound from bushes
and jutting rocks. The Indians of the Canadian north-west coast once
used regularly to collect this wool, spin it and weave it. They would
dye a proportion of the threads in bright colours and weave patterns
that nowadays look almost cubist or futuristic, although they always
represented some totemic animal.

This wool, the woollen cloth and the fleece of the mountain goat
were the first evidence of the animals' existence that explorers were to
discover. In 1778 off the coast of British Columbia Captain James Cook
wrote in the log of his voyage round the world that the natives had
brought 'pieces of polar bear fur and whole fleeces of young polar
bears'. Since there are no polar bears to be found in a radius of a
thousand miles of British Columbia and mountain goats were numerous

in the surrounding mountains, these must have been mountain goat fleeces. Alexander Mackenzie, the route of whose famous voyage to the mouth of the Mackenzie River in the Beaufort Sea I have followed by aeroplane, mentions 'white buffaloes' which were to be found in the mountains west of the river. I have flown for hours in a small aircraft along the gorges of the Richardson Range: he can only have been referring to the white Dall sheep, a few of which I was able to see and film, or possibly in those days they were mountain goats. Live mountain goats were first seen by a European, Alexander Henry, in 1811, when he hunted some and described them.

Around 1860 it was fashionable to have muffs and collars made out of the black and white fur of the African Guereza monkey. The black skins of these animals with their long dorsal mantle of white hairs increased in value to a great price, which led to imitations of them being made from partly-dyed mountain goat fleeces. This almost led to the extinction of these North American animals. Nowadays they are not only universally protected but since 1923 they have been successfully introduced into the Baranov Islands of Alaska and during the 'fifties on to Kodiak Island.

It is surprising that animals from such altitudes manage to survive as well as they do in zoos. In the New York Zoo a mountain goat buck lived from 1900 to 1909, dying at the age of ten, although when one was born in May 1963 at the Calgary Zoo in Canada this was still the first time for thirty-five years that a mountain goat had been born in captivity. One of the animal-catchers working for the New York Zoo reported: 'I did not have much trouble with the little mountain goat kids. I fed them about every three hours, day and night. When they got hungry they would jump up at me or climb all over me – I slept in the same compartment with them. Only when I left them alone did they get uneasy and tried every means to get out. As soon as I had fed the poor little orphans they all lay down close beside me and went to sleep. When they felt hungry again they would kick me with their forefeet. Their mothers must have had a hard time with them too, but they didn't have so many to care for as I did.' One of these little

animals weighs eight pounds at birth and can walk and jump after
half an hour.

It is not yet fully known whether mountain goats live in mono-
gamy, as many people claim, or in herds. They have glands behind
their horns which secrete an oily liquid, especially in the rutting season.
This they smear on branches and protruding rocks, presumably to
demarcate their territory – if one can judge from the behaviour of
other species. The females appear only to bear young every second year.

Near Banff, where I went to see the mountain goats, a Mr J. Brewster
witnessed a unique incident in which the incredible mountaineering
skill of these animals for once failed on the sheer faces of the Rockies.
In those days hunting mountain goat was still allowed and a party of
hunters was following a herd up a fissured crag. Finally the goats
climbed a rock-face whose upper edge had such an overhang that the
hunters lost sight of the animals. They returned to their camp in the
valley, but when they looked up at the cliff-face they saw their five
lost does standing high up on a narrow ledge. Night fell and they were
still there, motionless. Next morning the hunters discovered to their
amazement that the animals had not moved in the night, nor did they
throughout the following day. Brewster and his companions thus
became convinced that the mountain goats had trapped themselves
and were unable either to go on or turn back.

The little herd consisted of two adult does and three young ones.
The older animals had naturally led the way and the observers assumed
that the adult animals had been prevented from turning round because
the less experienced young does were blocking their way. Brewster
and his hunting party became so interested in the fate of these mountain
goats that they stayed in their camp to see the outcome of the tragedy.
One after the other these unfortunate beasts fell off their perch and were
killed as they crashed to the ground. The hunters only saw one of them
crash down; all the others fell during the night. The last one hung on
to the fatal ledge for ten days before she too fell to her death.

I have often explained in public why I think an educated German ought not to visit the bull-ring in Spain. Not because cattle are slaughtered there – we do that too in abattoirs. In most countries, however, it has become the accepted practice that in sport as in life matters should be arranged in a reasonably fair way and that both sides should have an equal chance. The bull's natural method of combat is the clash of brow on brow, the trial of strength. This can be properly seen in Thailand where a people with an ancient and highly developed culture provide public entertainment by pitting bull against bull and not bull against man. Their behaviour is positively chivalrous. If a bull is beaten the other does not pursue its opponent and never kills it. In Spain on the other hand the animal, which has been artificially irritated, is made to charge at flapping cloths and then stabbed from behind. The torero goads the powerful beast into charges in which it never encounters the honest resistance that it expects, until it is so breathless and exhausted that it almost loses interest in this pointless mock-combat. Virtually defenceless by then, it is stabbed to death because the spectators enjoy seeing blood and death. The bull dies every time, the torero always emerges unharmed – except for the occasional 'industrial accident'.

The object of bull-fighting being merely to satisfy the bloodlust of the spectators, which has nothing to do with sport, the tips of the fighting bull's horns are sawn off and then glued on again, so that the bull can't inflict a serious wound even if it unexpectedly succeeds in butting its tormentor. The Spanish newspapers have repeatedly described such scandals; others include numbing the bull with an injection, standing it on its head in the box for the journey to the bull-ring or hitting it in the kidneys with sandbags to reduce its mobility.

R

There have been no reports of an impresario or a bullfighter being disqualified for such practices, as would happen if an analogous case were to occur in some other form of sport.

Of course this does not make the Spaniards more cruel or less charming than other peoples. They have simply not reached the same stage of civilised development as the other European countries, just as about forty per cent of the inhabitants of the Iberian peninsula are said to be still illiterate. Once in Italy Christians were devoured by lions in the circus to amuse the masses, in Germany it is not so long since public executions were a general spectacle and a century ago in England cock-fighting was a most popular sport. Razor-sharp little knives were lashed to the cocks' spurs so that they could literally hack each other to death. People in these countries have progressed beyond such things. I would not like to prescribe to the Spaniards how they should slaughter their bulls. That is their business. For thirteen years one could be much more severely punished in Germany for maiming a dog than for murdering large numbers of Jews in agony. I dare not publish my views on bull-fighting, shooting song-birds or on kosher butchery in English magazines or on the London radio because I am a German and thereby give my opponents in other countries a perfect answer to all my objections. If I were Dutch, British or Swiss I could do so.

It nevertheless strikes me as unnecessary for non-Spanish writers and artists to lend this unsporting form of slaughter an undeserved halo, as for instance was done by Georges Bizet in 1875 with his Toreador's Song from *Carmen*, by the late Nobel prizewinner Ernest Hemingway in his books on Spain and by so many lesser would-be Hemingways. This form of free advertising may help toreros to progress slightly faster from being cowherds or muleteers to owning villas and being driven in Cadillacs; it does not make them into heroes.

Every German traveller to Spain to whom I have spoken has been fundamentally opposed to bull-fighting. But . . . one must have seen it once. German travel agencies arrange for a ticket to the bull-ring to be included in the price of the hotel – and nobody wants to waste their money by not making use of it. Hence the eighty or more coachloads of tourists that may be seen parked outside any bull-ring. On many occasions the audience consists of up to sixty per cent of Germans. The sport-loving young Spaniard of today has no time for the bloody, old-fashioned, fake glamour of the bull-ring; he prefers football. Bullfights exist chiefly as tourist-bait, paid for and largely kept going by Germans. To which I object.

And I am in good company. A great pope, Pius V – who was canonised in this century – issued a papal interdict on bullfighting on November 1, 1567. It declared that bull-fights and fights with other wild animals offended against Christian piety and charity; that therefore such cruel, shameful and diabolical performances were to be thenceforth abolished. All Christian princes, spiritual and temporal, whether vassals of the Holy Roman Emperor or not, together with cities and other bodies corporate would be punished for all eternity by instant exclusion from the Church if they allowed bullfights to be held anywhere within their jurisdiction. Anyone disobeying this command would be refused burial in consecrated ground. Both secular and monastic clergy were forbidden to attend such spectacles on pain of excommunication. 'All obligations, vows and pledges entered into by any person, university or college that have been or shall be made with regard to bullfighting, even if entered into ostensibly in honour of saints' days or festivities (which were better celebrated by praising the Holy Name and by good works than by games of this kind), we declare to be null and void for all time. We call upon all our reverend brethren, namely the patriarchs, primates, archbishops, bishops and all others in Holy Orders on pain of Divine punishment and eternal damnation to ensure suitable publication of this Bull among their flocks and on pain of punishment in the ecclesiastical courts to oversee its observance. All former pronouncements of our Apostolic See which conflict with this mandate, for whomsover they may have been made; under what form soever they may have been issued and with whatsoever clauses of exception and other more effective reservations with which they may have been furnished, be they general or particular, even if enacted without reference to papal initiative, are herewith rescinded. Before God and in the name of their duty of obedience to the Church we admonish all princes exactly to fulfil this mandate in their realms out of reverence for the name of God and thereby to ensure Divine recompense by their good works in executing this commandment.'

This Bull of Pius V had a great and lasting effect. Bullfights virtually ceased completely and were largely forgotten, even though popes Gregory XII, Sixtus V and Clement VII later mitigated the ban and in some instances removed it. In 1805 Charles IV of Spain specifically renewed the ban. Then, however, Joseph Bonaparte was foisted on the Spanish people as their king by his victorious brother, the emperor Napoleon I. This alien Frenchman was understandably disliked by the Spaniards; to curry favour among the masses and to spite the Catholic clergy, Joseph Bonaparte re-introduced the forbidden bullfights. When the French were driven out both Church and State forgot to re-affirm the ban. So now horses can still have their guts torn out in the arena to amuse the mob. Protestant theologians have nevertheless continued to denounce the savage spectacle.

Not long ago I was in Portugal. I went to the Lisbon Zoo with no very great expectations. Whereas England has ten large zoos, Holland two, Germany a good dozen and the USA many more, in all France there is only one of any size, in Italy only one really modern zoo and in Spain the Barcelona Zoo has only recently begun to flourish. The only zoo in Belgium is not in the French-speaking capital, Brussels, but in Antwerp, the centre of Flemish-speaking Belgium. In Switzerland the three zoos are all in German-speaking Switzerland; neither Geneva, Lausanne nor Lugano has a zoo. Interest in animals seems to be strongest among the North Americans, the northern Europeans, Slavs and Japanese; it is less marked in the Latin peoples, particularly those around the Mediterranean.

What a surprise, therefore, when after a seven-minute subway ride from the centre of Lisbon I found myself in a beautiful, spotlessly clean, generously laid-out zoological garden full of well-kept animals. In a country in which every third person is illiterate, the Lisbon Zoo maintains its own school for the keepers' children, and has just built a second one in which classes from other schools can be taught about animals after a visit to the zoo. There is a charming 'dogs' village' containing all the breeds of dog to be found in Portugal and behind it there is a dog's clinic open to the public. In a romantic corner of this zoo, which is housed in what was once the park of the famous prince Farrabo, there are always a few people who – believe it or not – come to pay a visit to the dogs' cemetery. It seemed that animals in Portugal had a happier lot than those in Spain.

Although they cost £5 or £6, tickets for the bullfight on Easter Sunday – as in Spain, the first of the season – were sold out. I had to go from official to official until I found the right one on the third floor of a renaissance palace. There I was given official permission to go into the arena if I wished to, whilst the press photographers and TV cameramen were confined to the upper rows.

This is what is called sport. In Spain the nobles, who once indulged in bullfighting, gave it up at the request of the church and of King Charles IV, who did not care for it. After the French Revolution and the alien rule of Bonaparte bullfighting became an amusement for the poorer townsfolk. In Portugal it has remained rural and aristocratic. At seaside resorts in Spain one can hire horses to ride which have had one eye removed – 'for the arena!' Wretched old nags are gored to pieces by maddened bulls which in their proper surroundings would never harm a horse. Here in Lisbon really brilliant horsemen on the noblest thoroughbreds face the bull across the yellow sand. The rider has no reins, but guides the horse with nothing but leg and spur. The horse prances towards the bull, circles round it, gallops towards it and then races away as soon as the beast really takes up the chase. No horse is injured in this contest; these highly-schooled animals are much too valuable for that and the riders too skilled. In addition the bull wears leather caps on the tips of its horns which makes them much less dangerous.

The Spanish torero, who always has an air of dicing with death every moment, would not make much of an impression here. Everything the Spaniards do the Portuguese do too. The bull is made to charge at the red cape, three times, six times, maybe twenty times. The bullfighter stands still, the bull runs round him in circles after the cape so that its flanks always brush the man's back or stomach. He could tickle the bull's back – and he does. Unfortunately they also stab the bull in the neck with the brightly coloured and barbed banderillas, just to show that they can do it as well as the Spaniards – but they do it on foot without the protection of a cape and from horseback without the use of the reins. Perhaps the angry, sweating bull really does not feel these darts very much; but we foreigners should patronise Portuguese bullfights more, lest the Portuguese feel obliged to adopt the cruel Spanish ways because they are apparently more commercially successful.

When the bull is exhausted and refuses to go on the Portuguese bullfighter calmly takes up his stance six feet from the horns with his back to the animal, or kneels down in front of it in the sand and looks the other way. Then he takes the cape and sword and shows how little skill is needed to stab such an exhausted bull. He shows it once, three times, seven times. But he makes no thrust. And excited young ladies throw him their elegant high-heeled left shoes into the arena, the men their hats, just the same.

When the bull leaves the arena to a round of applause it is clearly no man-eating monster but a domesticated beast brought in from pasture. Then come the 'forcados' and 'campinos', the cowherds from Ribatejo, the most famous cattle-raising district of Portugal. Just as they still do at home they come to the arena dressed in brilliantly-coloured jackets, short trousers, white knitted stockings and green tasselled caps. Eight or nine of them enter the arena, without a cape, without a sword, with nothing but their bare hands. They calmly hail the beast: the excited bull with the barbs in his neck recognises these bright figures from home. One of them cheekily crosses the arena towards it, his hands on his hips, and teases it. Finally he incites the bull to attack again. The 'campino' does not avoid the bull as the torero does. He seizes it by both horns, throws himself on to the broad forehead of the bull and holds tight there or is thrown into the air and, falling on the animal's back or flanks, glides off sideways. At the same moment one or two men have seized the bull by the tail and two or three more press up to him on either flank. They prevent the bull from turning round. During the bullfight that I saw, two of the 'campinos' were helped limping out of the arena with bruised hips.

If the heroic quadruped will still not budge, he is allowed to run free again, the campinos each seize a plain wooden stick, hold them out and urge the bull towards the gate as they would in their fields. If the bull turns and attacks, the man with his green tasselled cap simply jumps over his companions into the passage round the arena.

When all else fails, cows are used. If the bull still refuses to leave the ring, six or seven cows with tinkling bells are suddenly let in. They are driven towards the bull and surround it; since the herd instinct is stronger than the fun of barging about the ring, the hero trots peacefully out of the gate.

When Manitou the Great Spirit had wandered long enough on earth he resolved to fill it with animals. He took his long staff, broke off a piece from the bottom, rubbed it to splinters and threw them into the water. From these came the fishes. Then he pulled a few leaves from the trees, held them in the hollow of his hand and blew them into the air. They became birds. The middle length of his staff he broke into big and small pieces and they ran, hopped or crawled away as animals. Finally there remained only the stout, rounded end which until then he had kept in his hand. The Great Spirit considered awhile what he should make of it. In the end he turned it into a creature which was stronger and cleverer than all the other creatures. This was the grizzly bear. It was so strong and fierce that Manitou himself quickly had to flee from it and take refuge on the top of Mount Shasta.

62 *How the nobility went stag-hunting in the eighteenth century. The animals were driven into enclosures or into water, where they could then be slaughtered en masse without effort or danger. Similar methods were still used in Germany towards the end of the last century. Nowadays no one in Europe would dare to stage a hunt like this. (H. F. Flemming, Leipzig, 1719.)*

63 *A woodland reindeer in northern Canada. In the far north, beyond the tree-line, reindeer live chiefly off mosses. The moss attracts atmospheric dust and transmits into the bones of reindeer a particularly heavy concentration of the toxic Strontium 90 released by nuclear bomb tests. When the bones of Alaskan Eskimos were examined they were found to contain approximately twice as much Strontium 90 as people in the rest of the USA. Swedish Lapps from the far North, whose chief food is also reindeer meat, harboured Cesium 137 in quantities that were between thirty and forty times greater than those present in the inhabitants of southern Sweden. The genetic effects which this may have on these people is as yet unknown.*

In those days the grizzly bears still walked erect as men did later and they did not kill their prey with their teeth and claws but with clubs. Or so the Shasta Indians used to tell.

The Great Spirit was so pleased with life on his newly-created earth that he brought down his family and settled with them inside Mount Shasta. This mountain looked like a gigantic tent and Manitou made fire for his family inside it. Like a tepee, smoke came out of the mountain's top during the day and the glow of fire by night.

One spring day the youngest daughter of Manitou, a beautiful young girl with red hair, ran into the woods. The breeze was so warm, the flowers were in bloom and the birds sang so sweetly that she could not bear to turn round and by evening she was lost.

As father grizzly was returning home that evening from the hunt he found the sweet, red-haired child of God sleeping under a bush. He brought her home to his wife and they decided to bring up the foundling with their own children. The little daughter of the Great Spirit grew up with the young bears and when they were all of age the mother grizzly gave her foster-daughter to her son for a wife. All the other bears – in those days they could all still speak – came to the wedding. Some of the children of this mixed couple – they had a whole tribe of them – had the flesh, blood and nature of the Great Spirit whilst others were like grizzly bears. Their skin was reddish and hairless like that of their mother, the hair on their head grew long but black. They were as strong and brave as their father but they had the wisdom of their grandfather, the Great Spirit. So were created the red men, the first Indians.

64 *When stags fight they often rear up on their hind legs and belabour each other with their forefeet.*

65 *The ground squirrels, which include marmots, chipmunks and prairie dogs, have some most attractive and brightly-coloured varieties such as this striped chipmunk. Since the smaller predators and birds of prey have been largely exterminated, these social rodents often increase in numbers until they become vermin. Then man turns to gas and poison.*

When after many years their old foster-mother bear lay dying, their conscience was pricked. They sent a messenger to the Great Spirit to tell him what had become of his lost daughter. He was so angry at this misdeed that he came storming down the southern side of the mountain – the torn cliffside can be seen to this day. When Manitou met the grizzly bears he killed the old mother with a stroke of lightning. For having usurped the privilege of the Great Spirit by creating new beings, he awarded the grizzlies a terrible punishment. They were made to put aside their clubs, they lost their speech and could thenceforth only defend themselves with teeth and claws. Manitou broke their pride and forced them to the ground, where they were made to walk on all fours. Only when one of them is in the utmost danger and threatened with death does he rear up. Then at his last hour he stands erect again in the way of his forefathers and of Manitou, the Great Spirit.

These bears long remained the kings of North America, feared and respected by the Indians. It must have required considerable courage to fight this colossal beast with stone axes and stone arrowheads, even in bands of six or eight. The bears considered themselves the equals of men and made little attempt to avoid them.

This was a lesson which the first white men had to learn; with their muzzle-loaders, lead bullets and gunpowder permanently damp in the pan they were by no means greatly superior to the bears and the Indians. The redskins could shoot 'an arrow through a bison cow and still kill the calf on the other side of her'. While the first arrow was still humming through the air the second was already flashing from the quiver and many a marksman in those days could shoot off eight arrows in a row before the first one had touched the ground.

Henry Kelsey was the first white man to come face to face with a grizzly bear and describe it. He must have been quite a man. At the age of fourteen he left England for Canada as a pauper and was apprenticed to the Hudson's Bay Company. He got on better with the Indians than with white men. On a journey which lasted nearly two years he discovered not only the Canadian prairies and the bison but in 1691 he also found 'bears, bigger than any polar bear, not white, not black, but silver like our English rabbits —' Twenty years later he became Governor of Hudson Bay.

A hundred years later in many parts of America it was still uncertain as to who was the hunter and who the hunted. A Captain Lewis and his companions, who travelled the upper Missouri in the spring of 1805, were frequently forced to take flight from huge bears. A bear that had been shot at pursued the captain for seventy or eighty yards and only the bear's injuries enabled him to recharge his muzzle-loader twice and fire again. Two days later one of his comrades ran shouting to the river bank and at the last minute saved himself from a grizzly by leaping into the boat. A few days later six hunters at once fired at a bear and although four of them found their mark, the enraged animal jumped up and attacked them with wide open jaws. Two escaped into the boat, the others reloaded and fired again at the beast. They too had finally to throw away their guns and jump into the water – a means of escape to which the bear hunters who made this memorable journey had frequent recourse. When I reached the upper Missouri, with farms, villages, towns and cities along its banks I found it impossible to imagine that only just over a century ago those parts had been the haunt of bears and Indians.

In 1823, also on the banks of the Missouri, a certain Hugh Gulass wounded a grizzly bear; enraged, the animal attacked him. Gulass was just able to climb a tree, but the bear seized him, pulled him down and mauled him fearfully. Several more men came up but could not shoot for fear of hitting the bear's victim. When the beast finally let go and was about to make off, two or three of the men fired at once. The animal instantly turned round and took another bite at Gulass. This was repeated yet again until at last the monster collapsed dead on top of the crippled hunter.

Gulass was still alive, but he was so badly bitten and had so many broken bones that he could not even be moved, least of all carried away. They stitched him up as well as they could and decided to leave him there, as was then usual. Major Henry, who commanded the troop,

316 WILD ANIMAL, WHITE MAN

316 WILD ANIMAL, WHITE MAN

316 WILD ANIMAL, WHITE MAN

316 WILD ANIMAL, WHITE MAN

asked who would volunteer to stay behind. As there were hostile
Indians in the neighbourhood, to say nothing of bears, it was no easy
decision. After a long silence a very young man called Jim Bridger
stepped forward and another named Fitzgerald joined him on the
promise of a handsome bounty.

Jim Bridger later became one of the most famous scouts. He
described how the two of them stayed with the wounded man for five
days, but could see no sign that he was either dying or about to recover.
They therefore left him and took with them his gun, his horse and all
his possessions. They told the others that Gulass had died and that they
buried him.

But Gulass did not die; he dragged himself to the river to wash his
wounds and more crawling than walking he eventually reached a fort.
From there he made his way up the Missouri to find the men who had
abandoned him.

He found them. When he finally faced Bridger, the young man
thought that his last hour had come, but after so long a time Gulass'
thirst for revenge had abated. He merely gave Bridger a long stare and
then said: 'Where the devil are my gun and my horse?'

In the same year near Fort Kiowa, to which Gulass had managed to
drag himself, Captain Smith, who was leading a packhorse, was
suddenly attacked by a grizzly in the middle of a small valley. The
animal seized the man by the head, pulled him to the ground and
broke the butcher's knife which the man used to defend himself. One
of his companions has described in his clumsy way what happened
then:

'None of us had any knowledge of doctoring. One said, come on,
hold him up and the other answered, why don't you do it, and so we
stood around. I asked the captain what was the best thing to do. He
said for one or two to go and fetch water and if you have a needle and
thread, then out with it and sew up the wounds round about my head.
I cut off his hair with a pair of shears and began for the first time in my
life to stitch up wounds. It seemed that the bear had taken almost the
whole head in its mighty jaws, from close by the left eye on one side

to the right ear on the other side, laying the skull bare almost to the neck, at which it had left great white strips where its teeth had gone. One of the ears was torn from the head and was only hanging on by the skin. After I had patched up all the wounds as best I could according to the captain's directions, I said at last that I could do nothing with the ear. Ah, but you must try to stitch it somehow, said he. So I sewed on and laid the torn pieces together as best I might. About a mile away we found water; we all went there, camped for a while and then the captain was in a fit state to mount his horse. So we came to our camp where we put up the captain as well as we could. It gave us a lesson about the ways of the grizzly bear which none of us shall soon forget.'

Gradually times changed for these self-confident giants, the rulers of the American continent. Well over a hundred thousand of them must have lived in the United States of those days. However, the Indians meanwhile acquired metal arrowheads and then rifles and the white man's weapons were also becoming more accurate. Their bullets ploughed into animal bodies with ever greater velocity. Over a hundred million bison grazing on the prairies disappeared in a few decades. In 1848 five hunters returned from a year's stay in Oregon with seven hundred grizzly bear pelts.

The more efficient their weapons became, the bolder men acted towards their once-feared opponent. In California the Spaniards, who owned the territory at the time, used to round up the bears on horseback and lasso them. One day a US naval officer wanted to try it alone. He succeeded in lassoing a bear by the paw and started to try to pull the bear away. Nothing of the sort happened. The horse was unable to move an inch; it was as though it had been nailed to the spot. First the puzzled bear gave a few slaps at the taut lasso, then seized it with its teeth and pulled. The horse was forced to yield and was dragged along inch by inch. Finally the officer could do nothing but cut the lasso with a rapid stroke – to the laughter of the natives, who had ridden up to watch.

In those days in the southern states large captive bears were made to fight bulls in place of human bullfighters. The bear was fastened in the middle of the arena with a heavy chain round its neck, allowing it a restricted radius of movement. When the bull had finally been goaded into attacking the bear and had charged head down into the bear's ribs, the bear would generally grab the bull by the nose and hold tight. 'The bear lay on its back, held the bull's snout firmly between its teeth and gripped it round the neck with its fore-paws, whilst the bull did its best to kick the bear. This made the bear even wilder; it shook the bull furiously by the nose and after a fierce struggle the bear managed to floor its opponent. There was tremendous applause for the bear and everyone thought that it would quickly put an end to the bull, but the bull soon regained its legs, tore itself loose and ran away, whilst the bear crawled back into the hole that it had dug for itself. The bull was several times induced to attack again until it finally gave up and would move no more. The producer of this contest demanded two hundred dollars from the audience, which they threw down to him. A fresh bull was brought on and the affair began again. Finally both bulls were shot to put them our of their misery.'

With time the situation became still worse for the bears. In 1830 a hundred thousand domestic cattle were grazing on the Texas prairies, ten years later three hundred and thirty thousand and in 1850 there were three million five hundred thousand head. Wherever a dead cow was found that had been eaten by bears, the bears were branded as murderers, although as carrion-eaters they would naturally go for any animal that had died of sickness. They were hunted with packs of dogs, which was 'great sport'. The dogs flushed the bears and prevented them from attacking the hunters. The giant beasts were then easily killed. Every bear's head bore a price; poison was laid out. These massive animals, once so sure of their domination, became increasingly shy and fled to remote mountain valleys. For years now no case of a bear attacking a man has been reported. They seem to have completely changed their character, as though they were no longer the descendants of those dreaded beasts of yore. Have they learned to fear modern man and his arms or were all those gory hunters' tales exaggerated?

It is said of them nowadays that ninety-nine out of a hundred bears will never kill cows or large game. This was not always so. For about thirty-five years a bear called 'Old Moses' ruled the roost in Colorado and his dominion over a sixty-miles radius was only brought to an end in April 1904. He was said to have killed about eight hundred head of full-grown cattle, besides dozens of calves and small animals. He had killed at least five men who dared to oppose him, although if one were peacefully inclined he was no man-eater. Many people even credited him with a sense of humour. Now and again Old Moses would creep quietly up to the camp of some unsuspecting surveyors or travellers and then crash around with much roaring and snapping. Perhaps he wanted to scare the intruders out of his preserve, but it may have just been to enjoy watching them stumble off in all directions or climb up trees like frightened monkeys. He never wounded anybody who had not first attacked him with a gun.

Again and again Old Moses showed a clean pair of heels to any trapper who tried to earn the price that was put on his head. He simply jumped over silken trip-threads set to trigger off a loaded gun. Meat placed as bait in the middle of a wooden tunnel he reached by tearing off the roof-beams and carefully avoided stepping in at the two open ends, which were of course rigged with powerful traps.

McCracken, author of a good book on the American grizzly bear (from which I have taken many of these old anecdotes) also claims that in 1856 a man was frequently seen walking through the streets of San Francisco with two grizzlies following him like dogs. One was a female which her owner had reared from babyhood in the woods. She was said to have later defended him from wild grizzly bears, to have coupled with a wild bear one night in his camp and to have brought up the young alongside her master. As I believe I know something about bears and as this story was then published in book form by a journalist (the bear-tamer later appeared in Barnum's circus with his bears) I consider it to be highly exaggerated.

Today there are barely three hundred grizzly bears in the USA. Giant bears in greater numbers are now only to be found in the remote peninsula of Alaska; the biggest of all lead a peaceful life on offshore

Kodiak Island. Erect they are ten feet nine inches tall – the largest bears in the world. Some have been shot weighing fourteen hundred-weight and it is all the more remarkable that the new-born young often weigh only half a pound. Only once a year do these huge animals, which largely browse on grass and grub for roots, really turn carnivorous. This is in spring when the salmon begin to swim up the rivers. Already when the vast swarms of spawning fish begin to gather in the bays many bears are too impatient to wait. They wade out far into the salt water until only their heads are sticking out and make playful attempts to catch the big fish with their teeth or their paws. This is never very effective, but as soon as the salmon start on their way upstream, all the bears appear on the bank or sit down in shallow places in midstream. They carry the fish they have caught to land like dogs, carefully fillet the fish and leave only the head, the backbone and the tail.

Every year one million two hundred and fifty thousand head of big game are shot by hunters in the USA, not counting what is caught by poachers and by the remaining few Indians. 'This number is eight times the total American dead in World War II', a newspaper recently noted. Most of the grizzlies in America live in Yellowstone National Park. On my last visit there, the game wardens told me that there are about one hundred and eighty head – 'at any rate more than there are everywhere else in the United States taken together'. There they live on an almost completely vegetable diet, which again seems to confound those blood-soaked stories of old. Even so they have recently been obliged to kill some of these onetime 'lords of America', thanks to thoughtless behaviour by visitors. They had left garbage lying behind the huts and thrown food to the bears, inducing several grizzlies to pay frequent calls at their camp. The game wardens considered this behaviour too dangerous to be allowed to continue.

A few years ago a married couple with their children and grand-mother were sleeping in a tent in Yellowstone National Park. In the middle of the night one of the children woke up, because his brother was tickling him. The child began to complain and cry. This woke up the grandmother who saw that it was really a big bear standing in the middle of the tent and sniffing at the camp bed of one of the children. She was terrified and in her excitement threw a blanket over the bear's head. The result was a fearful scuffle, the tent was pulled down and torn to shreds and the bear, more frightened than any of them, fled in terror; no one was hurt.

Can you imagine brown bears being exported from Germany and Switzerland two thousand years ago? A memorial tablet was found near Cologne which provided the clue to the existence of this trade. According to the inscription, it had been erected in honour of Diana, goddess of the chase, in fulfilment of a pledge by a Captain of a Legion stationed in Bonn from AD 80 to 111. In six months he had caught fifty bears in the region round Bonn.

In those days there was a great demand for German bears in Rome. The emperor Caligula, who was murdered in AD 41, once arranged for a battle in the arena between four hundred bears and several gladiators assisted by a pack of large dogs. Gordian I, who died in AD 235, brought as many as a thousand bears into the amphitheatre; the emperor Probus (AD 276-282) had a whole artificial forest of trees planted in the Circus, in which two hundred leopards, one hundred lions and three hundred bears were despatched one after another with spears. Other Roman emperors amused themselves by keeping bears in their palaces; many are said to have been baited into attacking live men. It was thus a profitable trade to search the great forests of Germania and Helvetia for bears. The regions through which the captive bears passed on their way to Rome had to feed them. There are still sixty-two towns in Switzerland with bears on their coat of arms as a reminder of those days. The Swiss capital, Bern, is even named after the animal and the name of the old Swiss silver coin the 'batzen' is derived from 'Petz'.[1]

In 1578 the people of Canton Appenzell almost went to war with neighbouring St Gallen over a heraldic bear. They were very proud of the bear on their coat of arms. In the early fifteenth century the oppressed sheep-herding folk of Appenzell rebelled against the abbot

s

of St Gallen and the nobility. Like their symbol the alpine bear, they became raging beasts which spread terror among the nobility and even undertook bloody forays outside their territory, sacking five towns and sixty-four castles. When the angry alpine bear was finally driven back into the mountains, it had earned universal respect.

In 1578 the first printer in St Gallen, Leonhard Straub, printed a calendar showing the coats of arms of a number of regions. The Appenzellers discovered that their bear lacked the attributes of virility; it could equally have been taken for a she-bear. Since Appenzell was in any case involved in ceaseless disputes with St Gallen, this was regarded as an intentional insult. Therefore the magistracy of Appenzell sent the Clerk of the Canton, Zidler, and Brüllisauer, a master builder, as ambassadors to St Gallen and demanded a reply in three days. The mayor and corporation of St Gallen required fourteen days in which to deliberate, so the Appenzell envoys departed unsatisfied; the very next day an ultimatum, expiring in twenty-four hours, was delivered to St Gallen.

No reply was received and the Appenzellers' rage mounted. They prepared for a campaign. Considerable efforts by Abbot Joachim of St Gallen were required before both parties could be induced to meet round a table in January 1579. Straub the printer was made to destroy the pages of his calendar which showed the bear and to swear a solemn oath that he would never again disfigure the badge of the men of Appenzell. It transpired that Leonhard Straub had bought the block for the coat of arms from a printer in Basle, who had printed the same woodcut a year earlier without anyone objecting to it.

The Bernese have kept and bred their own heraldic beast in the famous bear-pit for over five hundred years. In 1575 two white bear cubs were born there, which was generally regarded as a miracle and an omen of great events. As the bear-pit was just outside the city walls, it was situated immediately alongside the prison, which from the blue uniform of its inmates was generally known as the 'Bluehouse'. Dumas has described how one stormy night a prisoner broke out of his cell with the help of a crow-bar. Now and again he could hear a noise as if someone on the outside was trying to help him. When he finally managed to break through part of the wall he was met by the snuffling and panting of a bear. His break-out had led him straight into the bear-pit.

The bear started back in fright and the prisoner made use of this moment to escape through the breach. When the warder opened the cell door next morning, he saw a bear on the palliasse instead of a prisoner. Horrified, he ran away, leaving the cell door open. The bear wandered out and finally reached the street. There he trotted up and down the fruit and vegetable market in the Bärenplatz sending all the people running. The bear gorged itself on the delicious fruit. It was some time before he was caught by a brave blacksmith and his apprentice. This story must have occurred after 1788, as the Bluehouse was built in that year.

A few more years later, on March 5, 1798, Bern was conquered by by the French. They captured three hundred cannon, about sixty thousand muskets and nineteen Bernese flags adorned with the bear. But their most important booty was the bullion of the Bernese treasury, kept in the vaults of the town hall. Eleven wagons drawn by forty-four horses drove out of the town laden with a hundred iron-bound chests containing seven million pounds of gold and silver. The good Bernese gold helped Napoleon to pay for his disastrous Egyptian campaign.

The French also removed the three bears from the pit. They were put into three large crates lined with sheet copper and driven on three wagons, each pulled by six captured horses, via Lausanne to Paris.

The Parisian air did not suit the poor beasts. They were put in the menagerie at the *Jardin des Plantes*, in cages so narrow that the animals could hardly turn round in them. Two of them soon died. The third one was found by a Bernese, as late as the 1820's, in a wretched state: 'It was being stared at as though it were a wounded soldier of a defeated army', wrote the man from Bern, his national pride still deeply wounded.

It really is a disgrace that with so many traditions connected with bears there are no more bears living wild in Switzerland. I think they could prove a great attraction to that country, depending as it does so much on tourism. As a result of the studies made by Dr Peter Krott, who spent two years with his family in the region inhabited by the last bears in the Italian Alps and there reared two young bears in freedom, we know with reasonable exactitude how this might be managed.

The last five alpine bears on Italian territory, which will soon become extinct, have been forced up too high into the mountains. Lower down, the high valleys in which the bears would subsist comfortably are inhabited by farmers. The bear, which is not a true hibernator, does not find enough food at such altitudes in winter, although – or rather because – it is predominantly vegetarian. So from time to time the animals are forced down by hunger, break through the roofs of the farmers' barns and do all kinds of damage. Now it has long been obvious that alpine farming is no longer economic. In large areas of the Alps the fields and pastures are being abandoned and the population is drifting down towards the lowlands, especially into industry. It really would not call for very much money to buy up a few desolate farms, merge the properties and make a nature reserve of reasonable size at the right altitude in which bears, lynx and other wild animals could live in freedom. Compared to the expenditure on tourism in the form of motor-roads, tunnels, etc., the cost of such a project would be ridiculously small.

We know today that bears are capable of living peacefully alongside humans, as they do in Slovakia, Yugoslavia, Sweden, in the Pyrenees, in Roumania, Poland and the Soviet Union, but especially in North America. Bears are the chief attraction of the national parks of the USA and Canada; every summer millions of tourists flock there to photograph bears in comfort from their cars or be photographed with them. The country which institutes an alpine nature reserve with bears, be it Austria, Italy or Switzerland, will undoubtedly attract the lion's share of all motorists passing through the Alps on their way south. There they could see not only bears but beavers, bison, wild horses, marmots and other European animals which elsewhere are hunted and therefore shy of humans, such as stags, deer, wild pig, alpine hares, rabbits, eagles, vultures and eagle owls.

I wonder if bears will ever again live wild in Switzerland – or anywhere else in the Alps?

[1] 'Petz' is an archaic German word for 'bear' which is still used as an affectionate nickname for a bear, equivalent to the English 'bruin'.

Once in mid-April, in a forest near Jablonec in Bohemia, a mountain cock, as the male capercaillie is called, barred the way to a forestry worker. He obviously had some objection to humans invading his territory. He appeared to pay hardly any attention to hen capercaillies, but made off if he was approached within more than fifty yards. At the end of May when the mating season was over, 'Joseph', as he came to be known, was seen no more. Next spring, however, he was there again, clearly recognisable by a tail feather which always remained shorter than the others. This time he was even cheekier and charged at people's legs. As he was specially irritated by the colour brown he was soon accused of 'hostility to the Party' (brown was the official colour of the Nazi Party) – for the incidents occurred in the middle of the last war. When he was caught and moved six miles away by lorry, he was back on his old stamping-ground punctually the next morning. By the following year he had even achieved a certain fame; many admirers from Reichenberg and Jablonec came to see him and took snapshots of him executing his courting display on people's heads. The Head Forester, G. Rehak, was unable to say whether or how he had survived the end of the war.

Eight years later on May 1 two hikers were strolling from the Frasdorf Hut in Upper Bavaria towards the Laubenstein. Suddenly from a distance of seven yards a large bird in display plumage came straight at them between the trees. Although they tried, as they put it, to 'tease' the bird with sticks and stones, it took scarcely any notice. After they had walked on for five minutes the running capercaillie charged straight at one of the hikers from a distance of five yards. 'I still had my stick in my hand and with it I hit the bird in the middle of its neck. The stick broke, the bird fell on its side, lay there for a few seconds, got up, gave itself a slight shake and stalked contemptuously, but rather more slowly, away from us into the woods. My companion wanted to throw another stone after it and I was tempted to hit it again with the remains of my stick. A shooting friend of ours thought that the bird was probably guarding its nest with a broody hen bird' – so ran the two brave men's story in a sporting paper. The cock was most certainly not guarding a broody hen; but what other motive could it have had for this suicidal behaviour?

Instances like this of 'mad' behaviour by capercaillies occur again and again. They will jump down from a tree as soon as a human approaches and execute their courting display, they will perch on car radiators and even on people's shoulders. They soon become one of the local 'sights' and almost invariably someone comes along and finishes them off. The cock capercaillie who lives in our Frankfurt Zoo appears to pay no attention to the brownish-coloured hen bird with whom he shares an enclosure. She spends most of her time hidden in the bushes, whilst he makes a furious rush at every spectator. Since the game birds in the Frankfurt Zoo are not kept in cages but are accessible to the visitors in aviaries, we have had to put calf-high wire netting round the capercaillie's territory to keep him away from people. Fortunately this is sufficient and he does not leap at their heads.

Every German knows what a capercaillie in display looks like, as they are a favourite subject for pictures and are often seen, stuffed and gathering dust, hanging on a wall above the sofa. Yet I don't suppose that as many as ten thousand out of the whole West German population have ever seen a live capercaillie nor, I would guess, have nine out of ten hunters ever seen one either. This is because most zoos do not keep them. The attitude of a capercaillie in display is quite similar to that of a domestic cock when crowing, except that the capercaillie can spread out its tail-feathers into a broad fan. This powerful, imposing bird with its wicked beak will perform, often before dawn, an amazingly muted version of its mating call, consisting of sounds reminiscent of whetting a knife, rattling and clicking. The capercaillie's windpipe is a good third longer than its neck; it therefore describes a big loop in the region of the crop, the purpose of which is presumably to induce a greater resonance. The mating call is a fairly exhausting pastime: a tame capercaillie, kept near Cracow by Professor J. Marchlewski, would make the call for two hours a day in its first year and four hours daily in its second year of life. At the Soviet Experimental Station at Stolby, the young capercaillies made their first attempts at the courting dance and mating call as early as August and the beginning of September, i.e. when they were three and a half months old; the following spring they were fully sexually mature.

During the 'whetting' or 'grinding' part of its mating call the capercaillie is supposed to be deaf. The stalker waits for exactly that moment before quickly advancing a few paces, according to books on the subject. Many theories have been put forward to explain the bird's deafness at this juncture; some maintain that the aural passages are blocked by increased blood-pressure, others that they are closed off at that moment by the particular attitude in which the head is held. Precise anatomical examination, however, does not support any of these explanations; probably the bird hears practically nothing else simply because it is itself producing a loud noise and is highly excited. It has been discovered from photography that it is exactly at this point that the bird's third eyelid, the nictitating membrane, closes over the eyeball and prevents it from seeing anything. Nevertheless a dozen capercaillies, performing their mating call at three am in some moorland pine spinneys, were all silenced as if by magic when the deep call of the eagle owl rang out in the darkness, as Leo Sonne has described. During the following nights the same behaviour was repeated. At first the capercaillies' fear of the eagle owl seemed exaggerated, until one morning a

66 *In the Canadian and American Rockies it is an exciting though by no means uncommon experience for bears to approach the traveller's car.*

67 *The end of a bout in the bull-ring. This bloody and unsporting Spanish show, staged to please the mob, has been condemned in most civilised countries, yet it is kept going by foreign tourists who feel that they must see at least one bullfight when they visit Spain so that they can show their indignation and feel superior to the Spaniards.*

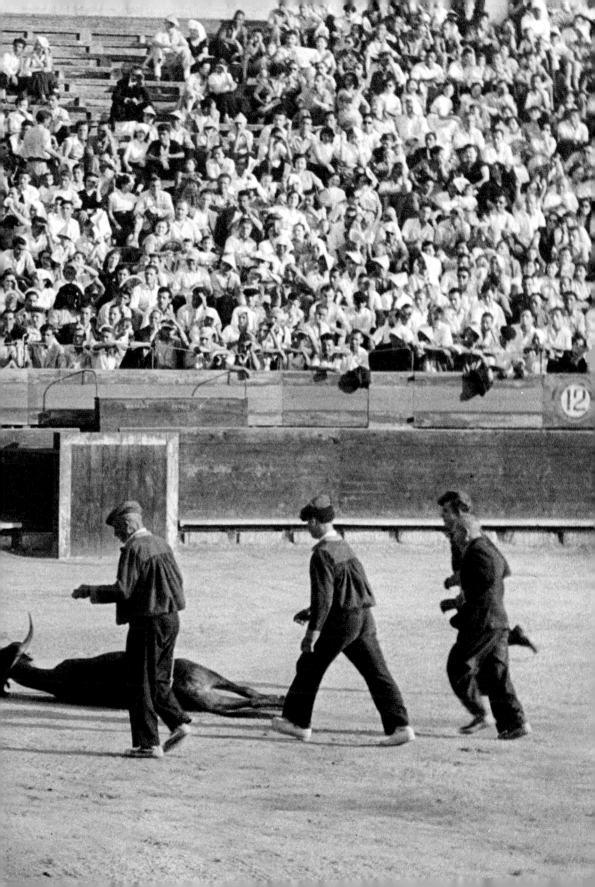

mountain cock was killed in mid-call by an eagle owl. The owl was shot, but the capercaillie was already dead.

The cocks have territories in which they perform their mating display or they perform in competition and greatly spur each other on. When there is no other capercaillie within sight or hearing, it is possible that the individual bird feels the lack of a rival against which it can unleash its fury. It is then that humans appear as a substitute; this is perhaps one explanation for the 'mad' behaviour of many capercaillies. In the case of the bird in the Frankfurt Zoo its familiarity with humans is clearly a result of its having been reared on a farm in Sweden. Cock birds brought up in this way will throughout their lifetime readily regard humans as friends, companions or rivals.

To pair with any hens which enter its territory and become excited by its mating display is all that the cock does to propagate its species – which is not very much. The broody hen incubates six to ten eggs on the ground for twenty-eight to thirty days; they are about as large as hens' eggs. Despite her modest and retiring habits she is even bolder and braver than the spectacular cock-bird. From 1946 to 1961 in Finland Illka Koivisto marked the wings of a total of one thousand and eighty-five young capercaillies. (Until then these birds had hardly ever been ringed because it is impossible to ring the chicks with a ring of appropriate size for an adult bird.) By 1963 3·2 per cent of the marked birds had been traced, which produced evidence that they do not venture very far out into the world: they were all found within a radius of a half to two-and-a-half miles. The hen-birds, on the other hand, went as far afield as three to fifteen miles. Even the oldest cock, who was shot, had gone no further in ten years than five-eighths of a mile from the spot where he was marked. Only in Sweden is a capercaillie known to have travelled twenty-four miles. Out of one thousand eight hundred and ninety-five ringed capercaillies which were set free in the Soviet Union, forty were reported again after having moved an average of

68 Occasionally capercaillie are so aggressive during the mating season that they jump on people's shoulders and are not put off by dogs. Although well known from pictures, they are seldom seen by most Europeans as they are practically never kept in zoos.

one and three-quarter miles; here too the greatest distance travelled was twenty-five miles. Alfred Brehm, on the other hand, estimated that a capercaillie in winter will 'cover seven to ten miles a day'.

When the hen capercaillie has chicks she can be amazingly brave. Once in the foothills of the Alps in Liechtenstein two hunters sat down to have supper against a huge fallen pine-trunk and chatted loudly for half an hour before they finally noticed the wing-coverts of a hen capercaillie beneath the tree-trunk. The feathers were being moved by the chicks sitting under her. 'After about five minutes of tense expectation I lost my patience,' said Herr Notar, one of the hunters, 'and gave the hen a gentle poke with my pipe. Now she too lost her patience, she realised that she had been discovered and shot out between my legs followed by at least ten of the sweetest little grey-brown bundles of wool. But the chicks only gave us a few seconds to see this splendid sight, as they and their mother disappeared into a thicket with amazing speed.'

On another occasion in the Grossenlüder Forest near Fulda a hen capercaillie remained sitting while women forestry workers slowly approached her as they planted out pine saplings. Even shouts failed to move her from her place. When finally a stout-hearted girl lifted up the bird and carried it a short distance away, the hen made not the slightest attempt to resist. Later she even ran after the woman to the spot where they stopped to eat their lunch, let them feed her with bread and cakes and spent the whole morning walking about among the girls as they worked. However, as soon as the forester appeared she made off. He was able to observe from a distance through binoculars that the hen rejoined them as soon as he left them. Three times the bird disappeared when a man approached and returned to the girls when he had gone. At midday a cock appeared and went through his courting display and mating call close to the spot where the girls were working. His call sounded like the noise of iron tools being sharpened and could be heard at a distance of two or three hundred paces.

Forestry workers brought five newly-found capercaillie eggs to Herr Fritz Zeliska, a Head Forester. He put them under a turkey hen and after thirty days five chicks hatched out. The young capercaillies, two cocks and three hens, would mostly roost in trees in the Schloss park while their turkey-hen foster-mother slept on the ground underneath the tree or on a low branch. The birds also flew up on to the roofs and even on to the housetops of the neighbouring small town. The following March the cocks were the first to vanish into the nearby woods.

Our children and grandchildren will have even less chance than those of our generation to see a live capercaillie because our native game birds are growing fewer and fewer. In 1964 the count was six thousand and two capercaillie, fourteen thousand seven hundred and eight black grouse and four thousand one hundred and twenty hazel hen in the whole Federal Republic. In Schleswig-Holstein the capercaillies have long since disappeared and there have been no more in Lower Saxony since 1958. In North Rhine-Westphalia there were still thirty in 1964, one hundred and forty in the Rhineland-Palatinate, none in the Saar, two hundred and fifty-five in Hesse, one thousand and sixty-five ('diminishing') in Baden-Württemberg and in the whole of Bavaria no more than four thousand five hundred and seventy-two which are also declining in numbers year by year. In 1961 there were four thousand and twenty-nine capercaillie alive in Czechoslovakia, of which nearly three-quarters were to be found in Slovakia (it is amazing how they were able to make such an exact count of these shy woodland birds). At the turn of the century the north of European Russia produced sixty-five thousand capercaillie a year, but now there are no more than a round eighteen hundred.

Is there still a chance of conserving our capercaillie and other, even rarer and slowly vanishing game birds? It depends whether we allow the growth of proper woodland again instead of timber plantations consisting of rank upon regimented rank of pine trees standing like drill-planted stalks of rye on weed-free arable. Our forestry officials often console us by telling us that the afforested areas of Germany have not been reduced in the last one hundred and fifty years but have on the contrary increased. However, there is not much cause to be proud of this. Where once there were mixed woods containing the most varied sorts of trees, broken up by fields, heath, clearings, bare patches, meadows, bog, pools and ponds there are now selected plantations of oak, beech and fir all of the same age. Because they are cheaper to establish and grow quicker, more and more conifers are planted every year at the expense of deciduous varieties, in spite of all advice to the contrary. Plantations of this kind are far more susceptible to wind damage and insect pests than is a real wood. In order to keep down bark-borers, forest moths and other woodland vermin huge sums are paid out in wages to remove, for instance, all the dead trees whose bark forms the breeding-ground for such creatures. The forest owners ceaselessly spray our plantations with chemicals to suppress the pests and in doing so they also destroy the ant-heaps and the birds which in a real wood serve to maintain the natural balance.

Nowadays – I almost said 'fortunately' – timber fetches such a low price that forestry has become uneconomic. Beech and pine plantations cost more than the same areas earn when cleared and ploughed. At the same time the masses are pouring out of the cities in their cars into the countryside. They want to see beautiful landscapes, to relax in the woods. In woods such as were sung by Eichendorff and the Romantics, not in plantations meant for nothing but builders' timber and wood-pulp. We can but hope that our forestry authorities will learn the lesson and allow the great German areas of afforestation which are mostly public property, to revert gradually to genuine woodland. Woodland in which birch, ash, maple, aspen, willow, poplar, lime, black alder, acacia, elm and all the many bushes, herbs, shrubs, flora and fauna are to be found, half of which we have allowed to disappear in the last three centuries.

Then the outlook for capercaillie will improve, for they prefer large, scrubby mixed woods broken up by heath and marshy ground. Christian Ludwig Brehm, a Thuringian parson and father of the author of *Brehms Tierleben* once examined ten mountain cocks shot during the mating season and found nothing but fir-, spruce- and pine-needles in the crops. They are probably in such a state of excitement during these hectic weeks that they cannot spare the time to look for any other food.

In winter the cock is said to spend as many as eight days in one tree and will devour practically all the needles on it.

Otherwise capercaillie are usually very fussy about their diet; this becomes clear when one keeps them in captivity. They want buds, young shoots and many sorts of berries. In Russia people used to catch them by making five-foot-high baskets and balancing a round piece of wood over the opening. Cranberries, held in place by horsehair netting, were put on the piece of wood and the capercaillies were tipped into the basket when they alighted to peck at the berries.

The chicks and young pullets feed almost entirely on beetles, caterpillars, larvae, flies, worms and snails. So much insecticide is sprayed over our timber plantations that there are no longer nearly enough of these, so that almost all attempts at artificially re-establishing capercaillie in their former haunts have failed. Their area of distribution should extend all the way across Northern Europe from Northern Spain as far as Lake Baikal and the Lena River in Asia. The first attempts at artificial re-establishment were made in Mecklenburg as early as 1630 by Wallenstein, the great Catholic commander of the Thirty Years War. Efforts to establish capercaillie in Ireland, in Denmark, on the Finnish Aaland Islands, in France, Italy and Switzerland and in various parts of Germany all failed.

They were, however, successfully re-introduced into Scotland after having been exterminated in the rest of Britain. Forty-eight of them were brought to Scotland in the years 1837-38, followed later by more capercaillie from Sweden. In addition capercaillie eggs were placed under black grouse to hatch. This method does, of course, run the risk of cross-breeding between blackcock and hen capercaillies; the reverse form of cross-breeding is rarer. These cross-breeds are roughly midway in appearance between their two parent varieties. Twenty years later the capercaillie stock in Scotland was reckoned at over a thousand birds.

The failure of all the other attempts at re-establishment was probably chiefly the result of setting out hen capercaillies that were too old for breeding; often no more than a single pair was put out. If the correct environment is present – large, unspoilt wooded areas interspersed with streams and heathland – the scraping sound of the mountain cock's mating call will be heard again in early spring, provided that the birds are introduced into the new area as chicks. This was done, for instance, in Poland, where they were released at the age of two to three months. But it is by no means easy to rear young capercaillies, as Oskar Heinroth and his wife discovered when they attempted to hand-rear a brood of capercaillie chicks: at the age of seven weeks five of the chicks suddenly died. They cared little for the broody hen which had hatched them out. They clearly did not understand their foster-mother's voice or the significance of her movements, but simply made use of her as a source of warmth. Obviously a hen capercaillie with young does not behave in the least like a domestic chicken. On the other hand the capercaillie chicks were strongly attracted to humans. Whenever they felt themselves abandoned, they would utter a long plaintive 'dee-ee' sound. Like young domestic cockerels they would indulge in mock fights, although they were less inclined to lunge at each other from the front and would try instead to peck each other's heads from behind.

In the Max Planck Institute at Seewiesen, Dietland Müller too lost nearly all his young capercaillies from various diseases. One which survived from a brood of nine became firmly attached to the scientist and would roost on the foot of his bed every night. If he worked too long the bird would settle down to sleep near him on the dining table or the desk. If it was left alone it would make the same sound of 'dee' which signified abandonment. Another group of fifteen capercaillie chicks, which he had kept for a year, could be induced to start 'crying' if Müller simply stood motionless. As soon as one of the chicks began to give the 'distress' call, the others would join in at once even though they had until then been happily feeding. If they heard Müller's voice, the whole flock would come running and fluttering towards him and would busy themselves round him with nibbling at insects, flowers and grass stalks. A grey parrot which lived in the same house quickly learned the 'distress' call. It imitated it so perfectly that Müller was frequently deceived by it into looking at his foster-brood. The Heinroths made the discovery that when the chicks are well feathered at four weeks old and weigh about a pound, they then go through no more than one complete change of feathers before they reach the brilliant, long-feathered plumage of the adult cock, whereas in *Brehms Tierleben* it still states that the cock goes through another change of feathers before attaining the full colours of adult plumage.

Once capercaillie chicks have been reared in human care they can grow to a ripe old age. One mountain cock lived eighteen years with a notary of Krainburg, Herr Sterger. The longest recorded life-span of a capercaillie in freedom was in a reserve at Orimatilas in Finland. As a three-day-old chick its wing was marked on July 1, 1950 and it was shot on September 25, 1960 weighing nine pounds. Capercaillies, the cock with a body length of three feet four inches and a weight of nine to ten pounds and the hen capercaillies with a weight of five to six pounds, are the largest of all game birds, which are – or rather were – distributed in eighteen species over all the temperate areas of the northern hemisphere.

Recently a leading West German daily newspaper published a picture of a Soviet postage stamp in honour of Richard Wagner. The newspaper added a controversial remark to the effect that we had, it seemed, to wait for the Soviets to commemorate a German composer on their stamps, whilst our Federal Post Office only saw fit to depict animals. It so happens that the Soviet Union has devoted whole series of stamps to threatened animal species and they have also been printed on millions of match-boxes. It is, however, typical of many West German journalists that they discount the natural world, regard it even as despicable in comparison with the works created by the mind of man.

If a producer of documentaries in Germany wishes to recover his heavy outlay by having them shown in the commercial cinema, he must first submit his films to the censors. Only then can he get the benefit of a reduction in entertainment tax without which his film would not be accepted by the cinemas. This obligatory censorship is in the hands of a 'Provincial Board of Censors'. An anonymous jury passes judgment on the film producer's opinions and artistic merits, then recommends changes – which are mandatory. This is the reason why I have stopped making films in Germany.

When I submitted the film *Serengeti Shall Not Die*, which I had shot jointly with my late son Michael, the censors demanded that we should cut the sentence, 'The world would be a better place if people behaved like lions' (because lions do not kill each other), and they also objected to our claim that it was just as important for mankind to safeguard what is left of wildlife as it is to preserve the Acropolis or the Louvre. They considered it intolerable to compare herds of zebras with such monuments of culture. Only when I refused these cuts – a number

of German scientists and newspapers unanimously took my side –
did the censors withdraw their demands.

A third more portentous example of the way the natural world is
underrated in comparison with things man-made: at a conference of
the Ministers of Education on September 29, 1960, a resolution was
passed, considerably restricting the extent to which biology should be
taught in the higher grades of German secondary schools. The total
extent of natural science subjects was actually curtailed. In addition,
many types of secondary schools in most of the Länder have been
allowed to make science subjects either partially or entirely optional.
This means that the majority of pupils in the higher grades are given an
inadequate introduction to the field of natural science, which is particularly grave for those pupils who, if they do not take up science or
technology as a career, never come into contact with natural sciences
at university level either.

In future, therefore, lawyers, judges, economists, clergymen,
journalists, politicians and most teachers in the Federal Republic – in
direct contrast to most other countries – will not have sufficient
grounding in the laws of nature and biology, which largely determine
the future of the nations and mankind. In apparent defiance of democratic procedure, the Ministers of Education passed this momentous
resolution without consulting the *Land* Parliaments. Admittedly, none
of the eleven Ministers had, in the course of his own university training,
studied any subjects which normally come under the heading of natural
sciences. They must have found it difficult to form a clear opinion about a
branch of knowledge which has since gained such enormous importance.

Most people tend to have a more limited outlook than the great
natural scientists, whose knowledge encompasses the entire planet and
the two thousand million years of its creatures' history. Prehistorians
think in tens of thousand of years, historians and philosophers in perhaps two to four thousand years, the majority of experts in art and
literature, and 'educated' people in general, only know about a few
centuries, while most country folk think in terms of decades, economists, politicians and fashion designers, as often as not, only in years.

T

To the natural scientist the thought of the infinitesimal span of our own life as compared with the complex, time-defying march of evolution is deeply impressive – it inspires him with modesty and awe. It makes him feel as if he were sitting in a fragile vessel, being propelled over the transparent surface of a great ocean of life, and looking down he divines how, far down and long ago, living creatures developed from single cells, acquired more efficient and more varied forms, learned to swim, walk, jump, fly, to cultivate the earth, to create the greatest diversity and magnificence.

Every single creature is a subject of the laws of nature, each can be extinguished by a mere blow, no matter whether it is an algae in the tropical seas or a President of the United States. No one knows whether the flow of evolution is directed towards a particular goal or whether life and existence is an aim in itself, but we do realise that in millions of years evolution has, intentionally or not, reached a unique climax – the human brain. With this instrument, of which so little is as yet known, life on earth can become conscious of itself, can reflect upon itself, can compare and study the sun, the moon, the waves, the birds and the fish. To quote Professor Wulf Ankel, the human spirit, whose connection with the brain is proven if intangible, allows man to confront and attempt to interpret the very nature that evolved him without his own doing.

Tracing the dead branches of the tree of life on earth, natural scientists have learnt that excessively specialised development imperils any species. Deer with too large antlers, saurians of too large proportions, species with highly developed defence mechanisms, often became extinct when their environment underwent a change. The human brain, too, is far from perfect. The tendency to overrate itself seems to be an innate fault, as does the faculty of plunging the whole of creation, mankind included, into mortal danger. Never before was any form of life so well endowed. From century to century, man has improved his capacity to change and destroy all other forms of life on this earth – and he does. He can change the whole planet. The consequence of this is the sin of hubris – the overweening arrogance of man.

The works of man tend to smother the natural world. At the same time our numbers are growing beyond all bounds. The less competent we become at peaceful co-existence and an equitable distribution of our food supplies, the bolder our technical constructions are, the less they impress or inspire us. We have long known that it is only a matter of time and money for technology to fulfil our least desires. We have no doubt that we shall eventually conquer the moon and Venus. We read in the papers of men circling round our planet in a few hours and at immense altitudes, but it seems far less exciting to us than the first steamer or the first tunnel through the Alps did in the previous century.

Only slowly, though in growing numbers in recent years, a few people of insight have come to realise the importance for us of animals which developed before us and without our aid, as a source of inspiration, pleasure, beauty and excitement nature has provided for us and which we are about to destroy for ever. The more vulnerable and rare the natural world becomes, the more its value to us increases.

There are three kinds of primates surviving today which number only a few thousand: anthropoid apes whose intelligence among living creatures is second only to us humans. If nothing drastic is done, one kind, the Asian orang-utan, will become extinct in our lifetime. Meanwhile we still know nothing about its habits, its intelligence or its behaviour. In the last two years a first attempt has been made by two young scientists, an Englishwoman and an American, to live among the two other kinds of anthropoids, the chimpanzees of Tanganyika and the mountain gorillas of the Virunga region in the Congo. They have discovered many exciting facts. According to the most modern micro-blood-tests, taken by my colleague Jakob Schmitt of the Frankfurt Zoo, the chimpanzee is the creature most closely related to man; when he lives in freedom he too occasionally hunts, kills and feeds on lower species of monkeys. Our next closest relation, the massive and much maligned gorilla, however, lives entirely on plants, is peaceful by nature, and his behaviour tends to avoid both hunting and killing his own species and fighting with other animals. A great opportunity to study our own character and earliest history will vanish if we allow the destruction of these creatures and their natural habitats.

Animals have made it possible for man to become truly human. The dog overtook the hunter's prey and prevented its escape until it could be killed with clubs, slings or arrows. Cattle fed his young and carried his possessions, allowing him to acquire things he could not have carried away himself. Man could thus establish patriarchal communities, regulate and refine his life. The horse made him free, bore him with incredible speed across continents, created a ruling caste of knights, who, relieved of the care for their daily bread, could devote their thoughts to astronomy, mathematics, the arts, science and politics, could conquer empires and found new civilisations. As little as one hundred and fifty years ago it seemed unthinkable that a nobleman should walk on foot.

Within the last few decades animals have become superfluous. But what folly to exterminate natural life around us, so that our children and grandchildren will never again be able to benefit from it! Do we know they may not be in dire need of it one day?

This is why there are a few of us – and there are more of us every year – who try to preserve what remains of nature, so that the flow of natural creation may not be stopped for good. We realise that with growing populations everywhere not all of nature can be protected, but at best only very small parts of it. The soundest way to do this is in

69 *Within approximately a hundred days the body of the male deer has to build up the bony structure of its antlers, which may weigh up to thirty-five pounds.*

70 *Anna Ivanovna, Empress of Russia (1730–40) amused herself by shooting down stags driven past the veranda of her hunting lodge. This form of hunting was a sport much in favour with princes of the time. (Picture by Surikov.)*

71 *Gillian Godfrey, a zoologist, kept track of moles (talpa europea) by putting radioactive rings round them and following them above ground with a Geiger counter as they burrowed. The young left the mother's nest on the thirty-third or thirty-fourth day; on the first occasion one young female mole only ventured five yards away, but by the fifth day it was moving around underground in a radius of ninety yards from the nest. Moles voluntarily enter water and are excellent swimmers.*

national parks, regions where people are not allowed to live or to change anything. For this we must fight, and it is worth while to examine how this can best be done.

One way, and by no means the least effective, is to inspire people with enthusiasm for wildlife. All governments nowadays agree that it is uncivilised, inhuman and unworthy to destroy the monuments of former generations. They preserve the Acropolis, dig up antique settlements from among ruins and conserve them; the United Nations have granted millions in order to save the temple of Abu Simbel from being submerged by the Aswan Dam project. But how much money is granted to preserve wildlife facing a far more deadly threat? Admittedly, there have been some encouraging signs. After the European colonial rulers had first destroyed nine-tenths of African wildlife from wantonness, greed or the thrill of killing, we believed that the newly independent peoples would soon complete the destruction. Instead, in spite of political upheavals, these last testimonials of a bountiful nature are being preserved by them. In spite of civil war in the Congo, the nature reserves, first established by the Belgians, have been maintained and protected as far as possible. In the now independent Tanganyika, notwithstanding poverty and need, the taxpayers reach deep into their

72 *Two North American Rocky Mountain goats; they are actually a species of antelope, like the European chamois. Rocky Mountain goats have been known to kill grizzly bears with a few rapid stabs to the heart.*

73 *Bull fighting in Portugal has remained an upper-class sport and has not degenerated into a blood-soaked spectacle for the masses. The bulls may not be killed; if one were killed the spectators would be indignant at such clumsiness.*

74 *A mere seven hours' drive southwards from Munich takes one to the habitat of the last wild alpine bears, in the Brenta and Bresanella group of the Alps, in the valleys round the Ortler and Admello. For centuries no human has ever been killed by one of these bears and their depredations among domestic animals are negligible. Nevertheless the numbers of these Italian bears decrease from decade to decade; today only five or six of them are left and their end, too, is in sight.*

pockets to protect the wildlife of their country – money that might well buy them schools, hospitals, or the improved living conditions they so urgently need. In its first two years of office, the new African government has already put its predecessors to shame by increasing the number of national parks from one to three, with current plans to establish three further parks, and last year raising the annual expenditure for the preservation of wildlife by a third. Are not these wise and clear-sighted people, who have few financial resources, justified in feeling that richer nations should help them to preserve values that are important for the future of *all* mankind?

These values are already beginning to be important to both Europeans and Americans. Increasing numbers of us seek recreation in travelling, and want to feast our eyes on things we are deprived of in our daily life. As little as eighty years ago eighty per cent of the population in Europe and America lived in villages, in daily contact with animals, horses, cows, sheep, chickens, encountering deer and hares in the course of their work in fields and forests. In the old days, European travellers, who had grown up in the country, took scant notice of the landscape they slowly traversed by mail coach, instead they described in their journals the towns, cathedrals, castles and royal residences they had seen. Even fifty years ago nobody could have foreseen that every spring millions of people would pour into Italy in search of sun, sea and scenery. Meanwhile more and more tourists begin to travel to Africa.

It does seem, though, that we Europeans, in co-operation with the Africans, might be able to save at least a small part of Africa's magnificent natural life, even if we are unable to preserve our own environment. In Europe, North America or Canada there are at present no national parks in which a proper natural equilibrium is maintained.

We have not yet been able to rid ourselves of the notion of 'harmful' animals, so our hunters kill our native beasts of prey or greatly reduce their numbers. In most national parks of America and Canada, and even the Soviet Union, the larger beasts of prey have been eliminated in favour of grazing animals – deer, antelopes, mountain sheep and goats.

In genuine nature reserves the beasts of prey do the killing and man need not appear in the role of hunter. The animals have therefore ceased to fear him; they no longer run away or attack when he approaches them by car.

Alas, there are no signs in Europe that genuine national parks will be established in which all wildlife, even wolves, would be protected and safe from human interference. Wolves, unlike lions, leopards and hyenas, go far afield, and national parks in our regions would therefore have to be very large and not surrounded by human dwellings. The opportunities to establish reserves of this kind, to preserve intact for our descendants parts of our northern regions probably only exist in some far off territories of Canada and Siberia. But so far no discernible efforts have been made in this direction. Let us hope that we white people may also manage to preserve part of our own natural life in its pristine state.

READING LIST

A. T. Bannikov, *Die Saiga-Antilope*, Neue Brehm-Bücherei, Wittenberg-Lutherstadt 1963

A. T. Bannikov, *L'écologie de Saiga tatarica L. en Eurasie, sa distribution et son exploitation rationnelle*, La terre et la vie, 1961. No. 1, p. 77–85

E. und G. Buchholz, *Rußlands Tierwelt und Jagd im Wandel der Zeit*, W. Schmitz, Gießen 1963

Victor H. Cahalane, *Mammals of North America*, Macmillan, New York 1947

Woldemar von Falz-Fein, *Askania Nowa*, J. Neumann-Neudamm, Berlin 1930

Harold McCracken, *The Beast That Walks Like Man*, Hannover House, New York 1955

Carl G. Hartman, *Possum*, University of Texas Press, Austin 1952

H. Hediger, *Jagdzoologie*, F. Reinhardt, Basel

L. Heiß, *Plötzlich jagt ein Sturm daher Die Geschichte eines Geschlechtes*, Robert Bardtenschlager, Reutlingen 1964

Gustav Hinze, *Unser Biber*, Neue Brehm-Bücherei, Wittenberg-Lutherstadt 1953

Fritz Koenen, *Der Feldhase*, Neue Brehm-Bücherei, Wittenberg-Lutherstadt 1956

Lili Koenig, *Beobachtungen über Murmeltiere*, Zschr. Tierpsychol. Bd. 14, S. 510 bis 521, 1957

Waldemar Lindemann, *Beobachtungen an wilden und gezähmten Luchsen*, Zschr. Tierpsychol. Bd. 7, S. 217–239, 1950

Wilhelm Linke, *Der Rothirsch*, Neue Brehm-Bücherei, Wittenberg-Lutherstadt 1957

Erna Mohr, *Das Urwildpferd*, Neue Brehm-Bücherei, Wittenberg-Lutherstadt 1959

Detlev Müller-Using, *Diezels Niederjagd*, Paul Parey, Hamburg 1954

Detlev Müller-Using, *Die Paarungsbiologie des Murmeltieres*, Zschr. Jagdwissensch. Bd. 3, S. 24–28, 1957

Detlev Müller-Using, *Großtier und Kulturlandschaft*, Musterschmidt-Verlag, Berlin 1960

Adolph Murie, *A Naturalist in Alaska*, Devin-Adair, New York 1961

Günther Niethammer, *Die Einbürgerung von Säugetieren und Vögeln in Europa*, Paul Parey, Hamburg 1963

S. J. Ognew, *Mammals of U.S.S.R. and Adjacent Countries*, Jerusalem 1963

Alvin Pedersen, *Der Eisbär*, Neue Brehm-Bücherei, Wittenberg-Lutherstadt 1957

Alvin Pedersen, *Der Moschusochse*, Neue Brehm-Bücherei, Wittenberg-Lutherstadt 1958

Jack K. Saunders, *Food Habits of the Lynx Cat in Newfoundland*, Journal of Wild-life Management, vol. 27, No. 3, p. 384 bis 390, 1963

Jack K. Saunders, *Movements and Activities of the Lynx Cat in Newfoundland*, Journ. Wildl. Manag. vol. 27, No. 3, p. 390–400, 1963

Alvin Pedersen, *Der Eisbär, Verbreitung und Lebensweise*, E. Brunn & Co., Kopenhagen 1945

Ernest Thompson Seton, *Lives of Game Animals*, vol. I–VIII. Branford, Boston 1953

Friedrich Aug. Volmar, *Das Bärenbuch*, Paul Haupt, Bern 1940

Wäscha-Kwonnesin, *Männer der letzten Grenze*, Franckh'sche Verlagshandlung, Stuttgart 1955

Eugene A. Healy

N.B. Italic numerals denote illustrations in monochrome, and roman numerals those in colour.

U